THE CHARLTON
STANDARD CATALOGUE OF
ROYAL WORCESTER
FIGURINES
MILLENNIUM EDITION

BY
ANTHONY CAST
JOHN EDWARDS

W. K. CROSS
PUBLISHER

The Charlton Press

PALM HARBOR, FLORIDA • TORONTO, ONTARIO

Canadian Cataloguing in Publication Data

The Charlton standard catalogue of Royal Worcester figurines

Biennial.
2nd ed. -
Continues: Charlton price guide to Royal Worcester figurines,
    ISSN 1208-9249
ISSN 1203-469X
ISBN 0-88968-189-9

1. Royal Worcester figurines—Catalogs. 2. Pottery, British—Catalogs.

NK4660.C49   738.8'2'029442   C99-901215-0

**Printed in Canada
in the Province of Ontario**

EDITORIAL TEAM

Editor	Jean Dale
Assistant Editor	Cindy Raycroft
Graphic Technician	Davina Rowan

ACKNOWLEDGEMENTS

The Charlton Press and the authors would like to thank all those who have helped with the second edition of *The Charlton Standard Catalogue of Royal Worcester Figurines.*

Contributors to the Second Edition

John Andrews; Gabrielle Doherty Bullock, Bygones of Worcester; Jennifer Campbell; Joseph Carr; Patrick Cerra; Freda and Jim Edmunds; Harry Frost; Elizabeth Greenshields; Ron Heberlee; M. Langham; Glenda J. May, Bruce Kodner Galleries; Peggy Rowbottom; Amanda Savidge; Helen Sinden; Ted Taylor; Nettie Wade

Special thanks to Wendy Cook, Curator of the Museum of Worcester Porcelain and Royal Worcester, for her assistance in putting the finishing touches on this guide.

A SPECIAL NOTE TO COLLECTORS

We welcome and appreciate any comments or suggestions in regard to *The Charlton Standard Catalogue of Royal Worcester Figurines*. If you would like to participate in pricing or supply previously unavailable data or information, please contact Jean Dale at (416) 488-1418, or e-mail us at chpress@charltonpress.com.

The Charlton Press

Editorial Office:
2040 Yonge Street, Suite 208, Toronto, Ontario M4S 1Z9
Telephone: (416) 488-1418 Fax: (416) 488-4656
Telephone: (800) 442-6042 Fax: (800) 442-1542
url: www.charltonpress.com; e-mail: chpress@charltonpress.com

HOW TO USE THIS PRICE GUIDE

THE PURPOSE

This book is designed to serve two specific purposes. First, to furnish the Royal Worcester enthusiast with accurate listings containing vital information and photographs to aid in the building of a rewarding figurine collection. Secondly, this publication provides Royal Worcester collectors and dealers with current market prices for Royal Worcester figures. Animal subjects are covered in *The Charlton Standard Catalogue of Royal Worcester Animals*, and candle extinguishers/snuffers, which may sometimes appear to be small hollow-bottomed figurines, will be treated separately in *The Charlton Standard Catalogue of Royal Worcester Collectables.*

Within the individual listings, the figures are catalogued in order of Royal Worcester (RW) model number. All listings include the modeller, height, colour, dates of issue and withdrawal, varieties and the series to which the piece belongs. Lastly, the suggested retail price is given in American, Canadian and British currencies.

VARIETY CLASSIFICATIONS

Collectors will note the following distinction concerning styles and versions:

STYLES: When two or more figurines have the same name but different physical modelling characteristics, they are listed as **Style One, Style Two**, and so on after their names. Such figurines will also have a different RW number.

VERSIONS: Versions are modifications to a minor style element.

VARIATIONS: Variations are modifications to a minor style element. A change in colour is a variation.

A WORD ON PRICING

In addition to providing accurate information, this catalogue gives the readers the most up-to-date retail prices for Royal Worcester figurines in American, Canadian and British currencies.

To accomplish this, The Charlton Press continues to access an international pricing panel of experts who submit prices based on both dealer and collector retail-price activity, as well as current auction results in the U.S.A., Canada and the U.K. These market prices are carefully averaged to reflect accurate valuations for figures in each of these markets. All discontinued figures are priced in this manner.

Please be aware that all prices given in a particular currency are for figures within that particular country. The prices published herein have not been calculated using exchange rates exclusively. They have been determined solely by supply and demand within the country in question.

A necessary word of caution: no pricing catalogue can be, or should be, a fixed price list. This catalogue, therefore, should be considered as a pricing guide only — showing the most current retail prices based on market demand within a particular region for the various figurines.

Current figures, however, are priced according to the manufacturer's suggested retail price. Please be aware that price or promotional sales discounting is always possible and can result in lower prices than those listed.

The prices published herein are for figures in mint condition. Collectors are cautioned that a repaired or restored piece may be worth as little as 25 per cent of the value of the same figure in mint condition. The collector interested strictly in investment potential will avoid damaged figurines.

THE INTERNET AND PRICING

The Internet is changing the way business is being done in the collectable market. Linking millions of collectors around the world through chat rooms, antique and collector malls, Internet auctions and producer web sites, e-commerce has become big business.

Some of the effects caused by the Internet and e-commerce on the collectable business are as follows:

1. Collectors deal directly with other collectors, changing the dynamics of the traditional customer/dealer relationship.

2. Information concerning new issues, finds and varieties is readily available, twenty-four hours a day. Collectors' wants are made known instantly to a wide spectrum of dealers and collectors.

3. Prices:
   (a) Price differentials disappear between global market areas as collectors and the delivery services team up to stretch the purchasing power of the collectable dollar/pound.

   (b) Prices of common to scarce items will adjust downward to compensate for the temporary expansion of merchandise supply. Conversely, prices of rare and extremely rare items will increase, a result of additional exposure to demand.

   (c) After a time even the prices of the common items will rise due to the growing worldwide demand for collectables.

4. Internet auction sites listing millions of items for sale on a daily basis continue to grow as more and more collectors discover the viability of using this method to buy and sell merchandise.

5. Traditional marketing strategies (retail stores, direct mail retailers, collectable shows and fairs, and collectable magazines and papers) face increased pressure in a more competitive environment.

The Internet is user-friendly; no travelling required, twenty-four hour accessibility, no face-to-face contact or other pressure to buy or sell. Without a doubt, the arrival of e-commerce will change the way a collector adds to their collection.

TABLE OF CONTENTS

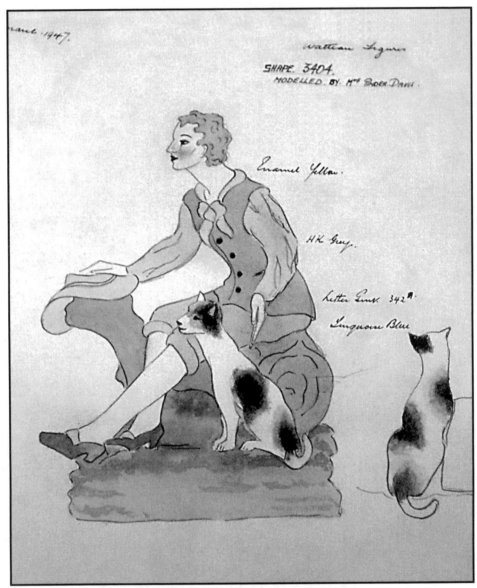

Copy of the *Watteau Figure (Male, seated)*
sketch by Agnes Pinder-Davis (RW3404)

INTRODUCTION

A HISTORY OF ROYAL WORCESTER

Porcelain, once an exorbitant luxury item exclusive to China, began production in Germany in 1711 (Meissen) and in the early eighteenth century in Italy and France (notably Sevres). Fifty years later it was manufactured in England, with factories developing in Shropshire, Derby, Plymouth, Bow, Lowestoft, Chelsea and Bristol, along with smaller operations scattered about Wales. The Worcester Tonquin Manufacture was formed in June 1751 by Dr. John Wall and fourteen other local businessmen, and is the oldest continually existing porcelain manufacturer in Britain. The newly formed company leased their first premises, Warmstry House, on the Severn in Worcester, and began making teapots and tableware.

Together with William Davis, an apothecary, Dr. Wall appears to have developed a soft-paste method using Cornish soapstone already in use at Benjamin Lund's factory at Bristol. Unlike its contemporaries, this formula made porcelain that would not crack when brought into contact with boiling water (the ingredients have remained largely unchanged over the past 250 years). The Worcester factories, along with similar operations in Caughley, Shropshire (called "Salop ware") and Liverpool, quickly surpassed the other outfits in sales of tea and dinner services.

While the Bow, Chelsea and Derby operations produce a number of figurines at that time on Continental models, the Worcester Porcelain Company concentrated on quality table ware. However, they and the Bristol plant (which merged with Worcester in 1752) did make a handful of unsophisticated figurines in their early years such as a white glazed Chinese man circa 1750. One early porcelain figure, "Cupid at Vulcan's Forge," was made at the Worcester factory in the 1760s. It is thought to be modelled by John Toulouse, who also produced some of the figurines made in the Worcester factory of Robert Chamberlain.

Dr. Wall retired in 1774 and died in 1776. William Davis was head of the factory until his death in 1783, whereupon the firm was purchased by the company's London agent, Thomas Flight. In 1789, following a visit to the factory by King George III and Queen Charlotte, the King granted the factory a Royal Warrant, hence the term "Royal Worcester." A London showroom was also opened at His Majesty's suggestion. The factory has continued to enjoy Royal Warrants until this day. Flight, together with his sons John and Joseph and various other family members, ran the Worcester factory until the 1840s, with the involvement of the Barr family, selling mostly tableware. At this time they merged with Chamberlain's factory. The operations were then moved from Warmstry house to Diglis, the site of Chamberlain's works, where the present factory stands. In 1851 the company was purchased by W. H. Kerr and R. W. Binns. The two men introduced Parian (a semi-matte material high in feldspar), first used by the Copeland factory in the 1840s, to the Worcester factory. This material was more lasting and easily coloured or gilded than earlier formulas, making it more suitable for the detailed modelling with which the name Worcester is now synonymous. This lead to an unpredecented expansion in both production of and demand for figurines, especially after the company issued stock and started trading as Worcester Royal Porcelain Company Ltd. in 1862.

The company also started hiring trained sculptors such as W. B. Kirk, E. J. Jones, and Charles Toft rather than factory workers to do their modelling. In the 1870s James Hadley produced the greatest number and variety of Worcester models, including a number or Oriental subjects, Middle Eastern figures and the *Countries of the World* series. Hadley left Worcester in 1876, and in 1896 he formed his own business with his sons. Two years after his death in 1903, his business was acquired by the Worcester Royal Porcelain Company, who had also bought their last major competitor in the city, the Grainger factory, in 1889.

At this time Royal Worcester won an important battle in the courts; another Worcester firm, Locke & Co., were using the word Worcester on their pieces. The judge ruled that "Worcester" would only be used to describe products manufactured by the Worcester Royal Porcelain Company. But the Company was entering a period of crisis. From 1900 to the First World War, Worcester produced a few animal figures, often modelled by the Evans family after Japanese Netsuke and Meissen style birds. During the War, the Worcester factory produced delicate porcelain figures in a style reminiscent of German crinolines, in a patriotic attempt to substitute British for German crafts. Though Frederick M. Gertner appears to have worked on these figurines, his best and most typical work was in the highly accurate *Historical and Regimental* series, which was also introduced at this time. A number of small nude figures of boys and girls also appeared at this time in Crownware. Crownware (a high-fired earthenware) was much cheaper to produce than Parian, which was phased out over this period. This proved, however, to be an unsuccessful move for the Worcester factory. Worcester tried to branch out by producing powder bowls, ashtrays and various jugs including Tobies, traditionally made by Staffordshire potters. Nothing, however, could prevent the factory from closing its doors when it went into receivership on July 24, 1930.

Queen Elizabeth I, Style One (RW2648)

Two weeks later the factory reopened under the direction of Joseph Grimson, who wisely discontinued Crownware production. The next few years found the Worcester factory producing ninety new figures. Grimson and C. W. Dyson Perrins, who bought the factory, were responsible for hiring new modellers, often on a freelance basis. From then on the company saw a period to rival their heyday of the 1700s, except during the blitz and immediately after the Second World War, when production ceased almost completely. The small *Wartime* series of 1941, modelled by Eileen Soper, was the most notable production. It was not a popular series and for this reason these pieces are hard to find in today's

The Drummer (RW3154) by Gwendolen Parnell

Take Cover (RW3351) by Eileen Soper

market.

Some of Worcester's most successful modellers over the next decades were Stella Crofts, Dorothy and Freda Doughty, Doris Lindner, Gwendolen Parnell, Agnes Pinder-Davis, husband and wife Ronald and Ruth Van Ruyckevelt, Eva Soper and Pheobe Stabler. Each modeller's individual taste was allowed to shine through, with extremely satisfying results. While Dorothy Doughty preferred modelling flora and fauna, such as her well-known *Birds* series, Freda enjoyed lifelike figurines of children, such as the *Nursery Rhyme*, *Months of the Year* and *Children of the Nations* series (the immensely popular *Days of the Week* series, which was launched in the late 1930s, is still in production today.) Eva Soper is known for her work on the *English Birds* series, while Doris Lindner worked primarily on animal models such as the *Equestrian* series, as well as Royal portraits. Gwendolen Parnell (who painted before modelling ceramics) is probably best known for her *Cries of London* series, though she also, like Angnes Pinder-Davis, did *Chinoiseries*. The Van Ruyckevelts were responsible for the tremendously popular *Victorian Ladies* series and the *Nursing Sisters* series, while Ronald also created fish, flowers and birds.

Royal Worcester has continued to expand in terms of technology and scope. Although soapstone from Cornwall in combination with the harder China Clay is the historically distinctive ingredient in Worcester ceramics, nowadays the

factory makes both hard-paste ceramics with China clay, feldspar and quartz, and bone china. Bone china gets it name because it contains 50% ash from cattle bones, giving it the characteristic whiteness and translucency. Royal Worcester continues to sell dinnerware as well as figurines. In recent years the factory, under the direction of John Morris, has continued to issue quality figurines such as the ever-popular women in nineteenth and early twentieth century costume series, and series of children. Among the more prominent modellers and designers in the past years have been Kenneth and Timothy Potts, Elizabeth Greenshields (the present Design Manager) and Maureen Halson. Royal Worcester also produces figurines in conjunction with organizations like the RSPCA and UNICEF, and now accepts commissions by other firms, such as Compton & Woodhouse.

The Tea Party (RW3700) by Ruth Van Ruyckevelt

Midnight Rendezvous (RW4633) by Elizabeth Greenshields

HOW TO COLLECT ROYAL WORCESTER FIGURINES

A collection may begin from a variety of sources. A chance gift, a souvenir picked up on holiday, or an appreciation of Royal Worcester craftsmanship can initiate a lifetime of extremely satisfying collecting. It is not unusual for very large collections to be created in a comparatively short time as one's enthusiasm rises.

For those aspiring to form a complete collection, it is advisable to keep up with all the current introductions, as they can become very elusive once discontinued. Those searching for that special piece sometimes face stiff competition, not to mention sky-high prices. Fortunately, today's collectors have a number of options when developing their collections. Auction houses and antique fairs are both excellent sources for collectors. Estate auctions are another area to explore, as are specialist dealers. The Internet can be an invaluable tool for purchasing items, as well as gathering information on a specific piece.

As accumulating every Royal Worcester figurine produced is a rather daunting task, it is wise to decide at the beginning exactly what type of collection you wish to develop. Collections are often based around one of four general criteria: series, subject, size or artist.

Collecting by Series

Collecting by series offers the collector a general theme upon which to build a grand display of figures. *Children of the World*, *Days of the Week*, or *Months of the Year* will all produce collections to be proud of. More elusive series such as *The Cries of London* will test the mettle of any series collector.

Collecting by Subject

Scanning through the following pages, you will find many and varied subjects around which to build a collection. A collection of historical figures, for example, could include figurines from the *Historical Military Figures*, *Military Commanders* and *Queen's Regnant* series. As subject and series collecting have a tendency to overlap, we have provided a "Collecting by Series" Appendix (pages 313 to 320) to help collectors stay on course with their collections.

Collecting by Size

In today's modern world with limited space, size can be an extremely important issue. The splendour of a collection of *Military Commanders* can easily be lost if one does not have adequate space in which to display their pieces. Figurines come in all sizes, so it is easy to select complimentary pieces in a size range that will result in a handsome display.

Collecting by Artist

The work of a specific modeller such as Frederick M. Gertner, Dorothy Doughty, Freda Doughty, Doris Lindner, Kenneth Potts or Elizabeth Greenshields may interest a collector.

CARE AND REPAIR

A Royal Worcester figurine collection can be enjoyed indefinately as long as care is taken when handling and cleaning. When dusting, in situ, a soft cosmetic brush or photographic lens brush is useful for getting into tight corners. When necessary, glazed figures should be washed in lukewarm water, using a mild liquid detergent, then rinsed thoroughly and dried naturally or buffed gently with a soft cloth. It is important that water does not get inside the figure, so the hole in the bottom should be blocked up beforehand, perhaps with a cork or a rubber bung. Care should be taken not to knock figures against the tap or against each other as this may cause chips or imperceptible cracks in the glaze which could open up at a later date.

If the worst does happen, a professional restorer should be consulted as they can work 'miracles' with damaged figures. Whether it be a small chip or a shattered body, pieces can be mended so that the repair is invisible to all but the most experienced eye. It follows that when buying figures on the secondary market, it is advisable to check for restorations. The head, the arms and any projecting accessories are the most vulnerable parts, so look at these areas carefully in a good light. Repaired cracks can be sometimes detected by looking inside the figure through the hole in the bottom. There are special ultraviolet lamps which highlight some types of restoration but these are not widely used, except by professionals. Restored figures should be priced less than perfect examples, according to the amount of damage and the quality of the repair. Always enquire about the condition of a piece when buying, as a reputable dealer will stand by any guarantees they give regarding restorations.

Insuring Your Collectables

As with any other valuables, making certain your collectables are protected is a very important concern. It is paramount that you display or store any porcelain items in a secure place, preferably one safely away from traffic in your home.

Your collectables are most often covered under your basic homeowner's policy. There are generally three kinds of such policies; standard, broad and comprehensive. Each has its own specific deductible and terms.

Under a general policy, your collectables are considered contents and are covered for all of the perils listed under the contractual terms of your policy (fire, theft, water damage and so on).

However, since collectables are extremely delicate, breakage is treated diferently by most insurance companies. There is usually an extra premium attached to insure collectables against accidental breakage by or carelessness of the owner. This is sometimes referred to as a fine arts rider.

You are advised to contact your insurance professional to get all the answers.

In order to help protect your collection, it is critical that you take inventory of your collectables and have colour photographs taken of all your pieces. This is the surest method of establishing clearly, for the police and your insurance company, the items lost or destroyed. It is also the easiest way to establish their replacement value in the event of a tragedy.

A GUIDE TO BACKSTAMPS AND DATING

In general, mainly puce marks were used between 1900 and 1940, and from 1941 to the present black backstamps have been used exclusively. Green marks were used for the *Boer War Soldiers* series, and the *First World War Soldiers*. Blue marks were used for a few series only, and red marks are known to exist.

The basic marking system, for Royal Worcester, including the crest of four linked W's surmounted by a crown, originated in 1862. From 1891, the words ROYAL WORCESTER ENGLAND appear ringed around the crest.

For every subsequent year through 1903 a dot is added near the crown, to the left side in even years, to the right in odd years. In 1904 dots are placed beneath the crest as well, one for each year until 1915.

In 1916 a star is used to replace all the dots that had accumulated, a single dot being added for each year thereafter until 1927.

Backstamps

The Puce Marks 1925-1940

1928	Small square
1929	Diamond
1930	Three horizontal lines
1931	OO (two circles)
1932	OOO (three circles)
1933 to	Three circles and one dot
1939	Then a dot for each year

The Black Marks 1938 to date

B-1	1938	Three circles and 6 dots
	1939	Three circles and 7 dots
	1940	Three circles and 8 dots

A blue wavy line was sometimes added for 1938, 1939 and 1940

B-2	1941	Three circles and 9 dots
	1942	Three circles and 10 dots

1943	The black mark with no date code
1944	Bone China in large letters

1945 to	The black mark with no date code
1948	Bone China in small letters

B-3	1949	Black mark with V

Backstamps Continued

B-4	1950	Black mark with W
	1951 to 1955	Black mark with W and one dot added for each year

1956 to 1972	Black mark which may or may not have dots added for years
1988	Black mark with M inside a diamond (M replaces the R)
1989	Black mark with N inside a diamond (N replaces the M)
1990 to date	Black mark with R inside a circle (Reverting back to the R inside a circle but with lithographer's numbers added to indicate the year)

B-5		Black mark with R inside a circle
	1956	R and 6 dots
	1957	R and 7 dots
	1958	R and 8 dots

ROYAL WORCESTER COLLECTORS SOCIETY

For many collectors, new series will be the most attractive option. By joining the Collectors Society, members are entitled to a free gift, the ability to purchase figurines unavailable to the general public, and a visit to the Factory, Visitor Centre and Museum. To join the Society, or get more information about Royal Worcester, contact the following:

ROYAL WORCESTER

In the United Kingdom

Royal Worcester
Severn Street, Worcester
Worcestershire WR1 2NE
Tel.: +44 (1905) 23221
Fax: +44 (1905) 23601

In the United States

The Royal China and Porcelain
  Companies Inc.
1265 Glen Avenue
Moorsetown, NJ 08057-0912
Tel.: (800) 257-7189

In Canada

Northdale Trading Ltd.
55-D East Beaver Creek Road
Richmond Hill
Ontario L4B 1E8
Tel.: (905) 731-9535

WHERE TO BUY

Discontinued Royal Worcester figurines can be found in antique shops, markets, autions, shows and fairs. Specialist dealers in Royal Worcester figures attend many of these venues and events below.

For Auction happenings it is necessary to subscribe to the catalogues provided by those Auction Houses that hold 20th Century Auctions.

UNITED KINGDOM
Land-based Auction Houses

BBR Auctions
Elsecar Heritage Centre
Nr. Barnsley
South Yorkshire S74 8HJ
England
Tel.: (01226) 745156
Attn: Alan Blakeman

Bonhams
65-69 Lots Road, Chelsea
London SW10 ORN
England
Tel.: +44 (0207) 393 3900
Fax: +44 (0207) 393 3906

Christie's South Kensington
85 Old Brompton Road
London SW7 3LD
England
Tel.: +44 (0207) 581 7611
Fax: +44 (0207) 321-3321
www.christies.com
Attention: Michael Jeffrey

Potteries Specialist Auctions
271 Waterloo Road
Stoke-on-Trent ST6 3HR
Staffordshire, England
Tel.: +44 (01782) 286622
Fax: +44 (01782) 213777
Attn.: Steve Anderson

Louis Taylor
Britannia House
10 Town Road, Hanley
Stoke-on-Trent ST1 2QG, England
Tel.: +44 (01782) 214111
Fax: +44 (01782) 215283
Attn: Clive Hillier

Phillips
101 New Bond Street
London W1Y OAS, England
Tel.: +44 (0207) 629 6602
Fax: +44 (0207) 629 8876
www.phillips-auctions.com
attn: Mark Oliver

Sotheby's
34-35 New Bond Street
London W1A 2AA, England
Tel.: +44 (0207) 293 5000
Fax: +44 (0207) 293 5989

Sotheby's Sussex
Summer's Place
Bilingshurst, Sussex RH1 9AF
England
Tel.: +44 (01403) 833500
Fax: +44 (01403) 833699

Thomson Roddick & Laurie
60 Whitesands
Dumfries DG1 2RS, Scotland
Tel.: +44 (01387) 255366
Fax: +44 (01387) 266236

Peter Wilson Auctioneers
Victoria Gallery, Market Street
Nantwich, Cheshire CW5 5DG
England
Tel.: +44 (01270) 623878
Fax: +44 (01270) 610508

Antique Markets

Alfie's Antique Market
13-25 Church Street
London
Tuesday - Saturday

Camden Passage Market
Islington, London N1
Wednesday and Saturday

New Caledonian Market
Bermondsey Square, London
Friday morning

Portobello Road Market
Portobello Road
London W 11
Saturday

UNITED STATES
Land-based Auction Houses

Bonhams
c/o William Doyle Galleries
175 East 87th Street
New York, NY 10128
Tel.: (212) 427-2730
Fax: (212) 369-0892

Christie's East
219 East 67th Street
New York, NY 10021
Tel.: (212) 606-040
www.christies.com
Attn: Timothy Luke

Sotheby's Arcade Auctions
1334 York Avenue
New York, NY 10021
Tel.: (212) 606-7000
www.sothebys.com
Attn: Andrew Cheney

Collectable Shows

Atlantique City
New Atlantic City Convention Center
Atlantic City, NJ
Usually March and October
For information on times and dates:
Brimfield and Associates
P.O. Box 1800, Ocean City, NJ 08226
Tel.: (609) 926-1800
www.atlantiquecity.com

O'Hare National Antiques Show & Sale
Rosemont Convention Center
Chicago, Illinois
Usually April, August and November
For information on times and dates:
Manor House Shows Inc.
P.O. Box 7320, Fort Lauderdale, Fl. 33338
Tel.: (954) 563-6747

CANADA
Land-based Auction Houses

Maynards
415 West 2nd Avenue
Vancouver, BC V5Y 1E3
Tel.: (604) 876-1311

Ritchie's
288 King Street East
Toronto, Ontario M5A 1K4
Tel.: (416) 364-1864 Fax: (416) 364-0704
Attn: Caroline Kaider

Collectable Shows

Canadian Art & Collectible Show & Sale
Kitchener Memorial Auditorium
Kitchener, Ontario
Usually early May
For information on times and location:
George or Jackie Benninger
P.O. Box 130, Durham, Ontario N0G 1R0
Tel.: (519) 369-6950

Canadian Doulton & Collectible Fair
Toronto, Ontario
Usually early September
For information on times and location:
George or Jackie Benninger
P.O. Box 130, Durham, Ontario N0G 1R0
Tel.: (519) 369-6950

E-COMMERCE

Auction Sites

http://www.amazon.com/
http://www.auctions.com/
http://www.Auctions-on-line.com/
http://www.ebay.com/
http://www.auctions.excite.com/
http://www.auctions.lycos.com/
http://www.auctions.shopping.com/
http://www.auctions.xoom.com/
http://www.auctions.yahoo.com/

Antique Mall Sites

http://www.icollector.co.uk.com/
http://www.tias.com/
http://www.worldcollectorsnet.com/

The Charlton Press does not endorse any of these sites, they are listed for convenience only.

FURTHER READING

The Charlton Price Guide to Royal Worcester Figurines: Models by Freda Doughty,
  by Anthony Cast and John Edwards

The Collector's Handbook of Marks and Monograms on Pottery and Porcelain,
  by William Chaffers (revised by Referick Litchfield)

The Country Life Collector's Pocket Book of China, by G. Bernard Hughes

Encyclopaedia of British Pottery and Porcelain Marks, by Geoffrey A. Godden

English Ceramics: The Frances & Emory Cocke Collection, by Donald C. Peirce

English Pottery and Porcelain, by W. B. Honey

A Guide to the Dating of Royal Worcester Porcelain Marks from 1862, by Derek Shirley

An Illustrated Encyclopaedia of British Pottery and Porcelain, by Geoffrey A. Godden

The Parian Phenomenon, by Paul Atterbury

A Picture Book of Royal Worcester Figurines, by H. E. Frost

Royal Worcester Porcelain and the Dyson Perrins Collection,
  by Harry Frost and Wendy Cook

The Sandon Guide to Royal Worcester Figurines 1900-1970,
  by David, John and Henry Sandon

Wigornia News (periodical)

ROYAL
WORCESTER
FIGURINES
1900 to the present

Copy of the *Pierrot Puff Bowl*
sketch by Henri Bargas (RW3126)

RW2101
HEBE

Modeller: Unknown
Height: 29 ¼", 74.3 cm
Colour: Parian:
        1. Coloured
        2. Shot silks
        3. White glazed
Issued: 1900

		Price		
Colourways	Backstamp	U.S. $	Can. $	U.K. £
1. Coloured	Puce	3,500.00	4,250.00	1,750.00
2. Shot silks	Puce	3,000.00	3,750.00	1,500.00
3. White glazed	Puce	2,500.00	3,125.00	1,250.00

RW2102
PSYCHE

Modeller: Unknown
Height: 30", 76.2 cm
Colour: Parian:
        1. Coloured
        2. Shot silks
        3. White glazed
Issued: 1900

		Price		
Colourways	Backstamp	U.S. $	Can. $	U.K. £
1. Coloured	Puce	3,000.00	3,750.00	1,500.00
2. Shot silks	Puce	3,000.00	3,750.00	1,500.00
3. White glazed	Puce	2,500.00	3,125.00	1,250.00

RW2103
CUPID WITH BOW

Modeller: Unknown
Height: 19 ¾", 50.2 cm
Colour: Parian:
        1. Coloured
        2. White glazed
Issued: 1900

		Price		
Colourways	Backstamp	U.S. $	Can. $	U.K. £
1. Coloured	Puce		Extremely rare	
2. White glazed	Puce		Extremely rare	

RW2104
CUPID WITH SHEATH

Modeller: Unknown
Height: 19 ¾", 50.2 cm
Colour: Parian:
    1. Coloured
    2. White glazed
Issued: 1900

Colourways	Backstamp	U.S. $	Price Can. $	U.K. £
1. Coloured	Puce		Extremely rare	
2. White glazed	Puce		Extremely rare	

RW2105
FLEMISH MAN AND WOMAN

Modeller: Unknown
Height: 12", 30.5 cm
Colour: Parian:
    1. Stained ivory
    2. Shot silks
    3. White glazed
Issued: 1900

Description	Backstamp	U.S. $	Price Can. $	U.K. £
1. Flemish Man	Puce		Extremely rare	
2. Flemish Woman	Puce		Extremely rare	

RW2106
SOLDIER OF THE IMPERIAL FORCES

Modeller: George Evans
Height: 7", 17.8 cm
Colour: 1. Khaki and cream; gilding
2. Shot silks
Issued: 1900
Series: Boer War Soldiers

Colourways	Backstamp	U.S. $	Price Can. $	U.K. £
1. Khaki/cream	Green	1,100.00	1,375.00	550.00
2. Shot silks	Green	1,000.00	1,250.00	500.00

RW2107
IMPERIAL YEOMAN

Modeller: George Evans
Height: 7", 17.8 cm
Colour: 1. Khaki and cream; gilding
2. Shot silks
Issued: 1900
Series: Boer War Soldiers

Colourways	Backstamp	U.S. $	Price Can. $	U.K. £
1. Khaki/cream	Green	1,100.00	1,375.00	550.00
2. Shot silks	Green	1,000.00	1,250.00	500.00

RW2108
COLONIAL TROOPER

Modeller: George Evans
Height: 7", 17.8 cm
Colour: 1. Khaki and cream; gilding
2. Shot silks
Issued: 1900
Series: Boer War Soldiers

Colourways	Backstamp	U.S. $	Price Can. $	U.K. £
1. Khaki/cream	Green	1,100.00	1,375.00	550.00
2. Shot silks	Green	1,000.00	1,250.00	500.00

RW2109A
SOLDIER OF THE BLACK WATCH
First Version

Modeller:	George Evans
Height:	7 ½", 19.1 cm
Colour:	1. Khaki and cream; gilding
	2. Shot silks
Issued:	1900
Series:	Boer War Soldiers

		Price		
Colourways	*Backstamp*	*U.S. $*	*Can. $*	*U.K. £*
1. Khaki/cream	Puce	1,100.00	1,375.00	550.00
2. Shot silks	Puce	1,000.00	1,250.00	500.00

RW2109B
SOLDIER OF THE BLACK WATCH
Second Version

Modeller:	George Evans
Height:	7 ½", 19.1 cm
Colour:	1. Khaki and cream; gilding
	2. Shot silks
Issued:	1900
Series:	Boer War Soldiers

		Price		
Colourways	*Backstamp*	*U.S. $*	*Can. $*	*U.K. £*
1. Khaki/cream	Puce	1,100.00	1,375.00	550.00
2. Shot silks	Puce	1,000.00	1,250.00	500.00

RW2110
HANDY MAN

Modeller:	George Evans
Height:	7", 17.8 cm
Colour:	1. Khaki
	2. Shot silks
Issued:	1900
Series:	Boer War Soldiers

		Price		
Colourways	*Backstamp*	*U.S. $*	*Can. $*	*U.K. £*
1. Khaki	Puce	1,100.00	1,375.00	550.00
2. Shot silks	Puce	1,000.00	1,250.00	500.00

RW2111
GUARDSMAN

Modeller:	George Evans
Height:	7 ¾", 19.7 cm
Colour:	1. Khaki and cream; gilding
	2. Shot silks
Issued:	1900
Series:	Boer War Soldiers

Colourways	Backstamp	U.S. $	Price Can. $	U.K. £
1. Khaki/cream	Green	1,100.00	1,375.00	550.00
2. Shot silks	Green	1,000.00	1,250.00	500.00

RW2161
WANDERING MINSTREL (Male)

Modeller:	Unknown
Height:	14 ½", 36.8 cm
Colour:	Parian:
	1. Stained
	2. White glazed
Issued:	1901

Colourways	Backstamp	U.S. $	Price Can. $	U.K. £
1. Stained	Puce		Extremely rare	
2. White glazed	Puce		Extremely rare	

RW2162
WANDERING MINSTREL (Female)

Modeller:	Unknown
Height:	14 ½", 36.8 cm
Colour:	Parian:
	1. Stained
	2. White glazed
Issued:	1901

Colourways	Backstamp	U.S. $	Price Can. $	U.K. £
1. Stained	Puce		Extremely rare	
2. White glazed	Puce		Extremely rare	

RW2213
JESTER
Style One

Modeller:	Ernest Evans
Height:	7", 17.8 cm
Colour:	1. Biscuit
	2. Black and red costume; mauve and green base
	3. Shot silks
	4. Stained ivory
	5. Yellow, orange, and blue costume; mauve and green base
	6. White glazed
Issued:	1902
Reissued:	c.1930-by 1953

		Price		
Colourways	Backstamp	U.S. $	Can. $	U.K. £
1. Coloured (as above)	Puce	1,300.00	1,600.00	650.00
2. White glazed	Puce	575.00	750.00	300.00

RW2214
SHEPHERDESS
Style One

Modeller:	Ernest Evans
Height:	7", 17.8 cm
Colour:	1. Shot silks
	2. Stained ivory
	3. White glazed
Issued:	1902-by 1953

			Price	
Colourways	Backstamp	U.S. $	Can. $	U.K. £
1. Shot silks	Puce			
2. Stained ivory	Puce		Extremely rare	
3. White glazed	Puce			

RW2322
THE BEADLE

Modeller:	Ernest Evans
Height:	6 ¾", 17.2 cm
Colour:	1. Acid gold
	2. Imperial blue
	3. Pale brown, pale green, red-brown and gold (shot silks)
	4. Stained ivory
	5. White glazed
Issued:	1904-by 1953

			Price	
Colourways	Backstamp	U.S. $	Can. $	U.K. £
1. Acid gold	Puce		Extremely rare	
2. Imperial blue	Puce		Extremely rare	
3. Pale brown/green	Puce	1,300.00	1,600.00	650.00
4. Stained ivory	Puce		Extremely rare	
5. White glazed	Puce	600.00	800.00	325.00

RW2374
ENGLISH COSTUME FIGURES

Modeller:	George Evans
Height:	12 ½", 31.7 cm
Colour:	Unknown
Issued:	1905-by 1927

Description	Backstamp	U.S. $	Price Can. $	U.K. £
1. English Costume Figure (male)	Puce		Extremely rare	
2. English Costume Figure (female)	Puce		Extremely rare	

RW2375
GREEK FIGURE WITH CAPE (Male)

Modeller:	George Evans
Height:	6 ½", 16.5 cm
Colour:	Unknown
Issued:	1905-by 1927

Colourways	Backstamp	U.S. $	Price Can. $	U.K. £
Unknown	Puce		Rare	

RW2376
GREEK FIGURE WITH CAPE (Female)

Modeller:	George Evans
Height:	6 ½", 16.5 cm
Colour:	Unknown
Issued:	1905-by 1927

			Price	
Colourways	Backstamp	U.S. $	Can. $	U.K. £
Unknown	Puce		Rare	

RW2377
GREEK FIGURE WITH POINTED HAT

Modeller:	George Evans
Height:	6 ¾", 17.2 cm
Colour:	Unknown
Issued:	1905-by 1927

			Price	
Colourways	Backstamp	U.S. $	Can. $	U.K. £
Unknown	Puce		Rare	

RW2378
GREEK FIGURE HOLDING FLOWERS (Female)

Modeller:	George Evans
Height:	6 ½", 16.5 cm
Colour:	Unknown
Issued:	1905-by 1927

			Price	
Colourways	Backstamp	U.S. $	Can. $	U.K. £
Unknown	Puce		Rare	

RW2379
GREEK FIGURE HOLDING DOG (Boy)

Modeller:	George Evans
Height:	6 ½", 16.5 cm
Colour:	Unknown
Issued:	1905-by 1927

			Price	
Colourways	Backstamp	U.S. $	Can. $	U.K. £
Unknown	Puce		Rare	

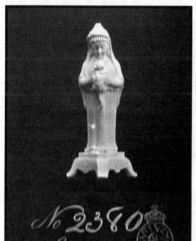

RW2380
GREEK FIGURE HOLDING KITTEN (Girl)

Modeller:	George Evans
Height:	6 ½", 16.5 cm
Colour:	Unknown
Issued:	1905-by 1927

			Price	
Colourways	Backstamp	U.S. $	Can. $	U.K. £
Unknown	Puce		Rare	

RW2387
BABY IN DRESSING GOWN

Modeller:	George Evans
Height:	5 ½", 14.0 cm
Colour:	Unknown
Issued:	1905-by 1927

			Price	
Colourways	Backstamp	U.S. $	Can. $	U.K. £
Unknown	Puce		Rare	

RW2388
WEIGHED OUT (Jockey)

Modeller:	George Evans
Height:	9", 22.9 cm
Colour:	Unknown
Issued:	1905-by 1927

			Price	
Colourways	Backstamp	U.S. $	Can. $	U.K. £
Unknown	Puce		Extremely rare	

RW2389
EARLY ENGLISH GENTLEMAN AND LADY

Modeller:	George Evans
Height:	8 ¼", 21.0 cm
Colour:	1. Delicate shot colours
	2. Shot silks
Issued:	1905-by 1927

			Price	
Description	Backstamp	U.S. $	Can. $	U.K. £
1. Early English Gentleman	Puce		Extremely rare	
2. Early English Lady	Puce		Extremely rare	

RW2391
MUSIC
Style One

Modeller: Unknown
Height: 15 ½", 39.4 cm
Colour: Delicate colours
Issued: 1905-by 1927

| | | | Price | |
Description	Backstamp	U.S. $	Can. $	U.K. £
1. Male (holding a lute)	Puce		Extremely rare	
2. Female (holding a music sheet)	Puce		Extremely rare	

RW2393
PIERETTE
PIERROT WITH RUFF

Modeller: Ernest Evans
Height: 8", 20.3 cm
Colour: Delicate shot colours
Issued: 1905-by 1927

Description	Backstamp	U.S. $	Price Can. $	U.K. £
1. Pierette	Puce		Extremely rare	
2. Pierrot with Ruff	Puce		Extremely rare	

RW2468
CLOWN'S HEAD

Modeller: Ernest Evans
Height: 3 ¼", 8.3 cm
Colour: Unknown
Issued: 1908-by 1927

Colourways	Backstamp	U.S. $	Price Can. $	U.K. £
Unknown	Puce		Extremely rare	

RW2523
LADY AND GENTLEMAN ON ROCOCO BASES

Modeller: Unknown
Height: 7", 17.8 cm
Colour: Unknown
Issued: 1911-by 1927

Description	Backstamp	U.S. $	Price Can. $	U.K. £
1. Lady on Rococo Base	Puce		Extremely rare	
2. Gentleman on Rococo Base	Puce		Extremely rare	

16

RW2582
FRENCH SOLDIER

Modeller:	Unknown
Height:	7 ½", 19.1 cm
Colour:	1. Blush ivory
	2. Blue and orange
	3. Shot colours
Issued:	1914-by 1927
Series:	First World War Soldiers

		Price		
Colourways	Backstamp	U.S. $	Can. $	U.K. £
1. Blush ivory	Puce	1,300.00	1,600.00	650.00
2. Blue and orange	Puce		Extremely rare	
3. Shot colours	Puce	1,300.00	1,600.00	650.00

RW2588
TERRITORIAL SOLDIER

Modeller:	Unknown
Height:	7 ½", 19.1 cm
Colour:	1. Blush ivory
	2. Shot colours
Issued:	1914-by 1927
Series:	First World War Soldiers

		Price		
Colourways	Backstamp	U.S. $	Can. $	U.K. £
Coloured (as above)	Puce	1,300.00	1,600.00	650.00

RW2591
SOLDIER OF THE WORCESTERSHIRE REGIMENT

Modeller:	Unknown
Height:	6", 15.0 cm
Colour:	1. Blush ivory
	2. Shot colours
Issued:	1917-by 1927
Series:	First World War Soldiers

		Price		
Colourways	Backstamp	U.S. $	Can. $	U.K. £
Coloured (as above)	Puce	1,300.00	1,600.00	650.00

16

RW2615
MOTHER AND TWO GIRLS

Designer: J. Wadsworth
Modeller: Frederick M. Gertner
Height: 5", 12.7 cm
Colour: White; black caps; lilac bows
Issued: 1916-by 1927

Colourways	Backstamp	U.S. $	Price Can. $	U.K. £
White/black/lilac	Green	900.00	1,100.00	450.00

RW2616
TWO LADIES

Designer: J. Wadsworth
Modeller: Frederick M. Gertner
Height: 4", 10.1 cm
Colour: Black capes with lilac bows; lilac mob caps with black bows;
            white skirts with painted flowers; black shoes
Issued: 1916-by 1927

Colourways	Backstamp	U.S. $	Price Can. $	U.K. £
Black/white/lilac	Green	900.00	1,100.00	450.00

RW2617
WIND

Designer: J. Wadsworth
Modeller: Frederick M. Gertner
Height: 5 ¾", 14.6 cm
Colour: 1. Black cape; black skirt trimmed with blue dots;
              turquoise-green mob cap
          2. Green cape; white and black skirt; green mob cap
          3. White cape with black checks; black mob cap with blue bow;
              black skirt with white lining; white mound base
Issued: 1916-by 1927

Colourways	Backstamp	U.S. $	Price Can. $	U.K. £
Coloured (as above)	Green	500.00	625.00	250.00

RW2618
BOY AND RABBIT

Modeller:	Frederick M. Gertner
Height:	3 ¼", 8.3 cm
Colour:	Unknown
Issued:	1916-by 1927

Colourways	Backstamp	U.S. $	Price Can. $	U.K. £
Unknown	Puce		Extremely rare	

RW2619
CRUCIFIX

Modeller:	Frederick M. Gertner
Height:	7 ¾" x 7 ¼", 19.7 x 18.4 cm
Colour:	White
Issued:	1916

Colourways	Backstamp	U.S. $	Price Can. $	U.K. £
White	Puce	800.00	1,000.00	400.00

RW2620
CRINOLINE FIGURE WITH CAP

Designer:	J. Wadsworth
Modeller:	Frederick M. Gertner
Height:	4 ¾", 12.1 cm
Colour:	1. Purple jacket and reticule; white skirt and hat with rose design
	2. White dress edged in black; black hat and reticule
	3. White dress edged in black, lilac flowers on skirt; black hat and reticule
Issued:	1916-by 1927

Colourways	Backstamp	U.S. $	Price Can. $	U.K. £
Coloured (as above)	Puce	400.00	500.00	200.00

Note: Issued as a dinner bell.

RW2621
CRINOLINE FIGURE WITH BOOK

Designer: J. Wadsworth
Modeller: Frederick M. Gertner
Height: 4 ½", 11.5 cm
Colour: 1. Black and green dress with pink roses; black book
            2. Green overjacket; white skirt with pink and green design
            3. White dress; black collar, lacing and edging; black bow and book
Issued: 1916-by 1927

Colourways	Backstamp	U.S. $	Price Can. $	U.K. £
Coloured (as above)	Green	400.00	500.00	200.00

Note: Issued as a dinner bell.

RW2625
THE IMMACULATE (VIRGIN MARY)

Modeller: Frederick M. Gertner
Height: 13 ¾", 34.9 cm
Colour: 1. Coloured
            2. Shot gold
            3. White glazed
Issued: 1916

Colourways	Backstamp	U.S. $	Price Can. $	U.K. £
1. Coloured (as above)	Puce	900.00	1,125.00	450.00
2. White glazed	Puce	600.00	750.00	300.00

RW2626
ST. JOSEPH

Modeller: Frederick M. Gertner
Height: 13 ¾", 34.9 cm
Colour: 1. Coloured
            2. Shot gold
            3. White glazed
Issued: 1916

Colourways	Backstamp	U.S. $	Price Can. $	U.K. £
1. Coloured (as above)	Puce	900.00	1,125.00	450.00
2. White glazed	Puce	600.00	750.00	300.00

RW2629
OFFICER OF THE FRENCH MARINES

Modeller: Frederick M. Gertner
Height: 10 ¾", 27.8 cm
Colour: Blue, red, white and black
Issued: 1916-by 1930
Series: Historical Military Figures

Colourways	Backstamp	U.S. $	Price Can. $	U.K. £
Blue/red/white/black	Puce	900.00	1,125.00	450.00

RW2632
GENTLEMAN IN EVENING DRESS WITH CIGAR

Modeller: Frederick M. Gertner
Height: 5", 12.7 cm
Colour: 1. Black jacket; grey trousers; green tablecloth
2. Purple jacket; lilac trousers; yellow tablecloth
Issued: 1916-by 1920

Colourways	Backstamp	U.S. $	Price Can. $	U.K. £
Coloured (as above)	Green	900.00	1,125.00	450.00

RW2633
GENTLEMAN WITH CLOAK AND OPERA HAT

Modeller: Frederick M. Gertner
Height: 5", 12.7 cm
Colour: 1. Blue cape, paler blue coat, hat and trousers
2. Lilac cape edged in black and lined in pale yellow;
black coat, hat, trousers
Issued: 1916-by 1920

Colourways	Backstamp	U.S. $	Price Can. $	U.K. £
Coloured (as above)	Green	900.00	1,125.00	450.00

RW2634
MARY, QUEEN OF SCOTS
Style One

Modeller: Frederick M. Gertner
Height: 8", 20.3 cm
Colour: Grey cape; pale pink and gold dress; gold headdress
Issued: 1916-by 1927
Reissued: c.1950-1979
Series: Historical Figures

Description	Backstamp	U.S. $	Price Can. $	U.K. £
1. Original issue	Puce	1,000.00	1,250.00	500.00
2. Reissued	Black	800.00	1,000.00	400.00

RW2635
OFFICER OF THE COLDSTREAM GUARDS 1815
First Version

Modeller: Frederick M. Gertner
Height: 10 ½", 26.7 cm
Colour: Red tunic; white trousers; black hat and boots; gold decoration
Issued: 1917-by 1927
Variations: RW2676 (Second Version), RW3675 (Third Version)
Series: Historical Military Figures

Colourways	Backstamp	U.S. $	Price Can. $	U.K. £
Red/white/black/gold	Puce	900.00	1,125.00	450.00

RW2637
HENRY VIII
Style One

Modeller: Frederick M. Gertner
Height: 9", 22.9 cm
Colour: Burgundy, yellow and black
Issued: 1916-by 1927
Reissued: c.1950-1979
Series: Historical Figures

Description	Backstamp	U.S. $	Price Can. $	U.K. £
1. Original issue	Puce	1,300.00	1,650.00	650.00
2. Reissued	Black	1,100.00	1,375.00	550.00

RW2643
EDWARD VI

Modeller:	Frederick M. Gertner
Height:	8 ½", 21.6 cm
Colour:	1. Black and gold
	2. Light blue-grey and gold
Issued:	1916-by 1927
Reissued:	c.1950-1979
Series:	Historical Figures

		Price		
Description	Backstamp	U.S. $	Can. $	U.K. £
1. Original issue	Puce	1,000.00	1,250.00	500.00
2. Reissued	Black	800.00	1,200.00	400.00

RW2645
SOLDIER OF THE FIRST WORLD WAR (Standing)

Modeller:	William Pointon
Height:	10 ¼", 26 cm
Colour:	Khaki
Issued:	1916
Series:	First World War Soldiers

		Price		
Colourways	Backstamp	U.S. $	Can. $	U.K. £
Khaki	Puce	1,200.00	1,500.00	600.00

RW2646
SOLDIER OF THE FIRST WORLD WAR (Seated)

Modeller:	William Pointon
Height:	5 ½", 14.0 cm
Colour:	Khaki
Issued:	1916
Series:	First World War Soldiers

		Price		
Colourways	Backstamp	U.S. $	Can. $	U.K. £
Khaki	Puce	1,100.00	1,375.00	550.00

RW2648
ELIZABETH I
Style One

Modeller:	Frederick M. Gertner
Height:	8 ¼", 21.0 cm
Colour:	Burgundy and gold dress; light blue cape
Issued:	1917-by 1927
Reissued:	c.1950-1979
Series:	Historical Figures

Description	Backstamp	U.S. $	Price Can. $	U.K. £
1. Original issue	Puce	1,300.00	1,600.00	650.00
2. Reissued	Black	900.00	1,125.00	450.00

RW2649
LADY WITH MIRROR - TRUTH

Modeller:	Frederick M. Gertner
Height:	11 ½", 29.2 cm
Colour:	1. Coloured
	2. White glazed
Issued:	1916-by 1930
Series:	Female Dancing Figures

Colourways	Backstamp	U.S. $	Price Can. $	U.K. £
1. Coloured	Puce		Extremely rare	
2. White glazed	Puce		Extremely rare	

RW2650
LADY WITH MASK - FALSEHOOD

Modeller:	Frederick M. Gertner
Height:	11 ½", 29.2 cm
Colour:	1. Coloured
	2. White glazed
Issued:	1916-by 1930
Series:	Female Dancing Figures

Colourways	Backstamp	U.S. $	Price Can. $	U.K. £
1. Coloured	Puce		Extremely rare	
2. White glazed	Puce		Extremely rare	

RW2651
CHARLES I

Modeller: Frederick M. Gertner
Height: 9 ½", 24.0 cm
Colour: 1. Dark blue jacket; dark green trousers; black hat; brown boots
           2. Mouse-grey jacket; red trousers; light blue shirt; black hat
Issued: 1917-by 1927
Reissued: c.1950-1979
Series: Historical Figures

Description	Backstamp	U.S. $	Price Can. $	U.K. £
1. Original issue	Puce	900.00	1,125.00	450.00
2. Reissued	Black	750.00	925.00	375.00

RW2652
ANNE BOLEYN

Modeller: Frederick M. Gertner
Height: 8 ¼", 21.0 cm
Colour: Blue dress; grey-gold robe and headdress; gold trim
Issued: 1917-by 1927
Reissued: c.1950-1979
Series: Historical Figures

Description	Backstamp	U.S. $	Price Can. $	U.K. £
1. Original issue	Puce	900.00	1,125.00	450.00
2. Reissued	Black	750.00	925.00	375.00

RW2654
FEMALE DANCING FIGURE
Style One

Modeller: Unknown
Height: 11", 27.9 cm
Colour: Unknown
Issued: 1916
Series: Female Dancing Figures

Colourways	Backstamp	U.S. $	Price Can. $	U.K. £
Unknown	Puce		Extremely rare	

RW2655
FEMALE DANCING FIGURE
Style Two

Modeller: Unknown
Height: 11", 27.9 cm
Colour: Unknown
Issued: 1916
Series: Female Dancing Figures

Colourways	Backstamp	U.S. $	Price Can. $	U.K. £
Unknown	Puce		Extremely rare	

RW2657
OFFICER OF THE SEAFORTH HIGHLANDERS 1812

Modeller: Frederick M. Gertner
Height: 11 ¾", 28.5 cm
Colour: Red jacket with gold epaulettes; green, blue and turquoise kilt; black bearskin
Issued: 1917-by 1927
Reissued: c.1950-1979
Varieties: Also called RW3677 Officer of the Scots Guards
Series: Historical Military Figures

Description	Backstamp	U.S. $	Price Can. $	U.K. £
1. Original issue	Puce	1,100.00	1,375.00	550.00
2. Reissued	Black	900.00	1,125.00	450.00

Note: This model is also known on a 'ground' base.

RW2658
OFFICER OF THE ROYAL ARTILLERY 1815

Modeller: Frederick M. Gertner
Height: 10 ½", 29.8 cm
Colour: Blue and red tunic; white trousers; black hat and boots; gold trim
Issued: 1917-by 1927
Reissued: c.1950-1979
Series: Historical Military Figures

Description	Backstamp	U.S. $	Price Can. $	U.K. £
1. Original issue	Puce	1,100.00	1,375.00	550.00
2. Reissued	Black	900.00	1,125.00	450.00

RW2659
CLASSICAL LADY WITH LYRE

Modeller: Frederick M. Gertner
Height: 14 ¼", 36.2 cm
Colour: 1. Gold, with ivory head and arms
           2. Traditional shot colours
Issued: 1916

Colourways	Backstamp	U.S. $	Price Can. $	U.K. £
Coloured (as above)	Puce		Extremely rare	

RW2660
CLASSICAL LADY WITH TAMBOURINE

Modeller: Frederick M. Gertner
Height: 14 ¼", 36.2 cm
Colour: 1. Gold, with ivory head and arms
           2. Traditional shot colours
Issued: 1916

Colourways	Backstamp	U.S. $	Price Can. $	U.K. £
Coloured (as above)	Puce		Extremely rare	

RW2661
THE ADMIRAL 1780

Modeller: Frederick M. Gertner
Height: 11 ½", 29.2 cm
Colour: Deep blue uniform with gold trim; cream waistcoat;
           black base
Issued: 1917-by 1927
Reissued: c.1950-1979
Series: Historical Military Figures

Description	Backstamp	U.S. $	Price Can. $	U.K. £
1. Original issue	Puce	950.00	1,200.00	480.00
2. Reissued	Black	800.00	1,000.00	400.00

The Museum *of*
Worcester Porcelain

Registered Charity No. 223753

A journey from 1751 to the present day

OPEN 7 DAYS A WEEK

Monday to Saturday: 9.00am - 5.30pm. Sunday: 11.00am - 5.00pm.

The Museum of Worcester Porcelain, Severn Street, Worcester, WR1 2NE. ENGLAND.
Tel: 01905 23221 • Fax: 01905 617807
Web: www.royal-worcester.co.uk • E-mail: museum@royal-worcester.co.uk

Collectors Society

Membership Benefits

- Exclusive complimentary gift, Royal Worcester's Fine Bone China figurine, Katie, when you join.

- Exclusive members offers.

- VIP invitation to Royal Worcester Visitor Centre, Factory & Museum.

- Royal Worcester's exclusive magazine for members, 'Society'.

- Invitation to Royal Worcester's Special Events.

Katie

COLLECTORS SOCIETY COMPLIMENTARY GIFT

Size:
14.5cm

Modelled by:
Maureen Halson

Year of Introduction:
2000

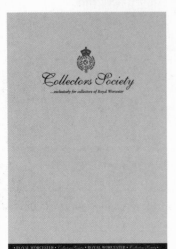

Above: Membership Pack & Membership Card
Right: Collectors Magazine 'Society'.

RW2668
SIR WALTER RALEIGH

Modeller: Frederick M. Gertner
Height: 9 ¾", 24.7 cm
Colour: Cream and burgundy cape; light green vest; black knickers; taupe hat
Issued: 1917-1927
Reissued: c.1950-1979
Series: Historical Figures

Description	Backstamp	U.S. $	Price Can. $	U.K. £
1. Original issue	Puce	950.00	1,200.00	480.00
2. Reissued	Black	750.00	925.00	375.00

RW2672
CHARLES II

Modeller: Frederick M. Gertner
Height: 9 ¾", 24.7 cm
Colour: 1. Burgundy coat
2. Taupe coat
Issued: 1917-1927
Reissued: c.1950-1979
Series: Historical Figures

Description	Backstamp	U.S. $	Price Can. $	U.K. £
1. Original issue	Puce	950.00	1,200.00	480.00
2. Reissued	Black	750.00	925.00	375.00

RW2673
MAIDEN WITH BALL IN RIGHT HAND

Modeller: Frederick M. Gertner
Height: 12", 30.5 cm
Colour: White
Issued: 1917

Colourways	Backstamp	U.S. $	Price Can. $	U.K. £
White	Puce		Extremely rare	

Note: Pair with RW2674 Maiden with Both Hands Outstretched.

RW2674
MAIDEN WITH BOTH HANDS OUTSTRETCHED

Modeller: Frederick M. Gertner
Height: 12", 30.5 cm
Colour: White
Issued: 1917

Colourways	Backstamp	U.S. $	Price Can. $	U.K. £
White	Puce		Extremely rare	

Note: Pair with RW2673 Maiden with Ball in Right Hand.

RW2675
OFFICER OF THE 3RD DRAGOON GUARDS 1806

Modeller: Frederick M. Gertner
Height: 11 ½", 29.2 cm
Colour: Red tunic; white trousers; black hat and boots; gold decoration
Issued: 1917-by 1927
Reissued: c.1950-1979
Series: Historical Military Figures

Description	Backstamp	U.S. $	Price Can. $	U.K. £
1. Original issue	Puce	1,050.00	1,300.00	525.00
2. Reissued	Black	850.00	1,050.00	425.00

RW2676
OFFICER OF THE COLDSTREAM GUARDS 1815
Second Version

Modeller: Frederick M. Gertner
Height: 11 ½", 29.2 cm
Colour: Red tunic; white trousers; black hat and boots; gold decoration
Issued: 1917-by 1930
Varieties: RW2635 (First Version), RW3675 (Third Version)
Series: Historical Military Figures

Colourways	Backstamp	U.S. $	Price Can. $	U.K. £
Red/white/black/gold	Puce	1,000.00	1,250.00	500.00

RW2677
OFFICER OF THE 17TH DRAGOON GUARDS 1814

Modeller:	Frederick M. Gertner
Height:	11 ¾", 29.8 cm
Colour:	1. Navy and white uniform; black base
	2. Navy and white uniform; black base; gilt metal wire on cap
Issued:	1917-by1930
Reissued:	c.1950-1979
Series:	Historical Military Figures

			Price	
Description	Backstamp	U.S. $	Can. $	U.K. £
1. Original issue	Puce	1,000.00	1,250.00	500.00
2. Reissued	Black	800.00	1,000.00	400.00

Note: Later models had a metal wire added to the cap.

RW2679
COLUMBINE
Style One

Modeller:	Frederick M. Gertner
Height:	9 ½", 24.0 cm
Colour:	Crownware:
	1. Ivory; powder blue costume and base
	Bone china:
	2. Pink and gold tutu, stockings and cap
Issued:	1917-by 1930

			Price	
Description	Backstamp	U.S. $	Can. $	U.K. £
1. Crownware	Puce	800.00	1,000.00	400.00
2. Bone china	Puce	1,000.00	1,250.00	500.00

Note: Crownware figures carry a CW number.

RW2680
HARLEQUIN
Style One

Modeller:	Frederick M. Gertner
Height:	9 ½", 24.0 cm
Colour:	Crownware:
	1. Ivory colourings; powder blue costume and base
	Bone china:
	2. Black costume, mask and cap
	3. Gold and white
Issued:	1917-by 1930

			Price	
Description	Backstamp	U.S. $	Can. $	U.K. £
1. Crownware	Puce	800.00	1,000.00	400.00
2. Bone china	Puce	1,000.00	1,250.00	500.00

RW2681
COLUMBINE
Style Two

Modeller:	Frederick M. Gertner
Height:	9 ½", 24.0 cm
Colour:	Crownware:
	1. Ivory colourings; powder blue costume and base
	Bone China:
	2. Gold costume, stockings, cap; white and gold base
Issued:	1917

		Price		
Description	Backstamp	U.S. $	Can. $	U.K. £
1. Crownware	Puce	800.00	1,000.00	400.00
2. Bone china	Puce	1,000.00	1,250.00	500.00

RW2682
PIERROT
Style One

Modeller:	Frederick M. Gertner
Height:	9 ½", 24.0 cm
Colour:	Crownware:
	1. Ivory colourings; powder blue costume and base
	Bone china:
	2. Yellow jacket, trousers, shoes and cap; flowered shirt;
	white, gold and black base
Issued:	1917

		Price		
Descripton	Backstamp	U.S. $	Can. $	U.K. £
1. Crownware	Puce		Extremely rare	
2. Bone china	Puce		Extremely rare	

RW2683
NUDE GIRL WITH FLOWERS (Seated)

Modeller:	Frederick M. Gertner
Height:	4 ¼", 10.8 cm
Colour:	Crownware:
	1. Light blue
	Bone china:
	2. Ivory finish; green circular base
Issued:	1917

		Price		
Description	Backstamp	U.S. $	Can. $	U.K. £
1. Crownware	Puce	500.00	625.00	250.00
2. Bone china	Puce	700.00	875.00	350.00

RW2684
NUDE BOY WITH FLOWERS (Seated)

Modeller: Frederick M. Gertner
Height: 4 ¼", 10.8 cm
Colour: Crownware:
     1. Light blue circular base
     Bone china:
     2. Ivory finish; green circular base
Issued: 1917

Description	Backstamp	U.S. $	Price Can. $	U.K. £
1. Crownware	Puce	500.00	625.00	250.00
2. Bone china	Puce	700.00	875.00	350.00

RW2685
NUDE BOY WITH FLOWERS (Standing)
Style One

Modeller: Frederick M. Gertner
Height: 6 ¼", 15.9 cm
Colour: 1. Green and ivory (matt)
     2. White glazed
Issued: 1917-by 1930

Description	Backstamp	U.S. $	Price Can. $	U.K. £
1. Crownware	Puce	350.00	450.00	180.00
2. Bone china	Puce	500.00	625.00	250.00

RW2686
NUDE GIRL WITH FLOWERS (Standing)

Modeller: Frederick M. Gertner
Height: 6", 15.0 cm
Colour: 1. Green and ivory (matt)
     2. White glazed
Issued: 1917

Description	Backstamp	U.S. $	Price Can. $	U.K. £
1. Crownware	Puce	350.00	450.00	180.00
2. Bone china	Puce	500.00	625.00	250.00

RW2687
NUDE CHILD (Seated)

Modeller: Frederick M. Gertner
Height: 5", 12.7 cm
Colour: Crownware:
         1. Light blue
         Bone china:
         2. Green and ivory
Issued: 1917

| | | Price | | |
Description	Backstamp	U.S. $	Can. $	U.K. £
1. Crownware	Puce	325.00	400.00	160.00
2. Bone china	Puce	525.00	650.00	260.00

RW2688
NUDE FEMALE LEANING ON A PEDESTAL

Modeller: Frederick M. Gertner
Height: 6", 15.0 cm
Colour: Crownware:
         1. Light blue
         Bone china
         2. Green and ivory
Issued: 1917-by 1927

| | | Price | | |
Description	Backstamp	U.S. $	Can. $	U.K. £
1. Crownware	Puce	325.00	400.00	160.00
2. Bone china	Puce	525.00	650.00	260.00

RW2689
NUDE FEMALE PUTTING SLIPPER ON FOOT

Modeller: Frederick M. Gertner
Height: 5 ¾", 14.6 cm
Colour: Crownware:
         1. Unknown
         Bone China:
         2. Ivory; yellow slippers, headband; matt green plinth
         3. Light blue; gold details
         4. Shagreen; gold details
Issued: 1917

| | | Price | | |
Description	Backstamp	U.S. $	Can. $	U.K. £
1. Crownware	Puce	350.00	450.00	180.00
2. Bone china	Puce	550.00	700.00	280.00

RW2690
NUDE BATHER RECLINING ON PLINTH
Style One

Modeller:	Unknown
Height:	7 ½", 19.1 cm
Colour:	Crownware:
	1. Ivory and light blue
	2. Ivory and matt green
	3. Strongly coloured
	Bone china:
	4. Light blue
	5. White glazed
Issued:	1. Crownware — 1917 2. Bone china — 1918-by 1930

		Price		
Description	Backstamp	U.S. $	Can. $	U.K. £
1. Crownware	Puce	450.00	550.00	220.00
2. Bone china	Puce	650.00	800.00	320.00
3. White glazed	Puce	350.00	475.00	200.00

*Photograph not
available
at press time*

RW2691
FEMALE NUDE, HAND ON BREAST

Modeller:	Frederick M. Gertner
Height:	7 ½", 19.1 cm
Colour:	Crownware:
	1. Ivory and light blue
	2. Ivory and matt green
	Bone china:
	3. Light blue
	4. Shagreen
	5. White glazed
Issued:	1. Crownware — 1918
	2. Bone China — 1918-by 1930

		Price		
Description	Backstamp	U.S. $	Can. $	U.K. £
1. Crownware	Puce	450.00	550.00	220.00
2. Bone china	Puce	650.00	800.00	320.00
3. White glazed	Puce	350.00	475.00	200.00

RW2692
FEMALE NUDE, HAND BEHIND SHOULDER

Modeller:	Frederick M. Gertner
Height:	7 ½", 19.1 cm
Colour:	Crownware:
	1. Ivory and light blue
	2. Ivory and matt green
	Bone china:
	3. Light blue
	4. Shagreen
	5. White glazed
Issued:	1. Crownware — 1918
	2. Bone china — 1918-by 1930

		Price		
Description	Backstamp	U.S. $	Can. $	U.K. £
1. Crownware	Puce	450.00	550.00	220.00
2. Bone china	Puce	650.00	800.00	320.00
3. White glazed	Puce	350.00	475.00	200.00

RW2693
NUDE FEMALE SLIPPER IN RIGHT HAND

Modeller: Frederick M. Gertner
Height: 5 ¾", 14.6 cm
Colour: Crownware:
    1. Unknown
    Bone china:
    2. Ivory
    3. Light blue; gold details
    4. Shagreen; gold details
Issued: 1. Crownware — 1917
    2. Bone china —1918-by 1930

		Price		
Description	Backstamp	U.S. $	Can. $	U.K. £
1. Crownware	Puce	450.00	550.00	220.00
2. Bone china	Puce	650.00	800.00	320.00

RW2694
NUDE BOY WITH FRUIT
Style One

Modeller: Unknown
Height: 7", 17.8 cm
Colour: Creamy glaze
Issued: 1918-by 1927

		Price		
Description	Backstamp	U.S. $	Can. $	U.K. £
1. Crownware	Puce	450.00	550.00	220.00
2. Bone china	Puce	650.00	800.00	320.00

RW2697
NUDE BATHER RECLINING ON PLINTH
Style Two

Modeller: Frederick M. Gertner
Height: 7 ¾", 19.7 cm
Colour: Crownware:
    1. Ivory and light blue
    2. Ivory and matt green
    3. Red-brown hair; green, pink and beige foliage
    Bone china:
    4. Light blue
    5. White glazed
Issued: 1. Crownware — 1917   2. Bone china — 1918-by 1930

		Price		
Description	Backstamp	U.S. $	Can. $	U.K. £
1. Crownware	Puce	350.00	450.00	180.00
2. Bone china	Puce	550.00	700.00	280.00
3. White glazed	Puce	225.00	325.00	150.00

RW2698
NAIAD (On plinth)

Modeller:	Frederick M. Gertner
Height:	8 ½", 21.6 cm
Colour:	1. Ivory
	2. Matt green
	3. Powder blue and gold
	4. White; light blue base
	5. White; shagreen base
Issued:	1. Crownware — 1918
	2. Bone china — 1918-by 1930
Varieties:	RW3030 Naiad; RW2783 Naiad Powder Bowl (First Version); RW2820 Naiad Power Bowl (Second Version)

		Price		
Description	Backstamp	U.S. $	Can. $	U.K. £
1. Crownware	Puce	550.00	700.00	280.00
2. Bone china	Puce	750.00	950.00	380.00

RW2702
NUDE BOY WITH DOLPHIN

Modeller:	Frederick M. Gertner
Height:	5 ¾", 14.6 cm
Colour:	Crownware:
	Cream body; red hair; green dolphin
Issued:	1919-by 1927

		Price		
Description	Backstamp	U.S. $	Can. $	U.K. £
Crownware	Puce	800.00	1,000.00	400.00

RW2703
NUDE BOY WITH SEAWEED

Modeller:	Frederick M. Gertner
Height:	7 ½", 19.1 cm
Colour:	Crownware:
	Creamy glaze
Issued:	1919-by 1927

		Price		
Description	Backstamp	U.S. $	Can. $	U.K. £
Crownware	Puce	800.00	1,200.00	400.00

RW2704
NUDE BOY WITH VINES (Standing)

Modeller:	Frederick M. Gertner
Height:	8 ½", 21.6 cm
Colour:	Crownware: Unknown
Issued:	1919-by 1927

Description	Backstamp	U.S. $	Price Can. $	U.K. £
Crownware	Puce	800.00	1,200.00	400.00

RW2705
NUDE BOY WITH FLOWERS (Standing)
Style Two

Modeller:	Frederick M. Gertner
Height:	8 ¼", 21.0 cm
Colour:	Crownware: Unknown
Issued:	1919-by 1927

Description	Backstamp	U.S. $	Price Can. $	U.K. £
Crownware	Puce	800.00	1,200.00	400.00

RW2706
NUDE BOY WITH FRUIT (Seated, facing right)
Style Two

Modeller:	Frederick M. Gertner
Height:	8 ½", 21.6 cm
Colour:	Crownware: Unknown
Issued:	1919-by 1927

Description	Backstamp	U.S. $	Price Can. $	U.K. £
Crownware	Puce	800.00	1,200.00	400.00

RW2707
NUDE BOY WITH FRUIT (Seated, facing left)
Style Three

Modeller: Frederick M. Gertner
Height: 8 ½", 21.6 cm
Colour: Crownware:
           Unknown
Issued: 1919-by 1927

Description	Backstamp	U.S. $	Price Can. $	U.K. £
Crownware	Puce	800.00	1,000.00	400.00

RW2715
NUDE GIRL WITH GARLAND OF LEAVES (Seated)

Modeller: Frederick M. Gertner
Height: 6", 15.0 cm
Colour: Crownware:
           Unknown
Issued: 1919

Description	Backstamp	U.S. $	Price Can. $	U.K. £
Crownware	Puce	700.00	875.00	350.00

RW2716
NUDE GIRL WITH GARLAND OF FRUIT AND LEAVES (Seated)

Modeller: Frederick M. Gertner
Height: 5 ¾", 14.6 cm
Colour: Crownware:
           Fleshtone; red-brown hair; green leaves; black base
Issued: 1919

Description	Backstamp	U.S. $	Price Can. $	U.K. £
Crownware	Puce	700.00	875.00	350.00

RW2717
NUDE BOY WITH ROSES (Standing)

Modeller: Frederick M. Gertner
Height: 6 ¼", 15.9 cm
Colour: Crownware:
    1. Light blue
    2. White glazed
Issued: 1919

Description	Backstamp	U.S. $	Price Can. $	U.K. £
Crownware	Puce	700.00	875.00	350.00

RW2718
NUDE GIRL WITH ROSES AND LEAVES (Standing)

Modeller: Frederick M. Gertner
Height: 6 ¼", 15.9 cm
Colour: Crownware:
    1. Light blue
    2. White; red-brown hair; green leaves; yellow roses
Issued: 1919

Description	Backstamp	U.S. $	Price Can. $	U.K. £
Crownware	Puce	700.00	875.00	350.00

RW2719
NUDE GIRL WITH BASKET OF ROSES (Seated)

Modeller: Frederick M. Gertner
Height: 5 ¼", 13.3 cm
Colour: Crownware:
    Unknown
Issued: 1919

Description	Backstamp	U.S. $	Price Can. $	U.K. £
Crownware	Puce	700.00	875.00	350.00

RW2720
NUDE GIRL WITH BOUQUET OF ROSES (Seated)

Modeller: Frederick M. Gertner
Height: 5 ¼", 13.3 cm
Colour: Crownware:
Unknown
Issued: 1919

Description	Backstamp	U.S. $	Price Can. $	U.K. £
Crownware	Puce	700.00	875.00	350.00

RW2723
DRUMMER BOY

Modeller: Frederick M. Gertner, altered from a James Hadley model
Height: 7 ½", 19.1 cm
Colour: Bone china:
Unknown
Issued: 1919

Description	Backstamp	U.S. $	Price Can. $	U.K. £
Bone china	Puce	900.00	1,125.00	450.00

RW2724
VIVANDIÈRE

Modeller: Frederick M. Gertner, altered from a James Hadley model
Height: 7 ½", 19.1 cm
Colour: Bone china:
Unknown
Issued: 1919

Description	Backstamp	U.S. $	Price Can. $	U.K. £
Bone china	Puce	900.00	1,125.00	450.00

RW2725
KATE GREENAWAY BOY
Style One (Hands in pockets)

Modeller:	James Hadley
Height:	6 ½", 16.5 cm
Colour:	1. Cream clothes edged in gilding
	2. Green trousers; lilac shirt with white ruff; yellow hat; black shoes
	3. Green suit; white ruff; straw hat
Issued:	1919

		Price		
Colourways	Backstamp	U.S. $	Can. $	U.K. £
Coloured (as above)	Puce	900.00	1,125.00	450.00

Note: Model RW2725 was based on RW800 originally issued in 1880. Also issued as sugar sifters.

RW2726
KATE GREENAWAY GIRL
Style One (Hands clasped in front)

Modeller:	James Hadley
Height:	6 ½", 16.5 cm
Colour:	1. Light green dress; grey collar; brown shoes and hat
	2. White dress with pink flowers and blue trim; black shoes
Issued:	1919

		Price		
Colourways	Backstamp	U.S. $	Can. $	U.K. £
Coloured (as above)	Puce	900.00	1,125.00	450.00

Note: Model RW2726 was based on RW800 originally issued in 1880. Also issued as sugar sifters.

RW2727
KATE GREENAWAY BOY
Style Two (Left arm behind back)

Modeller:	Frederick M. Gertner, altered from a James Hadley model
Height:	6 ¾", 17.2 cm
Colour:	Unknown
Issued:	1919

		Price		
Colourways	Backstamp	U.S. $	Can. $	U.K. £
Unknown	Puce	900.00	1,125.00	450.00

RW2728
KATE GREENAWAY GIRL
Style Two (Hands behind back)

Modeller:	Frederick M. Gertner, altered from a James Hadley model
Height:	6 ¾", 17.2 cm
Colour:	Pink bodice; cream fichu cuffs and apron; grey skirt; brown hat
Issued:	1919

		Price		
Colourways	Backstamp	U.S. $	Can. $	U.K. £
Pink/cream/grey	Puce	900.00	1,125.00	450.00

RW2732
COUNTRY GIRL WITH WALKING STICK

Modeller:	Frederick M. Gertner
Height:	6 ½", 16.5 cm
Colour:	Unknown
Issued:	1919

		Price		
Colourways	Backstamp	U.S. $	Can. $	U.K. £
Unknown	Puce		Extremely rare	

RW2733
COUNTRY GIRL WITH GLOVES

Modeller:	Frederick M. Gertner
Height:	6 ½", 16.5 cm
Colour:	Unknown
Issued:	1919

		Price		
Colourways	Backstamp	U.S. $	Can. $	U.K. £
Unknown	Puce		Extremely rare	

RW2734
YOUNG HUNTSMAN WITH WHIP

Modeller:	Frederick M. Gertner
Height:	7", 17.8 cm
Colour:	Unknown
Issued:	1919

		Price		
Colourways	Backstamp	U.S. $	Can. $	U.K. £
Unknown	Puce	Extremely rare		

RW2735
YOUNG HUNTSMAN WITH TOP HAT

Modeller:	Frederick M. Gertner
Height:	7", 17.8 cm
Colour:	Unknown
Issued:	1919

		Price		
Colourways	Backstamp	U.S. $	Can. $	U.K. £
Unknown	Puce	Extremely rare		

RW2783
NAIAD POWDER BOWL
First Version

Modeller:	Frederick M. Gertner
Height:	8", 20.3 cm
Colour:	1. Light blue
	2. Matt ivory
	3. Pink
	4. Shagreen
Issued:	1920
Varieties:	RW3030 Naiad; RW2698 Naiad (on plinth);
	RW2820 Naiad Powder Bowl (Second Version)

		Price		
Colourways	Backstamp	U.S. $	Can. $	U.K. £
Coloured (as above)	Puce	900.00	1,125.00	450.00

Note: Commissioned by DuBarry et Cie.

43

RW2798
ROSES

Modeller:	François Clemencin
Height:	10 ¼", 26.0 cm
Colour:	1. Full colours
	2. Light blue drapery
	3. Matt ivory
	4. Shot silk with gilding
Issued:	1922

Colourways	Backstamp	U.S. $	Price Can. $	U.K. £
Coloured (as above)	Puce	900.00	1,125.00	450.00

RW2799
GRAPES

Modeller:	François Clemencin
Height:	10 ¼", 26.0 cm
Colour:	1. Full colours
	2. Light blue drapery
	3. Matt ivory
	4. Shot silk with gilding
Issued:	1922

Colourways	Backstamp	U.S. $	Price Can. $	U.K. £
Coloured (as above)	Puce	900.00	1,125.00	450.00

RW2800
FEMALE NUDE WITH MIRROR

Modeller:	François Clemencin
Height:	9 ¾", 24.7 cm
Colour:	1. Full colours
	2. Light blue drapery
	3. Matt ivory
	4. Shot silk with gilding
Issued:	1922-by 1930

Colourways	Backstamp	U.S. $	Price Can. $	U.K. £
Coloured (as above)	Puce	900.00	1,125.00	450.00

RW2801
FEMALE NUDE WITH LEAVES (Seated)

Modeller:	François Clemencin
Height:	7 ½", 19.1 cm
Colour:	1. Full colours
	2. Light blue drapery
	3. Matt ivory
	4. Shot silk with gilding
Issued:	1922

		Price		
Colourways	Backstamp	U.S. $	Can. $	U.K. £
Coloured (as above)	Puce	800.00	1,000.00	400.00

RW2805
FEMALE NUDE (Seated, facing left)

Modeller:	Possibly François Clemencin
Height:	4 ½", 11.9 cm
Colour:	Crownware:
	1. Light blue and ivory
	2. Shot silk and ivory
	3. White glazed
Issued:	1922-by 1930

		Price		
Colourways	Backstamp	U.S. $	Can. $	U.K. £
1. Coloured (as above)	Puce	700.00	875.00	350.00
2. White glazed	Puce	225.00	300.00	125.00

RW2806
FEMALE NUDE (Seated, facing right)

Modeller:	Possibly François Clemencin
Height:	4 ½", 11.9 cm
Colour:	Crownware:
	1. Light blue and ivory
	2. Shot silk and ivory
	3. White glazed
Issued:	1922

		Price		
Colourways	Backstamp	U.S. $	Can. $	U.K. £
1. Coloured (as above)	Puce	700.00	875.00	350.00
2. White glazed	Puce	225.00	300.00	125.00

RW2807
INFANT POWDER BOWL

Modeller: Unknown
Height: 7" x 8", 17.8 x 20.3 cm
Colour: Pink bowl with gold trim; cream infant
Issued: 1922

Colourways	Backstamp	U.S. $	Price Can. $	U.K. £
Pink/cream	Puce	900.00	1,125.00	450.00

RW2820
NAIAD POWDER BOWL
Second Version

Modeller: Frederick M. Gertner
Height: 6 ½" x 6", 16.5 x 15.0 cm
Colour: 1. Light blue
2. Matt ivory
3. Pink
4. Shagreen
Issued: 1922
Varieties: RW3030 Naiad; RW2698 Naiad (on plinth);
RW2783 Naiad Powder Bowl (First Version)

Colourways	Backstamp	U.S. $	Price Can. $	U.K. £
Coloured (as above)	Puce	900.00	1,125.00	450.00

RW2848
CHINESE FAMILY GROUP

Modeller: Frederick M. Gertner
Height: 5 ½", 14.0 cm
Colour: Unknown
Issued: 1928

Colourways	Backstamp	U.S. $	Price Can. $	U.K. £
Unknown	Puce		Extremely rare	

RW2865
CORA

Modeller: Doris Lindner
Height: 6", 15.0 cm
Colour: 1. Fleshtone; green veil and base; black pigeon
2. Fleshtone; purple veil and base; silver pigeon
Issued: 1931-by 1940

Colourways	Backstamp	Price U.S. $	Can. $	U.K. £
Coloured (as above)	Puce	900.00	1,125.00	450.00

Note: This model is also known without the pigeon.

RW2866
HARLEQUIN AND COLUMBINE BOOKEND

Modeller: Doris Lindner
Height: 8", 20.3 cm
Colour: Harlequin: Chequered costume; black mask
Columbine: White costume
Curtain: Red
Issued: 1931

Description	Backstamp	Price U.S. $	Can. $	U.K. £
1. Single bookend	Puce	900.00	1,200.00	450.00
2. Pair: RW2866 and RW2867	Puce	1,750.00	2,250.00	900.00

RW2867
PIERROT BOOKEND

Modeller: Doris Lindner
Height: 8", 20.3 cm
Colour: White costume; black buttons; red curtain
Issued: 1931

Description	Backstamp	Price U.S. $	Can. $	U.K. £
1. Single bookend	Puce	900.00	1,200.00	450.00
2. Pair: RW2866 and RW2867	Puce	1,750.00	2,250.00	900.00

RW2868
HARLEQUIN
Style Two

Modeller:	Doris Lindner
Height:	6 ½", 16.5 cm
Colour:	1. Orange and grey checkered trousers; red shoes; grey base
	2. Orange, red, green and black checkered trousers; red shoes; black base
	3. Orange, yellow, black and beige checkered trousers; white shirt; black mask and base
Issued:	1931
Derivitive:	Bookend

Description	Backstamp	Price U.S. $	Can. $	U.K. £
1. Figure	Puce	1,200.00	1,500.00	600.00
2. Bookend, pair	Puce	2,300.00	2,875.00	1,150.00

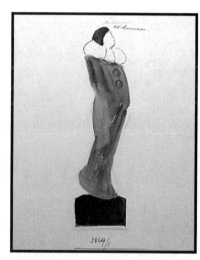

RW2869
PIERROT
Style Two

Modeller:	Doris Lindner
Height:	6", 15.0 cm
Colour:	1. Blue-green/white
	2. Green/silver
	3. Grey/black
	4. Red/black base
	5. White/black
Issued:	1931
Derivitives:	Bookend, Pen and Ink Tray

Description	Backstamp	Price U.S. $	Can. $	U.K. £
1. Figure	Puce	1,100.00	1,375.00	550.00
2. Bookend, pair	Puce	2,200.00	2,750.00	1,100.00
3. Pen and Ink Tray	Puce	1,200.00	1,500.00	600.00

RW2879
DREAMING

Modeller:	Phoebe Stabler
Height:	4", 10.1 cm
Colour:	Thick base:
	1. Chrome green; indigo base
	2. Ivory; indigo base
	3. Pink; indigo base
	4. Turquoise; black base
	5. Yellow; indigo base
	Shallow base:
	6. Pink; brown base
	7. Turquoise; brown base
Issued:	1931-by 1940

Varieties	Backstamp	Price U.S. $	Can. $	U.K. £
1. Thick base	Puce	600.00	750.00	300.00
2. Shallow base	Puce	650.00	800.00	320.00

RW2880
FLOWER GIRL
Style One

Modeller:	Phoebe Stabler
Height:	8", 20.3 cm
Colour:	Yellow dress; pink and blue striped shawl
Issued:	1931-by 1940

		Price		
Colourways	Backstamp	U.S. $	Can. $	U.K. £
Yellow/pink/blue	Puce	800.00	1,000.00	400.00

RW2881
SAUCE

Modeller:	Phoebe Stabler
Height:	Shallow base: 7 ¼", 18.4 cm
	Thick plinth: 8 ¾", 22.2 cm
Colour:	1. Emerald green dress and petticoat; blonde hair
	2. Green dress; yellow petticoat; blonde hair
	3. Mauve dress; orange petticoat; blonde hair
	4. Pink dress; white petticoat; blonde hair
	5. Sea-green dress
	6. Turquoise dress; gold and orange petticoat; red-brown hair
	7. Yellow dress and petticoat; brown hair
	8. Yellow dress; pink petticoat; light brown hair
Issued:	1931-1952

		Price		
Varieties	Backstamp	U.S. $	Can. $	U.K. £
1. Shallow base	Puce	750.00	950.00	380.00
2. Thick plinth	Puce	700.00	875.00	350.00

Note: The figure was available with either a shallow base, as illustrated, or a thick black plinth.

RW2882
BOY ON BOAR

Modeller: Phoebe Stabler
Height: 3 ½", 8.9 cm
Colour: Fleshtone; blonde hair; shaded brown pig; pale green oval base
Issued: 1931

Colourways	Backstamp	Price U.S. $	Can. $	U.K. £
Fleshtone/brown/green	Puce	1,300.00	1,600.00	650.00

RW2883
LITTLE DANCER

Modeller: Phoebe Stabler
Height: 3 ¼", 8.3 cm
Colour: 1. Blue
2. Flame
3. Light green
4. Pink
5. Turquoise
6. Yellow
Issued: 1931
Varieties: RW2938 Little Dancer Powder Bowl

Colourways	Backstamp	Price U.S. $	Can. $	U.K. £
Coloured (as above)	Puce	600.00	750.00	300.00

RW2884
COQUETTE
Style One

Modeller:	Phoebe Stabler
Height:	3 ¼", 8.3 cm
Colour:	1. Flame dress; beige hat; black base
	2. Light green dress; yellow hat; black base
	3. Pale blue dress; yellow hat; black or brown base
	4. Pink dress; beige hat; deep black base
	5. Pink dress; yellow hat; black base
	6. Pink and ivory dress; black base
	7. White dress and hat with lilac design; indigo base
	8. Yellow dress and hat; black base
Issued:	1931

Colourways	Backstamp	U.S. $	Price Can. $	U.K. £
Coloured (as above)	Puce	525.00	650.00	260.00

RW2885
THE MOTHER

Modeller:	Phoebe Stabler
Height:	7 ¾", 19.7 cm
Colour:	Green dress; pinkish-ivory body; blue stepped octagonal base
Issued:	1931

Colourways	Backstamp	U.S. $	Price Can. $	U.K. £
Green/pink-ivory/blue	Puce		Extremely rare	

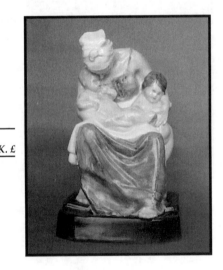

RW2886
THE OLD GOAT WOMAN

Modeller:	Phoebe Stabler
Height:	5 ¾", 14.6 cm
Colour:	1. Blue squares on dress; white apron and bonnet; ivory shoes; yellow pot; fawn goat; green base
	2. Flame and yellow dress; blue bonnet; beige apron; brown and white goat; green base
	3. Green dress and bonnet; white apron; lavender and yellow shawl; black and white goat
	4. Orange-red and mauve skirt; violet blouse; yellow and pink apron and shoes; orange-red and yellow bonnet and shawl; brown circular base
	5. Yellow apron with pink line; flame bonnet and cloak; ivory pot; purple and white goat; brown base
Issued:	1931-1938

Colourways	Backstamp	U.S. $	Price Can. $	U.K. £
Coloured (as above)	Puce	800.00	1,000.00	400.00

Note: This model was also used on a lamp base.

RW2887
PICK A BACK

Modeller:	Phoebe Stabler
Height:	8", 20.3 cm
Colour:	1. Mother: Burgundy striped jacket; green patterned skirt; yellow apron Child: Yellow coat; light blue trousers
	2. Mother: Yellow and grey striped coat; red and blue-grey shapes on dress Child: Yellow coat with shot shading; light blue trousers
Issued:	1931-by 1940

Colourways	Backstamp	U.S. $	Price Can. $	U.K. £
Coloured (as above)	Puce	1,300.00	1,625.00	650.00

RW2894
BOY WITH DONKEY

Modeller:	Stella R. Crofts
Height:	6", 15.0 cm
Colour:	Blue clothing; brown hair; grey donkey
Issued:	1931-by 1940

		Price		
Colourways	Backstamp	U.S. $	Can. $	U.K. £
Blue/brown/grey	Puce	1,900.00	2,375.00	950.00

RW2898
THE HARPIST

Modeller:	Ethelwyn Baker
Height:	9", 22.9 cm
Colour:	1. Cream dress with blue trim; cream and light green harp
	2. Green dress with light blue dots; orange, black and brown harp
	3. Grey dress with blue highlights; grey harp
	4. Ivory dress with light blue dots; orange, black and brown harp
	5. Pale yellow dress with blue dots; yellow harp
Issued:	1931-by 1949
Series:	Victorian Musicians

		Price		
Colourways	Backstamp	U.S. $	Can. $	U.K. £
Coloured (as above)	Puce	1,500.00	1,875.00	750.00

RW2899
THE LUTE PLAYER

Modeller:	Ethelwyn Baker
Height:	9", 22.9
Colour:	1. Claret coat; ivory trousers
	2. Grey coat and trousers with blue highlights
Issued:	1931-by 1949
Series:	Victorian Musicians

		Price		
Colourways	Backstamp	U.S. $	Can. $	U.K. £
Coloured (as above)	Puce	1,500.00	1,875.00	750.00

Note: This model was also available on a lamp base.

RW2901
THE FLUTE PLAYER

Modeller: Ethelwyn Baker
Height: 9", 22.9 cm
Colour: 1. Blue coat; yellow and lilac striped waistcoat; taupe trousers
2. Brown coat; lilac waistcoat; ivory trousers
3. Grey coat; waistcoat and trousers with blue highlights
Issued: 1931-by 1949
Series: Victorian Musicians

Colourways	Backstamp	Price U.S. $	Can. $	U.K. £
Coloured (as above)	Puce	1,500.00	1,875.00	750.00

Note: This model was also available on a lamp base.

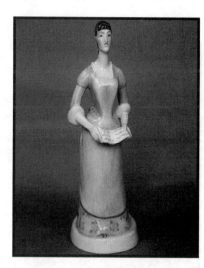

RW2902
THE SONG

Modeller: Ethelwyn Baker
Height: 8 ½", 21.6 cm
Colour: 1. Grey dress trimmed with blue
2. Orange dress; turquoise underskirt
3. Pink dress edged in yellow; flowered green underskirt
Issued: 1931-by 1949
Series: Victorian Musicians

Colourways	Backstamp	Price U.S. $	Can. $	U.K. £
Coloured (as above)	Puce	1,500.00	1,875.00	750.00

RW2903
BLUEBEARD

Modeller: Jessamine Bray, Sybil Williams
Height: 10 ¼", 26.0 cm
Colour: 1. Flame; green and black checkered base
2. Green robe with leaf print; purple pantaloons; red sash;
yellow and orange turban; brown slippers; green and
black checkered base
Issued: 1931-by 1940

Colourways	Backstamp	Price U.S. $	Can. $	U.K. £
Coloured (as above)	Puce	1,600.00	2,000.00	800.00

Note: This model was also available on a lamp base.

RW2904
FATIMA

Modeller:	Jessamine Bray, Sybil Williams
Height:	10", 25.4 cm
Colour:	1. Light green dress; shot turquoise and pink cloak with green and white decoration; ivory pantaloons; green and black base
	2. Yellow dress; brown top; grey-blue pantaloons and cloak
	3. Yellow jacket edged in flame; pale turquoise skirt; yellow pantaloons; flame shoes
Issued:	1931-by 1949

		Price		
Colourways	Backstamp	U.S. $	Can. $	U.K. £
Coloured (as above)	Puce	1,600.00	2,000.00	800.00

Note: This model was also available on a lamp base.

RW2905
NOEL

Modeller:	Jessamine Bray, Sybil Williams
Height:	1. Large — 7 ¼", 18.4 cm
	2. Small — 4 ½", 11.9 cm
Colour:	1. Blue dress and cloak; ermine trim; turquoise and green bonnet; pink balloons
	2. Crimson dress and cloak; ermine trim; blue bonnet; orange and green balloons
	3. Peacock and orange dress and cloak; ermine trim; pink bonnet; orange and red balloons
	4. Pink dress; blue-green cloak with ermine trim; green bonnet
	5. Turquoise dress and cloak; ermine trim; yellow and green bonnet; yellow and purple balloons
Issued:	1931-by 1959

		Price		
Size	Backstamp	U.S. $	Can. $	U.K. £
1. Large	Puce	550.00	700.00	280.00
2. Small	Puce	225.00	275.00	110.00

RW2906
JUNE
Style One

Modeller:	Jessamine Bray, Sybil Williams
Height:	1. Large — 6 ¾", 17.2 cm
	2. Small — 4 ¼", 10.8 cm
Colour:	1. Blue with shot gold

2. Deep blue dress; fawn and blue bonnet; flame and yellow flowers
3. Chrome green dress with darker green spotted frills; mauve and turquoise bonnet; pink and blue flowers
4. Golden orange with shot gold
5. Green dress; golden fawn and blue bonnet; pink and yellow flowers
6. Green with shot gold
7. Pink dress; lilac and yellow bonnet; blue and red flowers
8. Pink with shot gold
9. Pink dress with white spotted frills; mauve bonnet; red and blue flowers
10. Purple dress; orange-fawn bonnet; yellow and blue flowers
11. Ultramarine dress; golden fawn bonnet; pink, red and yellow flowers
12. Yellow dress; turquoise and pink bonnet; pink and blue flowers
13. Yellowish-green dress; mauve and yellow bonnet; pink and blue flowers
14. White dress with green and lilac design; blue and yellow bonnet; pink and blue flowers

Issued:	1931-by 1959

		Price		
Description	Backstamp	U.S. $	Can. $	U.K. £
1. Large size	Puce	550.00	700.00	280.00
2. Large size	Black	450.00	550.00	225.00
3. Small size	Puce	225.00	275.00	110.00
4. Small size	Black	175.00	225.00	90.00

RW2907
INDIAN CHIEF

Modeller:	Frederick M. Gertner
Height:	7", 17.8 cm
Colour:	Green, blue and red blanket; grey headdress
Issued:	1931-by 1940
Series:	Red Indian Series

		Price		
Colourways	Backstamp	U.S. $	Can. $	U.K. £
Green/blue/red	Puce	1,200.00	1,500.00	600.00

RW2908
INDIAN BRAVE

Modeller:	Frederick M. Gertner
Height:	7", 17.8 cm
Colour:	Brown blanket with black and red designs; black feather
Issued:	1931-by 1940
Series:	Red Indian Series

		Price		
Colourways	Backstamp	U.S. $	Can. $	U.K. £
Brown/black/red	Puce	1,200.00	1,500.00	600.00

RW2909
INDIAN SQUAW WITH CHILD ON BACK

Modeller:	Frederick M. Gertner
Height:	6 ¼", 15.9 cm
Colour:	Unknown
Issued:	1931-by 1940
Series:	Red Indian Series

		Price		
Colourways	Backstamp	U.S. $	Can. $	U.K. £
Unknown	Puce		Rare	

RW2910
INDIAN SQUAW WITH CHILD ON SHOULDER

Modeller: Frederick M. Gertner
Height: 6", 15.0 cm
Colour: Green, white, red and yellow
Issued: 1931-by 1940
Series: Red Indian Series

Colourways	Backstamp	U.S. $	Price Can. $	U.K. £
Green/white/red/yellow	Puce	1,200.00	1,500.00	600.00

RW2911
LADY WITH FAN

Modeller: Frederick M. Gertner
Height: 7 ¼", 18.4 cm
Colour:
1. Blue, green and pink dress with floral sprigs; purple ribbons; red fan
2. Blue dress with yellow flowered ribbons; multicoloured fan
3. Mottled blue and green dress; lilac ribbons; purple fan
4. Yellow dress with floral sprigs; pink ribbons; mauve fan
Issued: 1931-by 1940

Colourways	Backstamp	U.S. $	Price Can. $	U.K. £
Coloured (as above)	Puce	700.00	875.00	350.00

RW2912
MICHAEL

Modeller: Freda Doughty
Height: 2 ½", 6.4 cm
Colour:
1. Blue suit
2. Green suit
3. Red suit
4. Yellow suit
Issued: 1931-1957
Varieties: RW2928 Michael Powder Bowl / Bon-Bon Box
Series: Michael, Tommy, Mischief and Joan

Backstamp	U.S. $	Price Can. $	U.K. £
1. Puce	450.00	550.00	220.00
2. Black	375.00	450.00	190.00

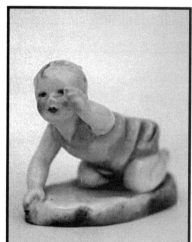

RW2913
TOMMY

Modeller:	Freda Doughty
Height:	4 ¼", 10.8 cm
Colour:	1. Flame shirt; mauve shorts
	2. Mauve shirt; blue shorts
	3. Pale green shirt; white shorts
	4. Pink shirt; turquoise shorts
	5. Sea-green shirt; blue shorts
	6. White shirt with blue and pink border; blue shorts
	7. Yellow shirt; grey shorts
Issued:	1931-1957
Series:	Michael, Tommy, Mischief and Joan

	Price		
Backstamp	U.S. $	Can. $	U.K. £
1. Puce	400.00	500.00	200.00
2. Black	325.00	400.00	160.00

RW2914
MISCHIEF

Modeller:	Freda Doughty
Height:	3 ½", 8.9 cm
Colour:	1. Flame dress; lilac and flame flowers
	2. Green sheen dress; yellow flowers
	3. Mauve sheen dress; yellow flowers
	4. Turquoise dress; lilac and yellow flowers
	5. Yellow dress; pink flowers
	6. Yellow dress with red dots; blue and mauve flowers
	7. Yellow dress with red dots; lilac flowers
Issued:	1931-1957
Series:	Michael, Tommy, Mischief and Joan

	Price		
Backstamp	U.S. $	Can. $	U.K. £
1. Puce	550.00	700.00	280.00
2. Black	475.00	600.00	240.00

RW2915
JOAN

Modeller: Freda Doughty
Height: 4 ¼", 10.8 cm
Colour: 1. Flame dress with spotted yellow smocking and sleeve line; yellow knickers
            2. White dress with blue dots; mauve knickers
            3. White dress with patterned yellow, red and green borders; pink knickers
            4. Yellow dress with green and purple design; purple knickers
Issued: 1931-1957
Series: Michael, Tommy, Mischief and Joan

		Price	
Backstamp	U.S. $	Can. $	U.K. £
1. Puce	475.00	600.00	240.00
2. Black	325.00	400.00	160.00

RW2916
THE MONGREL PUP

Modeller: Margaret Cane
Height: 7 ¾", 19.7 cm
Colour: 1. Blue and yellow dress
            2. Flame dress; blonde hair; brown and white puppy
            3. Turquoise dress trimmed with dots; brown hair; brown and white puppy
            4. Yellow dress; brown hair; black and white puppy
Issued: 1931-by 1959

			Price	
Colourways	Backstamp	U.S. $	Can. $	U.K. £
Coloured (as above)	Puce	1,500.00	1,875.00	750.00

RW2917
SEA URCHIN

Modeller:	Margaret Cane	
Height:	6 ¼", 15.9 cm	
Colour:	Fleshtones; light brown hair; dark green and brown base	
Issued:	1931-by 1948	

			Price	
Colourways	*Backstamp*	*U.S. $*	*Can. $*	*U.K. £*
Fleshtones/light brown	Puce	900.00	1,125.00	450.00

RW2918
SLEEPY BOY

Modeller:	Margaret Cane
Height:	3 ¼", 8.3 cm
Colour:	1. Blue sweater; brown shorts; fawn base
	2. Green sweater; brown shorts; indigo base
	3. Mauve sweater; brown shorts; green base
	4. Pink sweater; brown shorts; indigo base
	5. Orange-pink sweater; blue shorts; fawn base
	6. Ultramarine sweater; brown shorts; indigo base
	7. Yellow sweater; brown shorts; green base
Issued:	1931-by 1957

	Price		
Backstamp	*U.S. $*	*Can. $*	*U.K. £*
1. Puce	550.00	700.00	280.00
2. Black	450.00	550.00	220.00

RW2919
TANGLES

Modeller:	Anne Acheson
Height:	9 ½", 24 cm
Colour:	Fleshtones; yellow, pink and green ribbons and balloons
Issued:	1931-by 1940

			Price	
Colourways	*Backstamp*	*U.S. $*	*Can. $*	*U.K. £*
Fleshtones/yellow/pink/green	Puce		Extremely rare	

RW2920
LOUGH NEAGH MARY

Modeller: Anne Acheson
Height: 7", 17.8 cm
Colour: White and light blue apron; black dress; brown head shawl;
straw basket; green base
Issued: 1931-by 1940

Colourways	Backstamp	U.S. $	Price Can. $	U.K. £
White/light blue	Puce	700.00	875.00	350.00

RW2921
DUBLIN FLOWER GIRL

Modeller: Anne Acheson
Height: 6 ¼", 15.9 cm
Colour: Black dress; white apron; yellowish-lilac shawl;
yellow and blue flowers; pale lilac base
Issued: 1931-by 1940

Colourways	Backstamp	U.S. $	Price Can. $	U.K. £
Black/white/yellow	Puce	800.00	1,000.00	400.00

RW2922
DUTCH GIRL

Modeller: Possibly Frederick M. Gertner
Height: 5 ¼", 13.3 cm
Colour: 1. Flame skirt; mauve top
2. Turquoise skirt; blue top
3. White skirt with blue stripes; white apron with
checkered edge; black bodice; white hat and sleeves
Issued: 1931-by 1957

Backstamp	U.S. $	Price Can. $	U.K. £
1. Puce	400.00	500.00	200.00
2. Black	350.00	450.00	180.00

RW2923
DUTCH BOY

Modeller:	Possibly Frederick M. Gertner
Height:	5 ¼", 13.3 cm
Colour:	1. Blue trousers; green jacket
	2. Brown trousers; flame jacket
	3. Flame trousers; purple jacket
Issued:	1931-by 1957

		Price	
Backstamp	U.S. $	Can. $	U.K. £
1. Puce	550.00	700.00	280.00
2. Black	350.00	450.00	180.00

RW2924
THE FORTUNE TELLER

Modeller:	Freda Doughty
Height:	5 ¾", 14.6 cm
Colour:	1. Green dress; grey patterned shawl
	2. Lilac and red dress; green shawl
	3. Purple and orange dress; orangey-red shawl
Issued:	1931-by 1957
Varietes:	Also called "Mother Machree"

		Price	
Backstamp	U.S. $	Can. $	U.K. £
1. Puce	700.00	875.00	350.00
2. Black	600.00	750.00	300.00

RW2928
MICHAEL POWDER BOWL / BON-BON BOX

Modeller:	Freda Doughty
Height:	5 ¾", 14.6cm
Colour:	Boy: See RW2912 for possible colourways of Michael's suit
	Bowl: Grey bowl with blue, yellow and green design
Issued:	1931
Varieties:	RW2912 Michael

			Price	
Description	Backstamp	U.S. $	Can. $	U.K. £
Powder bowl/Bon-bon box	Puce	800.00	1,000.00	400.00

RW2930
BETTY

Modeller:	Anne Acheson
Height:	3 ½", 8.9 cm
Colour:	See below
Issued:	1931-by 1957

Model 2930 was issued in seven different colourways, with each of the colourway models being given an individual name.

Betty   Pale blue dress with gilt lustre; blue shoes; grey kitten; pale green base

Buttercup   Yellow dress and shoes

Lavender   Mauve dress and shoes; grey kitten; green base

Lily   Sea-green dress with gilt lustre; sea-green shoes; grey kitten; yellow-green base

Marigold   Flame dress and shoes; grey kitten; yellow and green base

Pansy   Shaded blue dress; blue shoes; black kitten; green base

Rose,   Rose-pink dress and shoes; grey kitten; green base
Style One

	Price		
Backstamp	*U.S. $*	*Can. $*	*U.K. £*
1. Puce	700.00	875.00	350.00
2. Black	500.00	625.00	250.00

RW2936
ARGENTINA

Modeller: Anne Acheson
Height: 8", 20.3 cm
Colour: 1. Flame and yellow dress; patterned blue shawl with black fringe
2. Green dress; red patterned shawl with red fringe
3. Green and black dress; patterned red shawl with red fringe
4 Green skirt with red flowers; blue bodice; patterned flame shawl with flame fringe
5. Orange skirt; patterned blue shawl with blue fringe
6. Pink skirt; white patterned shawl with yellow fringe
7. White dress; white shawl with pink, blue and yellow flowers and a yellow fringe
Issued: 1931-by 1949
Varieties: Also called "Spanish Lady"

Colourways	Backstamp	U.S. $	Price Can. $	U.K. £
Coloured (as above)	Puce	900.00	1,150.00	450.00

Note: This model was also available on a lamp base.

RW2937
GIRL AND RABBIT

Modeller: Unknown
Height: 4 ½", 11.9 cm
Colour: Unknown
Issued: 1932

Colourways	Backstamp	U.S. $	Price Can. $	U.K. £
Unknown	Puce		Extremely rare	

RW2938
LITTLE DANCER POWDER BOWL

Modeller: Phoebe Stabler
Height: 5 ½", 14.0 cm
Colour: Woman: See RW2883 for possible colourways of dress
Bowl: Grey bowl with blue, yellow and green design
Issued: 1932-by 1940
Varieties: RW2883 Little Dancer

			Price	
Description	Backstamp	U.S. $	Can. $	U.K. £
Powder bowl	Puce	900.00	1,125.00	450.00

RW2949
THE DANCERS

Modeller: Doris Lindner
Height: 9 ¾", 24.7 cm
Colour: 1. Blue-grey suit; red dress
2. Dark grey suit; pale grey dress
3. Steel grey suit; orange dress
Issued: 1932-by 1940

			Price	
Colourways	Backstamp	U.S. $	Can. $	U.K. £
Coloured (as above)	Puce	1,900.00	2,375.00	950.00

RW2999
COLUMBINE
Style Three

Modeller: Doris Lindner
Height: 6 ½", 16.5 cm
Colour: 1. Lilac and green dress; green shawl with pink and yellow flowers
2. Pale green dress; green shawl with pink and yellow flowers; green base
3. Red and yellow dress; blue and green shawl; black base
4. White dress; green shawl with pink and yellow flowers; grey base
Issued: 1932-by 1940

			Price	
Colourways	Backstamp	U.S. $	Can. $	U.K. £
Coloured (as above)	Puce	700.00	875.00	350.00

RW3001
GIRL WITH KITTEN POWDER BOWL

Modeller: Anne Acheson
Height: 6", 15.0 cm
Colour: Girl: See model RW2930 for colour variations on dress
Bowl: Grey with blue, yellow and green design
Issued: 1932-by 1940
Varieties: RW2930 Betty

Description	Backstamp	U.S. $	Price Can. $	U.K. £
Powder bowl	Puce	900.00	1,125.00	450.00

RW3006
SWEET NELL OF OLD DRURY

Modeller: Anne Acheson
Height: 9", 22.9 cm
Colour: 1. Green dress with white collar and bows
2. Grey-green dress
3. Mauve dress
4. Red dress with white collar, blue bows
5. Shaded pink dress with yellow collar, pale blue bows
6. Shot green and gold dress
7. Turquoise dress, with white collar, lilac bows
8. Turquoise dress with white collar and sleeves, red bows
8. Yellow dress with green collar and bows
Issued: 1933-by 1940

Colourways	Backstamp	U.S. $	Price Can. $	U.K. £
Coloured (as above)	Puce	900.00	1,125.00	450.00

RW3008
SEA BREEZE

Modeller: Freda Doughty
Height: 8 ½", 21.6 cm
Colour: 1. Blue-green dress; brown and blue base
2. Green and pink dress; brown and blue base
3. Mauve dress; brown and blue base
4. Pink and blue dress; green and blue base
5. Yellow and green dress; green and brown base
Issued: 1933-1959

| Backstamp | Price | | |
	U.S. $	Can. $	U.K. £
1. Puce	850.00	1,000.00	420.00
2. Black	700.00	875.00	350.00

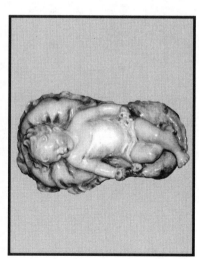

RW3009
THE TREASURE

Modeller: Freda Doughty
Height: 5", 12.7 cm
Colour: Fleshtones; pale pink clothing; deep pink cushion;
white daisies; green-brown base
Issued: 1932-by 1948
Varieties: Also called "Baby on Cushion" or "Sleeping Baby"

| Backstamp | Price | | |
	U.S. $	Can. $	U.K. £
1. Puce		Extremely rare	
2. Black		Extremely rare	

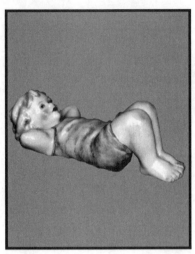

RW3010
HAPPY BOY

Modeller:	Freda Doughty
Length:	5", 12.7 cm
Colour:	1. Mauve bathing suit with green trim; blonde hair
	2. Pink bathing suit with yellow trim; blonde hair
Issued:	1932-1948

	Price		
Backstamp	*U.S. $*	*Can. $*	*U.K. £*
1. Puce	1,100.00	1,375.00	550.00
2. Black	900.00	1,125.00	450.00

RW3011
PETER PAN

Modeller:	Frederick M. Gertner
Height:	8", 20.3 cm
Colour:	1. Blue shirt and shorts; brown hair
	2. Green shirt and shorts; brown hair
	3. Pink shirt; brown shorts; yellow hair
	4. Red shirt; ultramarine shorts; brown hair
Issued:	1933-by 1958

	Price		
Backstamp	*U.S. $*	*Can. $*	*U.K. £*
1. Puce	750.00	950.00	380.00
2. Black	650.00	800.00	320.00

RW3012
SPRING
Style One

Modeller:	Freda Doughty
Height:	9", 22.9 cm
Colour:	1. Blue dress
	2. Lavender dress
	3. Pink dress
	4. Yellow dress
Issued:	1933-1959

	Price		
Backstamp	*U.S. $*	*Can. $*	*U.K. £*
1. Puce	750.00	950.00	380.00
2. Black	700.00	875.00	350.00

RW3014
MY FAVOURITE

Modeller:	Freda Doughty
Height:	5 ½", 14.0 cm
Colour:	1. Blue dress with pink dots; yellow hair; white rabbits; green base
	2. Blue dress with mauve highlights; yellow hair; brown and white rabbits; green base
	3. Chrome green dress; yellow hair; white rabbits; yellow flowers on base
	4. Dark green dress; yellow hair; white rabbits; yellow flowers on base
	5. Pink dress; yellow hair; white rabbits; pink flowers on green base
	6. White dress with blue dots; blue hairband; black and white rabbits
	7. Yellow dress; white rabbits; yellow flowers on base
Issued:	1932-1959

		Price	
Backstamp	U.S. $	Can. $	U.K. £
1. Puce	950.00	1,200.00	480.00
2. Black	750.00	950.00	380.00

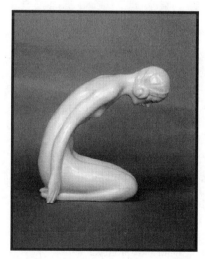

RW3030
NAIAD

Modeller:	Doris Lindner
Height:	4 ½", 11.9 cm
Colour:	Fleshtones; blonde hair
Issued:	1933-by 1948
Varieties:	RW2698 Naiad (on plinth); RW2783 Naiad Powder Bowl (First Version); RW2820 Naiad Powder Bowl (Second Version)

			Price	
Colourways	Backstamp	U.S. $	Can. $	U.K. £
Fleshtones	Puce	700.00	875.00	350.00

Note: This figure was produced exclusively for Aspreys, London, England. Originally, this figure sat on a mirror.

RW3040
THE KISS

Modeller:	Possibly Doris Lindner
Height:	4 ¾", 12.1 cm
Colour:	1. Green, pink and blue dress
	2. Ivory (matt)
	3. Peacock blue dress
Issued:	1933-by 1940

			Price	
Colourways	Backstamp	U.S. $	Can. $	U.K. £
Coloured (as above)	Puce		Rare	

RW3066
EGYPT

Designer:	Unknown
Modeller:	Freda Doughty
Height:	6", 15.0 cm
Colour:	Yellow robe with mauve and green stripes; red fez;
	orange shoes; brown mound
Issued:	1934-1959
Series:	Children of the Nations

		Price	
Backstamp	U.S. $	Can. $	U.K. £
1. Puce	750.00	950.00	380.00
2. Black	650.00	825.00	330.00

RW3067
ITALY / FLOWER GIRL (Style Two)

Modeller:	Freda Doughty
Height:	3 ¾", 9.5 cm
Colour:	1. **Italy:** Green blouse; white fichu and apron; yellow
	and pink headscarf; pink and purple flowers
	2. **Flower Girl:** Green blouse with purple decoration;
	mauve fichu and apron; yellow and pink kerchief;
	red, turquoise and purple flowers
Issued:	1934-1959
Series:	**Italy:** Children of the Nations

			Price	
Decsription	Backstamp	U.S. $	Can. $	U.K. £
1. Italy	Puce	900.00	1,125.00	450.00
2. Italy	Black	700.00	875.00	350.00
3. Flower Girl (Style Two)	Puce	900.00	1,125.00	450.00
4. Flower Girl (Style Two)	Black	700.00	875.00	350.00

RW3068
BURMAH

Modeller: Freda Doughty
Height: 5", 12.7 cm
Colour: Light blue loincloth with dark blue highlights; red necklace and
bracelets; brown and green base
Issued: 1934-1972
Series: Children of the Nations

Backstamp	U.S. $	Price Can. $	U.K. £
1. Puce	350.00	450.00	180.00
2. Black	240.00	275.00	120.00

RW3069
GREECE

Modeller: Freda Doughty
Height: 5 ½", 14.0 cm
Colour: Yellow blouse and stockings; black vest with orange and white trim;
red sash; white skirt; red cap; brown base
Issued: 1934-1959
Series: Children of the Nations

Backstamp	U.S. $	Price Can. $	U.K. £
1. Puce	750.00	950.00	380.00
2. Black	650.00	825.00	330.00

RW3070
SPAIN

Modeller: Freda Doughty
Height: 5 ¼", 13.3 cm
Colour: Pink dress; white apron with yellow and purple flowers;
black sash; dark brown hair; yellow and mauve parasol
Issued: 1934-1959
Series: Children of the Nations

Backstamp	U.S. $	Price Can. $	U.K. £
1. Puce	750.00	950.00	380.00
2. Black	650.00	825.00	330.00

RW3071
INDIA

Modeller:	Freda Doughty
Height:	3 ½", 8.9 cm
Colour:	1. White robe with purple highlights; blue turban; metal pipe
	2. Yellow robe with purple highlights; blue turban; metal pipe
Issued:	1934-1959
Series:	Children of the Nations

		Price	
Backstamp	U.S. $	Can. $	U.K. £
1. Puce	360.00	450.00	180.00
2. Black	240.00	300.00	120.00

RW3072
JAPAN

Modeller:	Freda Doughty
Height:	3 ½", 8.9 cm
Colour:	Flowered pink kimono; light green obi; dark brown hair; yellow fan
Issued:	1934-1959
Series:	Children of the Nations

		Price	
Backstamp	U.S. $	Can. $	U.K. £
1. Puce	1,000.00	1,250.00	500.00
2. Black	800.00	1,000.00	400.00

RW3073
CHINA

Modeller:	Freda Doughty
Height:	2 ½", 6.4 cm
Colour:	1. Light green shirt with blue-green highlights; lavender trousers; maroon shoes; beige bowl
	2. Yellow shirt; blue trousers; purple shoes; turquoise bowl
Issued:	1934-1959
Series:	Children of the Nations

		Price	
Backstamp	U.S. $	Can. $	U.K. £
1. Puce	325.00	400.00	160.00
2. Black	240.00	300.00	120.00

RW3074
HOLLAND

Modeller: Freda Doughty
Height: 5 ½", 14.0 cm
Colour: Blue blouse; white skirt with blue checks;
pink and white scarf; white hat; fawn clogs
Issued: 1934-1959
Series: Children of the Nations

Backstamp	Price U.S. $	Can. $	U.K. £
1. Puce	750.00	900.00	380.00
2. Black	675.00	750.00	335.00

RW3075
ENGLAND

Modeller: Freda Doughty
Height: 5 ¾", 14.6 cm
Colour: 1. Blue dress; yellow hair; white flowers; white flowers on
green and yellow base
2. Pink dress; yellow hair; white flowers; white flowers on
green and yellow base
Issued: 1934-1959
Series: Children of the Nations

Backstamp	Price U.S. $	Can. $	U.K. £
1. Puce	700.00	900.00	360.00
2. Black	550.00	725.00	320.00

RW3076
WOODLAND DANCE

Modeller: Freda Doughty
Height: 4", 10.1 cm
Colour: 1. Blue dress; brown hair; light brown rabbits;
red-brown squirrel; green base
2. Pink dress; yellow hair; light brown rabbits;
brown squirrel; green base
3. Sea-green dress; brown hair; light brown rabbits;
brown squirrel; green base
4. Yellow dress; yellow hair; brown rabbits;
red squirrel; green base
Issued: 1934-1972

Backstamp	Price U.S. $	Can. $	U.K. £
1. Puce	550.00	700.00	280.00
2. Black	400.00	625.00	230.00

RW3081
GRANDMOTHER'S DRESS

Modeller:	Freda Doughty
Height:	6 ½", 16.5 cm
Colour:	1. Blue dress, white frills; white mob cap with blue ribbon; gloss
	2. Blue dress, white frills; blue mob cap; gold highlights; matt
	3. Creamy-yellow dress, blue frills and hem; white mob cap with blue frill; gloss
	4. Creamy-yellow dress, pink frills and hem; white mob cap with pink frill; gloss
	5. Green dress, white frills; white mob cap with green ribbon; gloss
	6. Green dress, white frills; green mob cap; gold highlights; matt
	7. Pink dress, white frills; white mob cap with pink ribbon; gloss
	8. Pink dress, white frills; pink mob cap; gold highlights; matt
	9. Red dress, white frills; red mob cap; gloss
	10. Red dress, white frills; red mob cap; gold highlights; matt
	11. Yellow dress; white frills, white mob cap, yellow ribbon; gloss
	12. Yellow dress; white frills; yellow mob cap; gold highlights; matt
Issued:	1935-1983

		Price		
Colourways	Backstamp	U.S. $	Can. $	U.K. £
1. Coloured (as above)	Puce	350.00	425.00	180.00
2. Coloured (as above)	Black	200.00	275.00	120.00

Note: This model is also known with the left hand flat to the dress.
See also miniature version RW4155 Little Grandmother's Dress.

RW3082
THE FIRST CUCKOO

Modeller:	Freda Doughty
Height:	6 ½", 16.5 cm
Colour:	1. Blue dress
	2. Mauve dress
	3. Pink dress; white petticoat; blonde hair; yellow flowers
	4. White dress shaded in yellow; turquoise and purple trim
	5. Yellow dress; purple flowers
Issued:	1935-1959

		Price		
Colourways	Backstamp	U.S. $	Can. $	U.K. £
1. Coloured (as above)	Puce	750.00	950.00	380.00
2. Coloured (as above)	Black	625.00	725.00	320.00

RW3083
SUNSHINE

Modeller:	Freda Doughty
Height:	5", 12.7 cm
Colour:	1. Ivory dress; mauve flowers
	2. Pink dress; mauve flowers
	3. Turquoise dress; yellow flowers
	4. Yellow dress; mauve flowers
	5. Yellow dress; orange-brown flowers
Issued:	1935-1959

			Price	
Colourways	*Backstamp*	*U.S. $*	*Can. $*	*U.K. £*
1. Coloured (as above)	Puce	1,000.00	1,250.00	500.00
2. Coloured (as above)	Black	700.00	900.00	400.00

RW3084
THE DANDELION

Modeller:	Freda Doughty
Height:	4", 10.1 cm
Colour:	1. Pale blue suit; blonde hair; yellow dandelion; white rabbits; green base
	2. Yellow suit; blonde hair; yellow dandelion; white rabbits; green base
Issued:	1935-1959

			Price	
Colourways	*Backstamp*	*U.S. $*	*Can. $*	*U.K. £*
1. Coloured (as above)	Puce	1,000.00	1,250.00	500.00
2. Coloured (as above)	Black	700.00	900.00	400.00

RW3086
LADY WITH A ROSE

Modeller:	Doris Lindner
Height:	8", 20.3 cm
Colour:	1. Blue-grey dress with gold shading; blonde hair; red shoes
	2. Ivory dress with gold lustre (matt)
Issued:	1935-by 1940

			Price	
Colourways	*Backstamp*	*U.S. $*	*Can. $*	*U.K. £*
Coloured (as above)	Puce	1,600.00	2,000.00	800.00

RW3087
BOY WITH PARAKEET

Modeller:	Freda Doughty
Height:	6 ½", 16.5 cm
Colour:	1. Blue suit with white frills; lavender bird; gloss
	2. Blue suit with white frills; gold highlights; lavender bird; matt
	3. Creamy-yellow suit with blue frills; yellow bird; gloss
	4 Pink suit with white frills; purple bird; gloss
	5. Pink suit with white frills; gold highlights; purple bird; matt
	6. Red suit with white frills; grey bird; gloss
	7. Red suit with white frills; gold highlights; grey bird; matt
	8. Yellow suit with white frills; green bird; gloss
	9. Yellow suit with white frills; gold highlights; green bird; matt
Issued:	1935-1983
Varieties:	Also called "Parakeet"

		Price		
Colourways	Backstamp	U.S. $	Can. $	U.K. £
1. Coloured (as above)	Puce	375.00	450.00	190.00
2. Coloured (as above)	Black	200.00	275.00	120.00

Note: See also miniature version RW4163 Little Parakeet Boy.

RW3088
DANCE

Modeller:	Doris Lindner
Height:	8 ½", 21.6 cm
Colour:	1. Gold dress; red shoes; blonde hair
	2. Ivory dress with gold lustre; matt
	3. Mottled grey
Issued:	1935-by 1940

		Price		
Colourways	Backstamp	U.S. $	Can. $	U.K. £
Coloured (as above)	Puce	1,600.00	2,000.00	800.00

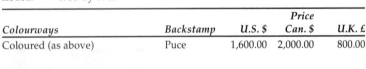

RW3089
KING GEORGE V

Modeller:	Gwendolen Parnell
Height:	9", 22.9 cm
Colour:	Blue uniform with gold trim; red sash
Issued:	1935 in a limited edition of 250

		Price		
Colourways	Backstamp	U.S. $	Can. $	U.K. £
Blue/gold/red	Puce	1,400.00	2,000.00	700.00

Note: Only 72 pairs (RW3089 and 3090) were issued.

RW3090
QUEEN MARY

Modeller:	Gwendolen Parnell
Height:	9", 22.9 cm
Colour:	White gown, blue cape and sash
Issued:	1935 in a limited edition of 250

		Price		
Colourways	Backstamp	U.S. $	Can. $	U.K. £
White/blue	Puce	1,400.00	2,000.00	700.00

RW3091
KING GEORGE V (Bust)

Modeller:	Gwendolen Parnell
Height:	1. 4 ½", 11.9 cm (with porcelain plinth)
	2. 2 ½", 6.4 cm (with wooden base)
Colour:	1. Navy jacket; blue sash; gold collar, epaulettes
	2. White Parian
Issued:	1935-1935

		Price		
Description	Backstamp	U.S. $	Can. $	U.K. £
1. On porcelain plinth	Puce	500.00	625.00	250.00
2. On wooden base	Unmarked	250.00	300.00	120.00

RW3092
QUEEN MARY (Bust)

Modeller:	Gwendolen Parnell
Height:	1. 4 ½", 11.9 cm (with porcelain plinth)
	2. 2 ½", 6.4 cm (with wooden base)
Colour:	1. White gown, blue sash
	2. White Parian
Issued:	1935-1935

Description	Backstamp	U.S. $	Price Can. $	U.K. £
1. On porcelain plinth	Puce	500.00	650.00	250.00
2. On wooden base	Unmarked	230.00	300.00	120.00

RW3095
"GOOD LUCK TO YOUR FISHING"

Modeller:	Gwendolen Parnell
Height:	5 ¾", 14.6 cm
Colour:	Fleshtone body; pink wings; blonde hair; blue water; marbled white base with inscribed title in black
Issued:	1935-by 1948

Colourways	Backstamp	U.S. $	Price Can. $	U.K. £
Fleshtone/pink/blue	Puce	950.00	1,200.00	480.00

RW3097
LADY BOUNTIFUL

Modeller:	Gwendolen Parnell
Height:	7 ¾", 19.7 cm
Colour:	1. Blue jacket; white cuffs and bodice; white skirt with pink flower print; yellow bonnet
	2. Green jacket; pink skirt; white bodice with blue design; white bonnet
Issued:	1935-by 1959

Colourways	Backstamp	U.S. $	Price Can. $	U.K. £
1. Coloured (as above)	Puce	750.00	950.00	380.00
2. Coloured (as above)	Black	550.00	725.00	320.00

RW3099
FLOWER GIRL
Style Three

Modeller:	Miss Stewart
Height:	7 ½", 19.1 cm
Colour:	Unknown
Issued:	1935

			Price		
Colourways	Backstamp	U.S. $	Can. $	U.K. £
Unknown	Puce		Extremely rare	

RW3103
WALES

Modeller:	Freda Doughty
Height:	5 ½", 14 cm
Colour:	Pink dress; white apron; black hat; yellow flowers; green and yellow base
Issued:	1935-1959
Series:	Children of the Nations

	Price		
Backstamp	U.S. $	Can. $	U.K. £
1. Puce	700.00	800.00	360.00
2. Black	550.00	700.00	320.00

RW3104
SCOTLAND

Modeller:	Freda Doughty
Height:	5 ½", 14 cm
Colour:	Deep rose jacket; green and yellow kilt; brown and beige sporran; yellow hair; purple and green base
Issued:	1935-1959
Series:	Children of the Nations

	Price		
Backstamp	U.S. $	Can. $	U.K. £
1. Puce	700.00	800.00	360.00
2. Black	550.00	700.00	320.00

RW3105
"HIT!"

Modeller:	Gwendolen Parnell
Height:	7 ¼", 18.4 cm
Colour:	1. Blue tunic; red sandals; brown bow
	2. White tunic; red sandals; purple bow
	3. White tunic; pink sandals; blue and brown bow
Issued:	1935-by 1948

		Price		
Colourways	*Backstamp*	*U.S. $*	*Can. $*	*U.K. £*
Coloured (as above)	Puce	950.00	1,200.00	480.00

RW3106
THE DUCHESS' DRESS
First Version (Hand beneath rose - 9")

Modeller:	Freda Doughty
Height:	9 ½", 24.0 cm
Colour:	1. Pink dress with red and green flower design
	2. Rose-pink dress
	3. Turquoise dress with mauve highlights
	4. Yellow dress
Issued:	1935-1959

		Price		
Colourways	*Backstamp*	*U.S. $*	*Can. $*	*U.K. £*
1. Coloured (as above)	Puce	800.00	1,000.00	400.00
2. Coloured (as above)	Black	525.00	675.00	300.00

Second Version (Hand to the side of rose - 6 ½")

Modeller:	Freda Doughty
Height:	6 ½", 16.5 cm
Colour:	1. Pink dress with red and green flower design
	2. Rose-pink dress
	3. Turquoise dress with mauve highlights
	4. Yellow dress
Issued:	1935-1959

		Price		
Colourways	*Backstamp*	*U.S. $*	*Can. $*	*U.K. £*
1. Coloured (as above)	Puce	500.00	600.00	275.00
2. Coloured (as above)	Black	400.00	500.00	225.00

RW3107
APPLAUSE

Modeller: Gwendolen Parnell
Height: 7 ¼", 18.4 cm
Colour: 1. Green dress with floral pattern; black hair
         2. Pink dress; ivory and turquoise fringe
         3. Yellow bodice and peplum with flower print; green skirts;
            yellow gloves; black hair
Issued: 1935-by 1948

Colourways	Backstamp	Price U.S. $	Price Can. $	Price U.K. £
Coloured (as above)	Puce	800.00	1,000.00	400.00

RW3108
AMARYLLIS

Modeller: Gwendolen Parnell
Height: 9 ¾", 24.7 cm
Colour: 1. Black, yellow, green and white
         2. Green and yellow dress
         3. Pink dress; white skirt with orange
         4. Turquoise dress; white skirt with orange flowers
         5. Yellow, purple, white and green
Issued: 1935-by 1959

Colourways	Backstamp	Price U.S. $	Price Can. $	Price U.K. £
1. Coloured (as above)	Puce	900.00	1,100.00	480.00
2. Coloured (as above)	Black	675.00	875.00	380.00

RW3111
BAL MASQUÉ

Modeller: Gwendolen Parnell
Height: 9 ½", 24.0 cm
Colour: 1. Blue and green dress; mauve and pink underskirt; green shoes
         2. Pink dress; green, yellow and grey underskirt; yellow shoes
         3. Pink dress; turquoise, green and yellow underskirt; yellow shoes
         4. Shot green dress; ivory and claret underskirt; green shoes
         5. Turquoise dress; mauve, yellow and grey underskirt; green shoes
Issued: 1935-c.1965

Colourways	Backstamp	Price U.S. $	Price Can. $	Price U.K. £
1. Coloured (as above)	Puce	900.00	1,100.00	480.00
2. Coloured (as above)	Black	675.00	875.00	380.00

Note: Earlier models had a square base, later models an oval base.

RW3114
AT THE MEET

Modeller:	Doris Lindner
Height:	7 ¼", 18.4 cm
Colour:	1. Rider: Black habit, hat and boots
	Horse: Grey
	2. Rider: Navy habit, hat and boots
	Horse: Bay
Issued:	1935-1981
Series:	Equestrian Series

			Price	
Colourways	Backstamp	U.S. $	Can. $	U.K. £
1. Coloured (as above)	Puce	850.00	1,000.00	420.00
2. Coloured (as above)	Black	625.00	800.00	350.00

RW3115
HUNTSMAN AND HOUNDS

Modeller:	Doris Lindner
Height:	With plinth: 9", 22.9 cm
	Without plinth: 7 ½", 19.1 cm
Colour:	Rider: Red riding habit; white jodhpurs and cravat;
	black hat, metal whip
	Horse: Light grey
	Dogs: White with light brown and black patches
Issued:	1936-1981
Series:	Equestrian Series

		Price	
Backstamp	U.S. $	Can. $	U.K. £
1. Puce	900.00	1,150.00	450.00
2. Black	700.00	900.00	400.00

RW3116
OVER THE STICKS

Modeller:	Doris Lindner
Height:	With plinth: 9 ¾", 24.7 cm
	Without plinth: 7 ¼", 18.4 cm
Colour:	Rider: Various coloured silks
	Horse: Chestnut
Issued:	1936-1986
Series:	Equestrian Series

		Price	
Backstamp	U.S. $	Can. $	U.K. £
1. Puce	900.00	1,150.00	450.00
2. Black	700.00	900.00	400.00

Note: Many colourway variations of this model may exist as the rider's silks could be painted to order.

RW3117
CANTERING TO THE POST

Modeller: Doris Lindner
Height: 7 ¾", 19.7 cm
Colour: Rider: Various coloured silks
           Horse: Bay
Issued: 1936-1986
Series: Equestrian Series

Backstamp	U.S. $	Price Can. $	U.K. £
1. Puce	900.00	1,150.00	450.00
2. Black	700.00	900.00	400.00

Note: Many colourway variations of this model may exist as the rider's silks
could be painted to order.

RW3126
PIERROT PUFF BOWL

Modeller: Henri Bargas
Height: 6 ½", 16.5 cm
Colour: Girl: Aquamarine dress with pink lining
           Pierrot: Fawn top with clover ruff; yellow pants with clover design;
           clover shoes; black hat and pompons
Issued: 1936-by 1940

Colourways	Backstamp	U.S. $	Price Can. $	U.K. £
Aquamarine/pink/fawn/yellow	Puce		Extremely rare	

RW3127
BABY BON BON-BOX / POWDER BOWL

Modeller: Henri Bargas
Height: 5", 12.7 cm
Colour: Baby: Fleshtones
           Bowl: Cream with embossed leaves and fruits
Issued: 1936-by 1940

Colourways	Backstamp	U.S. $	Price Can. $	U.K. £
Fleshtone/cream	Puce		Extremely rare	

RW3138
THE PLANTER'S DAUGHTER

Modeller: Gwendolen Parnell
Height: 7 ½", 19.1 cm
Colour: Daughter: Pink and white dress; fawn bodice;
blue and green hair ribbons
Servant: Purple coat; green shoes; white and green turban
Issued: 1936- by 1948

Colourways	Backstamp	U.S. $	Price Can. $	U.K. £
Pink/white/purple	Puce	1,300.00	1,600.00	650.00

RW3139
RECOLLECTIONS

Modeller: Gwendolen Parnell
Height: 12", 30.5 cm
Colour: 1. White coat with pink and brown designs; black and
gold hat; black shoes; white plinth
2. Yellow coat; black and green hat and shoes; marbled plinth
Issued: 1936

Colourways	Backstamp	U.S. $	Price Can. $	U.K. £
Coloured (as above)	Puce		Rare	

Note: Possibly issued as a bookend.

RW3140
THE POWDERING MASK

Modeller: Gwendolen Parnell
Height: 7", 17.8 cm
Colour: Woman: Blue dress, white skirt with brown pattern; blue
headdress; white cloth over shoulders; brown chair and mirror
Servant: Yellow coat; pale brown pants; white turban; white sash
with purple fringes
Issued: 1936-by 1948

Colourways	Backstamp	U.S. $	Price Can. $	U.K. £
Blue/white/yellow/brown	Puce	1,300.00	1,600.00	650.00

RW3142
THE FROG

Modeller: Gwendolen Parnell
Height: 7 ¾", 19.7 cm
Colour: Primrose and white dress; black hat and shoes; green frog
Issued: 1936

Colourways	Backstamp	Price U.S. $	Can. $	U.K. £
Primrose/white	Puce	1,000.00	1,250.00	500.00

RW3143
THE SUMMIT

Modeller: Gwendolen Parnell
Height: 9", 22.9 cm
Colour: Unknown
Issued: 1936

Colourways	Backstamp	U.S. $	Price Can. $	U.K. £
Unknown	Puce		Extremely rare	

RW3144
MAGNOLIA BUD

Modeller: Gwendolen Parnell
Height: 4 ½", 11.9 cm
Colour: 1. Pink, white and blue tabard; pink headdress
         2. Turquoise tabard with pink edging
Issued: 1936-c.1955

Backstamp	U.S. $	Price Can. $	U.K. £
1. Puce	500.00	625.00	280.00
2. Black	400.00	500.00	230.00

RW3145
THE THIEF

Modeller: Gwendolen Parnell
Height: 4 ½", 11.9 cm
Colour: 1. Pink skirt; spotted and striped pink and white
          turban; marbled white plinth
      2. Turquoise skirt with pink edging; marbled white plinth
Issued: 1936-c.1955

		Price	
Backstamp	U.S. $	Can. $	U.K. £
1. Puce	500.00	625.00	280.00
2. Black	400.00	500.00	230.00

RW3147
CHILD WITH LAMB, FLOWERS IN ARMS

Modeller: Guero
Height: Unknown
Colour: Unknown
Issued: 1936

			Price	
Colourways	Backstamp	U.S. $	Can. $	U.K. £
Unknown	Unknown	Extremely rare		

RW3148
CHILD WITH LAMB IN ARMS

Modeller: Guero
Height: Unknown
Colour: Unknown
Issued: 1936

			Price	
Colourways	Backstamp	U.S. $	Can. $	U.K. £
Unknown	Unknown	Extremely rare		

RW3149
SISTER

Modeller: Freda Doughty
Height: 6 ¾", 17.2 cm
Colour: 1. Sister: Pink dress; Brother: Green jacket; white trousers
2. Sister: Rose-pink dress; Brother: Yellow suit
3. Sister: Yellow dress with red flower design; Brother: Blue suit
4. Sister: White dress with red flower design; Brother: Blue suit
Issued: 1936-1959

Colourways	Backstamp	Price U.S. $	Can. $	U.K. £
1. Coloured (as above)	Puce	950.00	1,200.00	480.00
2. Coloured (as above)	Black	675.00	850.00	380.00

RW3150
TWO BABIES

Modeller: Freda Doughty
Height: 3 ¾", 9.5 cm
Colour: 1. Blue vest; yellow shorts; white and brown
puppy; yellow flowers on green and brown base
2. White vest with blue trim; white and grey puppy;
yellow flowers on green and brown base
Issued: 1936-by 1959

Colourways	Backstamp	Price U.S. $	Can. $	U.K. £
1. Coloured (as above)	Puce	675.00	850.00	380.00
2. Coloured (as above)	Black	550.00	725.00	320.00

RW3151
WATER BABY

Modeller: Freda Doughty
Height: 6 ¼", 15.9 cm
Colour: Flesh colouring; yellow hair; brown rock; blue and turquoise base
Issued: 1936-1959

Backstamp	Price U.S. $	Can. $	U.K. £
1. Puce	800.00	1,000.00	420.00
2. Black	675.00	850.00	380.00

RW3154
THE DRUMMER

Modeller:	Gwendolen Parnell
Height:	7", 17.8 cm
Colour:	1. Imperial red and golden orange dress; dark brown gloves
	2. Ivory and red dress; green gloves
	3. Yellow dress with red and black decoration; green gloves
Issued:	1936-by 1959
Varieties:	Also called "The Drum"

		Price		
Colourways	Backstamp	U.S. $	Can. $	U.K. £
1. Coloured (as above)	Puce	850.00	1,100.00	420.00
2. Coloured (as above)	Black	750.00	900.00	380.00

RW3157
CHILD WITH BUTTERFLY

Modeller:	Anne Acheson
Height:	4 ¾", 12.1 cm
Colour:	1. Blue butterfly; checkered clothing; turquoise and yellow base
	2. Pink butterfly; flowered clothing; turquoise and green base
Issued:	1936-by 1959

		Price		
Colourways	Backstamp	U.S. $	Can. $	U.K. £
1. Coloured (as above)	Puce	900.00	1,125.00	450.00
2. Coloured (as above)	Black	800.00	1,000.00	400.00

RW3160
BUBBLES

Modeller:	Freda Doughty
Height:	6 ½", 16.5 cm
Colour:	1. Pale blue dress; white bowl with blue band; white circular base with blue band
	2. Pink dress; white bowl with pink band; white circular base with pink band
	3. Pink dress; white bowl with pink band; white circular base with pink, yellow and white patterned band
Issued:	1936-1959

		Price		
Colourways	Backstamp	U.S. $	Can. $	U.K. £
1. Coloured (as above)	Puce	1,200.00	1,500.00	600.00
2. Coloured (as above)	Black	875.00	1,125.00	500.00

Note: The glass bubble, which was made at Stourbridge Glass Works, was added separately.

RW3161
MERMAID

Modeller:	Anne Acheson
Height:	5 ¼", 13.3 cm
Colour:	1. Fleshtone skin with orange on tail; blonde hair; pale turquoise fish and waves
	2. Fleshtone skin with sea-green on tail; blonde hair; sea-green fish and waves
	3. All-over sea-green
Issued:	1936

		Price		
Colourways	Backstamp	U.S. $	Can. $	U.K. £
1. Coloured (as above)	Puce	1,250.00	1,500.00	650.00
2. Coloured (as above)	Black	950.00	1,200.00	550.00

RW3163
POLO PLAYER

Modeller:	Doris Lindner
Height:	With plinth: 8 ¼", 21.0 cm
	Without plinth: 6 ¾", 17.2 cm
Colour:	1. Jockey: Blue, red and yellow shirt; white jodhpurs and cap; black boots
	Horse: Chestnut (gloss or matt)
	2. Jockey: Yellow shirt; white jodhpurs and cap; brown metal polo stick, reins
	Horse: Chestnut (gloss or matt)
Issued:	1936-1981

		Price		
Colourways	Backstamp	U.S. $	Can. $	U.K. £
1. Coloured (as above)	Puce	950.00	1,200.00	480.00
2. Coloured (as above)	Black	800.00	1,000.00	400.00

RW3164
HOG HUNTING

Modeller:	Doris Lindner
Height:	With plinth: 8 ½", 21.6 cm
	Without plinth: 6 ¾", 17.2 cm
Colour:	Rider: Khaki clothes and hat; painted metal spear
	Horse: Bay
	Hog: Dark grey
Issued:	1936-1981

	Price		
Backstamp	U.S. $	Can. $	U.K. £
1. Puce	1,150.00	1,450.00	580.00
2. Black	950.00	1,200.00	480.00

RW3165
BANBURY CROSS

Modeller: Geraldine Blake
Height: 8", 20.3 cm
Colour: Unknown
Issued: 1936-by 1945

Colourways	Backstamp	U.S. $	Price Can. $	U.K. £
Unknown	Puce	1,100.00	1,375.00	550.00

RW3166
HIGHWAYMAN

Modeller: Geraldine Blake
Height: 8 ½", 21.6 cm
Colour: Rider: Pale blue jacket; green shirt; black hat, eye mask, boots
           Horse: Black; brown saddle
Issued: 1936-by 1945

Colourways	Backstamp	U.S. $	Price Can. $	U.K. £
Blue/green/black/brown	Puce	1,100.00	1,375.00	550.00

RW3167
YONDER HE GOES

Modeller: Geraldine Blake
Height: 8", 20.3 cm
Colour: Rider: Red riding habit; white jodhpurs; black hat and boots
           Horse: Black
Issued: 1936-by 1945

Colourways	Backstamp	U.S. $	Price Can. $	U.K. £
Red/white/black	Puce	1,100.00	1,375.00	550.00

RW3168
BENGAL LANCER

Modeller: Geraldine Blake
Height: 8 ½", 21.6 cm
Colour: Rider: Blue tunic and leggings; brown sash and belt; white turban with blue stripes
Horse: Brown
Issued: 1936-by 1945

Colourways	Backstamp	U.S. $	Price Can. $	U.K. £
Blue/brown	Puce	1,100.00	1,375.00	550.00

RW3169
YOUNG ENTRY

Modeller: Geraldine Blake
Height: 7", 17.8 cm
Colour: Rider: Dark yellow habit; black riding hat
Horse: White with brown patches
Issued: 1936-by 1945

Colourways	Backstamp	U.S. $	Price Can. $	U.K. £
Yellow/black/white/brown	Puce	1,100.00	1,375.00	550.00

RW3171
ANITA / SOUBRETTE

Modeller: Rachel Greaves
Height: 5 ¾", 14.6 cm
Colour: **Anita:** 1. Asprey grey dress
2. Blue-green dress
3. Sea-green dress; blue slippers
Soubrette: White; gold-lined base
Issued: **Anita:** 1936
Soubrette: 1982-1985
Series: **Anita:** Ballet Dancers
Soubrette: Art Deco

Description	Backstamp	U.S. $	Price Can. $	U.K. £
1. Anita	Puce		Extremely rare	
2. Soubrette	Black	375.00	475.00	220.00

RW3172
TAMARA / JOY (Style One)

Modeller:	Rachel Greaves
Height:	5 ¾", 14.6 cm
Colour:	**Tamara:** 1. Asprey grey dress
	2. Blue-green dress
	3. Sea-green dress
	Joy: White; gold-lined base
Issued:	**Tamara:** 1936
	Joy: 1982-1985
Series:	**Tamara:** Ballet Dancers
	Joy: Art Deco

			Price	
Description	Backstamp	U.S. $	Can. $	U.K. £
1. Tamara	Puce		Extremely rare	
2. Joy (Style One)	Black	375.00	475.00	220.00

RW3173
TATIANA

Modeller:	Rachel Greaves
Height:	5 ¾", 14.6 cm
Colour:	1. Asprey grey dress
	2. Blue-green dress
	3. Sea-green dress
Issued:	1936
Series:	Ballet Dancers

			Price	
Colourways	Backstamp	U.S. $	Can. $	U.K. £
Coloured (as above)	Puce		Extremely rare	

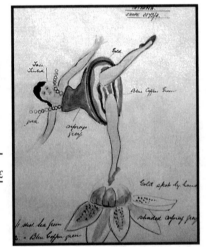

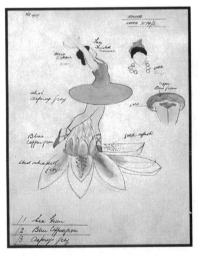

RW3174
ANNA

Modeller:	Rachel Greaves
Height:	6 ½", 16.5 cm
Colour:	1. Asprey grey dress
	2. Blue-green dress
	3. Sea-green dress
Issued:	1936
Series:	Ballet Dancers

			Price	
Colourways	Backstamp	U.S. $	Can. $	U.K. £
Coloured (as above)	Puce		Extremely rare	

RW3175
ALICIA / BLITHE SPIRIT

Modeller:	Rachel Greaves
Height:	5 ¼", 13.3 cm
Colour:	**Alicia:** 1. Asprey grey dress
	2. Blue-green dress
	3. Sea-green dress
	Blithe Spirit: White; gold-lined base
Issued:	**Alicia:** 1936
	Blithe Spirit: 1982-1985
Series:	**Alicia:** Ballet Dancers
	Blithe Spirit: Art Deco

			Price	
Description	Backstamp	U.S. $	Can. $	U.K. £
1. Alicia	Puce		Extremely rare	
2. Blithe Spirit	Black	375.00	475.00	220.00

RW3176
NATASHA (Style One) / PIROUETTE

Modeller:	Rachel Greaves
Height:	6 ½", 16.5 cm
Colour:	**Natasha:** 1. Asprey grey dress
	2. Blue-green dress
	3. Sea-green dress
	Pirouette: White; gold-lined base
Issued:	**Natasha:** 1936
	Pirouette: 1982-1985
Series:	**Natasha:** Ballet Dancers
	Pirouette: Art Deco

			Price	
Description	Backstamp	U.S. $	Can. $	U.K. £
1. Natasha (Style One)	Puce		Extremely rare	
2. Pirouette	Black	375.00	475.00	220.00

RW3177
IRINA / GRACE (Style Two)

Modeller:	Rachel Greaves
Height:	5 ¾", 14.6 cm
Colour:	**Irina:** 1. Asprey grey dress
	2. Blue-green dress
	3. Sea-green dress
	Grace: White; gold-lined base
Issued:	**Irina:** 1936
	Grace: 1982-1985
Series:	**Irina:** Ballet Dancers
	Grace: Art Deco

			Price	
Description	Backstamp	U.S. $	Can. $	U.K. £
1. Irina	Puce		Extremely rare	
2. Grace (Style Two)	Black	375.00	475.00	220.00

RW3178
IRELAND

Modeller:	Freda Doughty
Height:	5 ¾", 14.6 cm
Colour:	1. Green dress and scarf; white apron; brown hair; light brown basket
	2. Green and white striped dress; pink scarf; white apron; brown hair; brown basket
Issued:	1936-1959
Series:	Children of the Nations

		Price		
Colourways	Backstamp	U.S. $	Can. $	U.K. £
1. Coloured (as above)	Puce	675.00	850.00	380.00
2. Coloured (as above)	Black	550.00	700.00	320.00

RW3180
IN THE RING

Modeller:	Doris Lindner
Height:	With plinth: 14 ¾", 37.5 cm
	Without plinth: 10 ¼", 26.0 cm
Colour:	Rider: Yellow dress with red stars and white trim; white and yellow plume
	Horses: Grey
Issued:	1936-c.1970

	Price		
Backstamp	U.S. $	Can. $	U.K. £
1. Puce	6,000.00	7,500.00	3,000.00
2. Black	4,000.00	5,000.00	2,000.00

Note: For the companion piece, RW3179 Three Circus Horses Rearing, see *The Charlton Standard Catalogue of Royal Worcester Animals*.

RW3186
BALLET DANCER
Style One

Modeller:	Dorothea Charol
Height:	11 ¼", 28.5 cm
Colour:	1. Asprey grey bodice with blue bows; blue skirt and slippers
	2. Ivory with blue bows
Issued:	1937-by 1948

		Price		
Colourways	Backstamp	U.S. $	Can. $	U.K. £
Coloured (as above)	Puce		Extremely rare	

RW3192
BALLET DANCER
Style Two

Modeller:	Dorothea Charol
Height:	10 ¼", 26.0 cm
Colour:	1. Grey and gold costume; blue shoes
	2. Grey and pink costume; pink shoes
	3. Lilac and white costume; pink shoes
	4. Turquoise costume and shoes
Issued:	1937-by 1948

Colourways	Backstamp	U.S. $	Price Can. $	U.K. £
Coloured (as above)	Puce		Extremely rare	

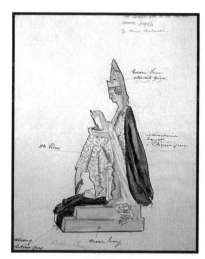

RW3193
THE QUEEN IN THE PARLOUR

Modeller:	Anne Acheson
Height:	6", 15.0 cm
Colour:	Pink dress and shoes; turquoise cloak; gold, fawn and pink headdress
Issued:	1937-by 1948

Colourways	Backstamp	U.S. $	Price Can. $	U.K. £
Pink/turquoise/gold	Puce		Extremely rare	

RW3194
CHINESE DANCER (Male)

Modeller:	Gwendolen Parnell
Height:	9 ½", 24.0 cm
Colour:	Black, green, grey and cream; edged in red
Issued:	1937-by 1948
Series:	Chinese Dancers

Colourways	Backstamp	U.S. $	Price Can. $	U.K. £
Black/green	Puce	1,250.00	1,500.00	650.00

RW3195
CHINESE DANCER (Female)

Modeller: Gwendolen Parnell
Height: 9 ½", 24.0 cm
Colour: Black, green, grey and cream; edged in red
Issued: 1937-by 1948
Series: Chinese Dancers

Colourways	Backstamp	U.S. $	Price Can. $	U.K. £
Black/green	Puce	1,250.00	1,500.00	650.00

RW3202
PIERROT GROUP

Modeller: Dorothea Charol
Height: 10 ½", 26.7 cm
Colour: Pierrot: Grey suit; black shoes
 Columbine: White dress with pink bows and roses
Issued: 1937-by 1948

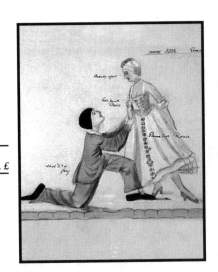

Colourways	Backstamp	U.S. $	Price Can. $	U.K. £
Grey/white/pink	Puce		Extremely rare	

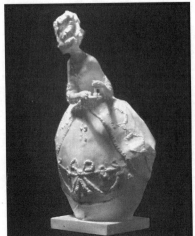

RW3222
THE CANDLESTICK

Modeller: Gwendolen Parnell
Height: 10", 25.4 cm
Colour: Unknown
Issued: 1937-by 1959

Backstamp	U.S. $	Price Can. $	U.K. £
1. Puce	1,100.00	1,350.00	550.00
2. Black	900.00	1,125.00	450.00

RW3224
THE BRIDESMAID
Style One

Modeller: Freda Doughty
Height: 8 ¼", 21.0 cm
Colour: 1. Blue dress with white highlights; yellow shoe;
pink flowers; brown hair; blue headband
2. White dress; green shoe; pink flowers; brown hair;
green headband
3. Yellow dress; green shoe; purple flowers; brown hair;
green headband
Issued: 1938-1955
Varieties: Also called "Rose Maiden"

Colourways	Backstamp	U.S. $	Price Can. $	U.K. £
1. Coloured (as above)	Puce	1,100.00	1,375.00	550.00
2. Coloured (as above)	Black	775.00	1,000.00	450.00

RW3225
DANCING WAVES

Modeller: Freda Doughty
Height: 8 ¾", 22.2 cm
Colour: 1. Pink dress; blue, yellow and white base
2. Turquoise dress; blue and white base
Issued: 1938-1959

Colourways	Backstamp	U.S. $	Price Can. $	U.K. £
1. Coloured (as above)	Puce	1,000.00	1,250.00	500.00
2. Coloured (as above)	Black	700.00	900.00	400.00

RW3226
ONLY ME

Modeller: Freda Doughty
Height: 5 ½", 14.0 cm
Colour: 1. Pink and rose dress; lilac base
2. Pink dress with deep pink star design; brown hair;
pink base with star design
3. White dress with pink bodice and pink dots on skirt;
white base
Issued: 1938-1972

Description	Backstamp	U.S. $	Price Can. $	U.K. £
1. Coloured (as above)	Puce	475.00	600.00	240.00
2. Coloured (as above)	Black	300.00	400.00	180.00

Note: See also miniature version RW4206 Solitaire.

RW3227
"DELICATE COWCUMBERS TO PICKLE"

Modeller:	Gwendolen Parnell
Height:	6 ¼", 15.9 cm
Colour:	Pink coat; brown skirt; green apron; fawn hat
Issued:	1938-by 1948
Series:	The Cries of London

	Price		
Backstamp	U.S. $	Can. $	U.K. £
1. Puce	900.00	1,125.00	450.00
2. Black	800.00	1,000.00	400.00

RW3246
AUTUMN (Bust)

Modeller:	Rachel Greaves
Height:	9", 22.9 cm
Colour:	Glazed cream bone china
Issued:	1938-by 1959

	Price		
Backstamp	U.S. $	Can. $	U.K. £
1. Puce	1,000.00	1,250.00	500.00
2. Black	800.00	1,000.00	400.00

RW3247
SPRING (Bust)

Modeller:	Rachel Greaves
Height:	9", 22.9 cm
Colour:	Glazed cream bone china
Issued:	1938-by 1959

	Price		
Backstamp	U.S. $	Can. $	U.K. £
1. Puce	1,000.00	1,250.00	500.00
2. Black	800.00	1,000.00	400.00

RW3250
"RIPE 'SPERAGUS"

Modeller:	Gwendolen Parnell
Height:	6", 15.0 cm
Colour:	Sea-green dress; orange apron; yellow cloak; clover shoes with red bows; purple and mauve hat
Issued:	1938
Series:	The Cries of London

		Price	
Backstamp	U.S. $	Can. $	U.K. £
1. Puce	900.00	1,125.00	450.00
2. Black	800.00	1,000.00	400.00

RW3252
"A MERY NEW SONG"

Modeller:	Gwendolen Parnell
Height:	6 ¼", 15.9 cm
Colour:	Pink dress with yellow and brown stripes; tan apron and hat; mauve shoes
Issued:	1938-by 1959
Series:	The Cries of London

		Price	
Backstamp	U.S. $	Can. $	U.K. £
1. Puce	900.00	1,125.00	450.00
2. Black	800.00	1,000.00	400.00

RW3256
SUNDAY'S CHILD (Boy)

Modeller:	Freda Doughty
Height:	4 ¾", 12.1 cm
Issued:	See below
Colour:	Blue outfit; blonde hair; green ball with red and blue stripes; yellow sandy base
Series:	The Days of the Week

			Price	
Issued	Colourways	Backstamp	U.S. $	Can. $	U.K. £
1938 to 1942	As above	Blue	475.00	700.00	240.00
1943 to 1961	As above	Black	350.00	525.00	180.00
1962 to 1984	As above	Black, circle	300.00	450.00	160.00
1996 to date	As above	Black, diamond	—	225.00	100.00

Note: See also miniature version RW4164 Sunshine Days.

RW3257
MONDAY'S CHILD (Girl) / SUSIE

Modeller:	Freda Doughty
Height:	6 ½", 16.5 cm
Colour:	**Monday's Child:**
	1. Blue dress trimmed with yellow frills and sash; white base with blue and yellow design
	2. Creamy-white dress trimmed with blue frills and sash; light blue base
	Susie:
	Purple dress trimmed with yellow frills and sash
Issued:	See below
Series:	**Monday's Child:** The Days of the Week

				Price	
Issued	Colourways	Backstamp	U.S. $	Can. $	U.K. £
Monday's Child					
1938 to 1942	As above	Blue	475.00	700.00	240.00
1943 to 1961	As above	Black	350.00	525.00	180.00
1962 to 1984	As above	Black, circle	300.00	450.00	160.00
1996 to date	As above	Black, diamond	—	225.00	100.00
Susie:					
1982 to 1983	As above	Black, circle		Very rare	

Note: See also miniature version RW4194 Birthday Girl.

RW3258
TUESDAY'S CHILD (Girl) / RED SHOES

Modeller:	Freda Doughty
Height:	8 ½", 21.6 cm
Colour:	**Tuesday's Child:** Yellow and white tutu trimmed with orange; yellow and red slippers
	Red Shoes: White tutu; red slippers
Issued:	See below
Series:	**Tuesday's Child:** The Days of the Week

				Price	
Issued	Colourways	Backstamp	U.S. $	Can. $	U.K. £
Tuesday's Child					
1938 to 1942	As above	Blue	475.00	700.00	240.00
1943 to 1961	As above	Black	350.00	525.00	180.00
1962 to 1984	As above	Black, circle	300.00	450.00	160.00
1996 to date	As above	Black, diamond	—	225.00	100.00
Red Shoes					
1982 to 1983	As above	Black, circle		Very rare	

Note: See also miniature version RW4188 Ballerina.

RW3259
WEDNESDAY'S CHILD (Girl)

Modeller:	Freda Doughty
Height:	7", 17.8 cm
Colour:	Rose-pink dress; blue shoes; red hair; green and base
Issued:	1938-1942
Series:	The Days of the Week

		Price		
Colourways	Backstamp	U.S. $	Can. $	U.K. £
Coloured (as above)	Blue	475.00	600.00	240.00

RW3260
THURSDAY'S CHILD (Boy) / SMILING THROUGH

Modeller:	Freda Doughty
Height:	6 ½", 16.5 cm
Colour:	**Thursday's Child:** Light blue coat; red hat, sandals; brown staff
	Smiling Through: Light blue coat; brown hat, sandals; brown staff
Issued:	See below
Series:	**Thursday's Child:** The Days of the Week

Issued	Colourways	Backstamp	U.S. $	Price Can. $	U.K. £
Thursday's Child					
1938 to 1942	As above	Blue	475.00	700.00	240.00
1943 to 1961	As above	Black	350.00	525.00	180.00
1962 to 1984	As above	Black, circle	300.00	450.00	160.00
1996 to date	As above	Black, diamond	—	225.00	100.00
Smiling Through					
1982 to 1983	As above	Black, circle	Very rare		

Note: See also miniature version RW4201 Country Boy.

RW3261
FRIDAY'S CHILD (Boy) / MY PET

Modeller:	Freda Doughty
Height:	7", 17.8 cm
Colour:	**Friday's Child:** Beige, white; green shorts; orange sandals; grey cat
	My Pet: Turquoise shirt and shorts; brown hair and sandals; grey cat
Issued:	See below
Series:	**Friday's Child:** The Days of the Week

Issued	Colourways	Backstamp	U.S. $	Price Can. $	U.K. £
Friday's Child					
1938 to 1942	As above	Blue	475.00	700.00	240.00
1943 to 1961	As above	Black	350.00	525.00	180.00
1962 to 1984	As above	Black, circle	300.00	450.00	160.00
1996 to date	As above	Black, diamond	—	225.00	100.00
My Pet					
1982 to 1983	As above	Black, circle	Very rare		

Note: See also miniature version RW4193 Old Friends.

RW3262
SATURDAY'S CHILD (Girl)

Modeller: Freda Doughty
Height: 7", 17.8 cm
Colour: 1. Blue dress; yellow wool; black and white kitten
2. White dress trimmed with dark blue; red wool; black and white kitten; lavender base
Issued: See below
Series: The Days of the Week

Issued	Colourways	Backstamp	U.S. $	Price Can. $	U.K. £
1938 to 1942	As above	Blue	475.00	700.00	240.00
1943 to 1961	As above	Black	350.00	525.00	180.00
1962 to 1984	As above	Black, circle	300.00	450.00	160.00
1996 to date	As above	Black, diamond	—	225.00	100.00

Note: See also miniature version RW4154 Katie.

RW3270
PLAYMATES

Modeller: Freda Doughty
Height: 6 ¾", 17.2 cm
Colour: 1. Pink dress with white highlights; white and brown dog; green and brown base
2. Pale blue dress with lavender highlights; white and brown dog; green and brown base
Issued: 1938-1959

Colourways	Backstamp	U.S. $	Price Can. $	U.K. £
1. Coloured (as above)	Puce	950.00	1,200.00	480.00
2. Coloured (as above)	Black	750.00	950.00	420.00

RW3271
"LONDON GAZETTE HERE"

Modeller: Gwendolen Parnell
Height: 6 ¼", 15.9 cm
Colour: Primrose and orange dress; clover cloak, hat and shoes
Issued: 1938
Series: The Cries of London

Backstamp	U.S. $	Price Can. $	U.K. £
1. Puce	1,000.00	1,250.00	500.00
2. Black	775.00	1,000.00	450.00

RW3272
REPOSE

Modeller:	Dorothea Charol
Height:	7", 17.8 cm
Colour:	1. Green dress; blonde hair
	2. Purple dress; blonde hair
	3. Turquoise dress; pink bodice; brown hair
Issued:	1938- by 1948

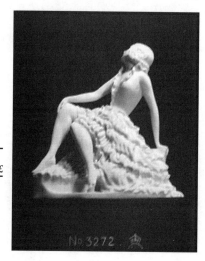

			Price		
Colourways	Backstamp	U.S. $	Can. $	U.K. £
Coloured (as above)	Puce		Extremely rare	

RW3288
GIRL WITH BEADS

Modeller:	Dorothea Charol
Height:	4", 10.1 cm
Colour:	Golden fawn skin; shot tan hair and features; green necklace
Issued:	1939-by 1948
Varieties:	Also called "The Necklace"

			Price		
Colourways	Backstamp	U.S. $	Can. $	U.K. £
Golden fawn	Puce		Rare	

RW3289
BATHING GIRL

Modeller:	Dorothea Charol
Height:	8 ¼", 21.0 cm
Colour:	1. Blue bathing suit; blue headband and sandals; blonde hair
	2. White bathing suit; red headband and sandals; brown hair
Issued:	1939-by 1948
Varieties:	Also called "Hesitation"

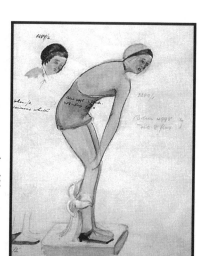

			Price		
Colourways	Backstamp	U.S. $	Can. $	U.K. £
Coloured (as above)	Puce		Rare	

RW3296
HACKING IN THE PARK

Modeller: Doris Lindner
Height: 6 ¾", 17.2 cm
Colour: Rider: Light brown jacket; white jodhpurs; black boots
Horse: Brown; tan saddle
Issued: 1939-by 1970

Backstamp	Price U.S. $	Can. $	U.K. £
1. Puce	1,000.00	1,250.00	500.00
2. Black	800.00	1,000.00	400.00

RW3299
"FINE WRITEING INKES"

Modeller: Gwendolen Parnell
Height: 6", 15.0 cm
Colour: Mauve skirt; ultramarine apron; blue cloak; green shoes; white hat
Issued: 1940-by 1959
Series: The Cries of London

Backstamp	Price U.S. $	Can. $	U.K. £
1. Puce	1,000.00	1,250.00	500.00
2. Black	900.00	1,100.00	450.00

RW3300
"FAIR CHERRYES"

Modeller: Gwendolen Parnell
Height: 6 ½", 16.5 cm
Colour: Yellow dress; pink pinafore; light green hat; blue
shoes; red cherries; light grey base
Issued: 1940-by 1959
Series: The Cries of London

Backstamp	Price U.S. $	Can. $	U.K. £
1. Puce	1,000.00	1,250.00	500.00
2. Black	900.00	1,100.00	450.00

RW3301
LITTLE MISS MUFFET

Modeller: Freda Doughty
Height: 4 ½", 11.9 cm
Colour:
1. Blue outer dress; yellow sleeves; cream underdress with red pattern; blue bowl; green tuffet; brown and black spider
2. Rose outer dress; yellow sleeves; white underdress with pink and green pattern; blue bowl; green tuffet; brown and black spider
Issued: 1940-1959
Series: Nursery Rhymes

| Colourways | Backstamp | Price | | |
		U.S. $	Can. $	U.K. £
1. Coloured (as above)	Puce	700.00	900.00	400.00
2. Coloured (as above)	Black	525.00	675.00	300.00

RW3302
BABES IN THE WOOD

Modeller: Freda Doughty
Height: 6 ¼", 15.9 cm
Colour:
1. Older girl: Pink pinafore; lilac blouse and shoes
   Younger girl: Turquoise dress; lilac cap trimmed with white
2. Older girl: Yellow pinafore; white blouse and shoes
   Younger girl: White dress with red pattern; pink cap trimmed with white
Issued: 1940-1959

| Colourways | Backstamp | Price | | |
		U.S. $	Can. $	U.K. £
1. Coloured (as above)	Puce	875.00	1,125.00	500.00
2. Coloured (as above)	Black	700.00	675.00	400.00

RW3303
POLLY PUT THE KETTLE ON

Modeller: Freda Doughty
Height: 6", 15.0 cm
Colour:
1. White dress; pink apron; white cap trimmed with pink; brown shoes; gold kettle
2. White dress; pink apron; white cap trimmed with pink; brown shoes; silver kettle
3. Pink dress; green apron; gold kettle
4. Pink dress; green apron; silver kettle
Issued: 1940-1983
Series: Nursery Rhymes

| Colourways | Backstamp | Price | | |
		U.S. $	Can. $	U.K. £
1. Coloured (as above)	Puce	500.00	625.00	280.00
2. Coloured (as above)	Black	375.00	475.00	220.00

Note: Earlier versions of this model, c.1940, had either black or white kettles. See also miniature version RW4205 Mother's Helper.

RW3304
GOOSEY GOOSEY GANDER

Modeller:	Freda Doughty
Height:	6", 15.0 cm
Colour:	Yellow smock with white collar; green shorts; white and grey goose; orange beak, feet; green and beige base
Issued:	1940-1959
Series:	Nursery Rhymes

	Price		
Backstamp	U.S. $	Can. $	U.K. £
1. Puce	775.00	1,000.00	450.00
2. Black	675.00	850.00	380.00

RW3305
LITTLE JACK HORNER

Modeller:	Freda Doughty
Height:	4 ½", 11.9 cm
Colour:	1. Green and beige tunic; white blouse; yellow breeches; green stockings; beige shoes; blonde hair
	2. Turquoise and yellow tunic; white blouse; yellow breeches; turquoise stockings; orange shoes; blonde hair
Issued:	1940-1959
Series:	Nursery Rhymes

		Price		
Colourways	Backstamp	U.S. $	Can. $	U.K. £
1. Coloured (as above)	Puce	775.00	1,000.00	450.00
2. Coloured (as above)	Black	675.00	850.00	380.00

RW3306
LITTLE BOY BLUE

Modeller:	Freda Doughty
Height:	3 ½", 8.9 cm
Colour:	Blue suit with white collar, blue hat and shoes; yellow horn; white sheep with lavender and beige highlights; beige base
Issued:	1940-1959
Series:	Nursery Rhymes

	Price		
Backstamp	U.S. $	Can. $	U.K. £
1. Puce	775.00	1,000.00	450.00
2. Black	675.00	850.00	380.00

MODELS BY PHOEBE STABLER

Pick a Back

The Mother

The Old Goat Woman

Coquette, Style One

NUDE FIGURES

Naiad (On Plinth)

Nude Bather Reclining on Plinth, Style Two

Tangles

Nude Boy with Dolphin

FIGURES BY STYLE

Columbine, Style One

Harlequin, Style One

Kate Greenaway Girl, Style One

Columbine, Style Two

Harlequin, Style Two

Kate Greenaway Girl, Style Two

HISTORICAL FIGURES

Sir Walter Raleigh

Elizabeth I, Style One

Edward VI

PAPAL GUARD

The Privy Chamberlain of the Sword
and Cape to The Pope in the
Spanish Costume

Trooper of the Swiss Guard
of His Holiness The Pope

Papal Gendarmé

HISTORICAL MILITARY FIGURES

Officer of the 3rd
Dragoon Guards 1806

Officer of the Royal
Artillery 1815

Officer of the 29th Foot
(Worcestershire Regiment) 1812

Officer of the Coldstream
Guards 1815, Second Version

Officer of the
Seaforth Highlanders 1812

Officer of the 17th
Dragoon Guards 1814

CHINOISERIE SAYINGS

Wise as an Owl

Slow Coach

Early Bird

Mad as a Hatter

WARTIME SERIES

The Rescue

Evacuees

Take Cover

Stowaway

VICTORIAN MUSICIANS

The Lute Player

The Harpist

The Flute Player

DANCERS

Lady with a Rose

The Dancers

Dance

RW3330
BOGSKAR

Modeller: Doris Lindner
Height: 9", 22.9 cm
Colour: 1. Rider: Blue and gold silks; white jodhpurs
Horse: Brown
2. White
Issued: 1940-by 1942

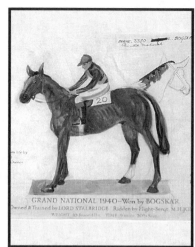

Colourways	Backstamp	U.S. $	Price Can. $	U.K. £
1. Blue/gold/white/brown	Puce		Rare	
2. White	Puce		Rare	

Note: "Bogskar," owned by Lord Stalbridge, was the Grand National winner in 1940.

RW3339
SUMMER
Style One

Modeller: Gwendolen Parnell
Height: 4 ¾", 12.1 cm
Colour: 1. Pink dress; green underskirt with white dots; white apron with flower print; light green base surrounded with flowers
2. Yellow dress; white underskirt with pink pattern; yellow apron; white base surrounded by flowers
Issued: 1941-by c.1960
Series: The Four Seasons, Series One

Colourways	Backstamp	U.S. $	Price Can. $	U.K. £
1. Coloured (as above)	Puce	675.00	850.00	380.00
2. Coloured (as above)	Black	525.00	675.00	300.00

RW3340
WINTER
Style One

Modeller: Gwendolen Parnell
Height: 4 ¾", 12.1 cm
Colour: 1. Red hooded cloak and shoes; pink skirt with red flowers; white apron; green bag
2. White cloak and apron trimmed in blue; pink skirt; brown bag
Issued: 1941-by c.1960
Series: The Four Seasons, Series One

Colourways	Backstamp	U.S. $	Price Can. $	U.K. £
1. Coloured (as above)	Puce	600.00	775.00	350.00
2. Coloured (as above)	Black	525.00	675.00	300.00

RW3341
AUTUMN
Style One

Modeller: Gwendolen Parnell
Height: 4 ¾", 12.1 cm
Colour: 1. White skirt with red design; mauve apron; red shoes;
                green foliage; orange apples
            2. Yellow and white dotted dress; blue shoes; green foliage;
                orange apples
Issued: 1941-by c.1960
Series: The Four Seasons, Series One

Colourways	Backstamp	Price U.S. $	Can. $	U.K. £
1. Coloured (as above)	Puce	775.00	1,000.00	450.00
2. Coloured (as above)	Black	700.00	900.00	400.00

RW3342
SPRING
Style Two

Modeller: Gwendolen Parnell
Height: 4 ¾", 12.1 cm
Colour: 1. Blue dress; yellow overskirt; white sleeves and apron;
                straw hat with lilac ribbon; green surround with pink flowers
            2. Pink dress with white and red patterned top; white apron;
                red shoes; yellow hat
Issued: 1941-by c.1960
Series: The Four Seasons, Series One

Colourways	Backstamp	Price U.S. $	Can. $	U.K. £
1. Coloured (as above)	Puce	675.00	850.00	380.00
2. Coloured (as above)	Black	550.00	725.00	320.00

RW3346
THE RESCUE

Modeller: Eileen Soper
Height: 4 ½", 10.8 cm
Colour: 1. Pink dress; blue coat; blonde hair; brown shoes; black kitten
            2. White
Issued: 1941-by 1943
Series: Wartime

Colourways	Backstamp	Price U.S. $	Can. $	U.K. £
1. Pink/blue	Puce	2,500.00	3,375.00	1,500.00
2. White	Puce	750.00	950.00	375.00

RW3347
EVACUEES

Modeller: Eileen Soper
Height: 4 ½", 11.9 cm
Colour: 1. Jenny: Blue coat; pink kerchief; grey shoes
Tommy: Orange jersey; blue scarf; grey shorts; brown shoes
2. White
Issued: 1941
Series: Wartime

Colourways	Backstamp	U.S. $	Price Can. $	U.K. £
1. Blue/pink/orange/grey	Puce	3,000.00	3,950.00	1,750.00
2. White	Puce	800.00	1,000.00	400.00

3348
CHINOISERIE GIRL (Head down)

Modeller: Gwendolen Parnell
Height: 6 ¼", 15.9 cm
Colour: Black, turquoise and white robes with Chinese red details; grey squirrel
Issued: 1941
Series: Chinoiserie Children

Colourways	Backstamp	U.S. $	Price Can. $	U.K. £
Black/turqouise	Black	450.00	575.00	260.00

3349
BOY AND DOLPHIN

Modeller: Frederick M. Gertner
Height: Unknown
Colour: Unknown
Issued: 1941

Colourways	Backstamp	U.S. $	Price Can. $	U.K. £
Unknown	Black		Extremely rare	

Photograph not available at press time

RW3351
TAKE COVER

Modeller:	Eileen Soper
Height:	4 ½", 11.9 cm
Colour:	1. Boy: Blue shirt; grey shorts; brown shoes and hair; brown and white puppy
	Girl: Yellow dress; white and yellow dotted sleeves and collar; blonde hair
	2. White
Issued:	1941
Series:	Wartime

			Price	
Colourways	Backstamp	U.S. $	Can. $	U.K. £
1. Blue/yellow	Puce	2,875.00	3,700.00	1,650.00
2. White	Puce	750.00	950.00	375.00

RW3352
SPITFIRE

Modeller:	Eileen Soper
Height:	6 ½", 16.5 cm
Colour:	1. Older boy: Blue vest and cap; paler blue checkered shirt; light brown trousers; brown shoes
	Younger boy: Red jersey; pale grey trousers; light brown shoes
	2. White
Issued:	1941
Series:	Wartime

			Price	
Colourways	Backstamp	U.S. $	Can. $	U.K. £
1. Blue/brown/red/grey	Puce	2,875.00	3,725.00	1,650.00
2. White	Puce	750.00	950.00	375.00

RW3353
SEAWEED

Modeller:	Frederick M. Gertner
Height:	7", 17.8 cm
Colour:	Unknown
Issued:	1941-by 1953

			Price	
Colourways	Backstamp	U.S. $	Can. $	U.K. £
Unknown	Puce		Rare	

RW3354
CHINOISERIE BOY

Modeller: Gwendolen Parnell
Height: 5", 12.7 cm
Colour: Black trousers and hair; turquoise jacket; grey shirt
Issued: 1941
Series: Chinoiserie Children

Colourways	Backstamp	U.S. $	Price Can. $	U.K. £
Black/turquoise	Black	325.00	400.00	180.00

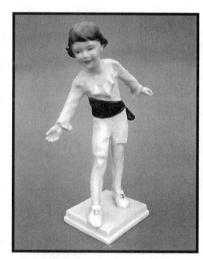

RW3359
THE BOW

Modeller: Freda Doughty
Height: 7 ½", 19.1 cm
Colour: 1. Creamy-white suit with white and grey collar and cuffs; burgundy sash; brown hair; green and cream base
2. Turquoise suit with white collar and cuffs; burgundy sash; yellow hair; brown shoes; cream base
Issued: 1941-1974
Varieties: Also called "Masquerade Boy"

Colourways	Backstamp	U.S. $	Price Can. $	U.K. £
Coloured (as above)	Black	350.00	450.00	200.00

RW3360
THE CURTSEY
Style One

Modeller: Freda Doughty
Height: 6 ¼", 15.9 cm
Colour: 1. Cream dress edged with blue dots; cream bows; silver shoe; yellow hair
2. Pink dress with green bows; green shoe; brown hair
3. Turquoise dress; brown hair and shoe
Issued: 1941-1974
Varieties: Also called "Masquerade, Style One"

Colourways	Backstamp	U.S. $	Price Can. $	U.K. £
Coloured (as above)	Black	485.00	625.00	280.00

RW3362
CHINOISERIE GIRL (Head up)

Modeller:	Gwendolen Parnell
Height:	5", 12.7 cm
Colour:	Black, turquoise and white robe; Chinese red shoes
Issued:	1941-by 1952
Series:	Chinoiserie Children

Colourways	Backstamp	Price U.S. $	Can. $	U.K. £
Black/turquoise/white	Black	325.00	425.00	190.00

RW3369
STOWAWAY

Modeller:	Eileen Soper
Height:	5 ¾", 14.6 cm
Colour:	1. Blue dress; white pinafore edged with blue; red beret and scarf
	2. Mauve dress; cream pinafore edged with green; pink beret and scarf
	3. White
Issued:	1941-by 1942
Series:	Wartime

Colourways	Backstamp	Price U.S. $	Can. $	U.K. £
1. Coloured (as above)	Puce	2,800.00	3,600.00	1,600.00
2. White	Puce	800.00	1,000.00	400.00

RW3370
SALVAGE

Modeller:	Eileen Soper
Height:	5 ½", 14.0 cm
Colour:	1. White shirt; blue dungarees; red, brown and green toys; brown and white dog; white sign
	2. White
Issued:	1941-by 1942
Series:	Wartime

Colourways	Backstamp	Price U.S. $	Can. $	U.K. £
1. White/blue/brown	Puce	3,000.00	4,000.00	1,800.00
2. White	Puce	800.00	1,000.00	400.00

RW3373
NUDE BOY WITH CORNUCOPIA

Modeller: Frederick M. Gertner
Height: 7 ¾", 19.7 cm
Colour: Unknown
Issued: 1942-by 1953

Colourways	Backstamp	U.S. $	Price Can. $	U.K. £
Unknown	Black		Extremely rare	

RW3374
NUDE GIRL WITH CORNUCOPIA

Modeller: Frederick M. Gertner
Height: 7 ¾", 19.7 cm
Colour: Unknown
Issued: 1942-by 1953

Colourways	Backstamp	U.S. $	Price Can. $	U.K. £
Unknown	Black		Extremely rare	

RW3380
CHILD (Seated)

Modeller: Freda Doughty
Height: 4", 10.1 cm
Colour: Fleshtone; yellow hair
Issued: 1942-1955

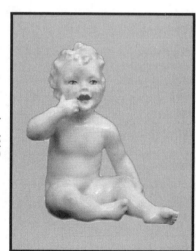

Colourways	Backstamp	U.S. $	Price Can. $	U.K. £
Fleshtone	Black	1,000.00	1,350.00	600.00

RW3381
CHILD (Crawling)

Modeller: Freda Doughty
Height: 3 ½", 8.9 cm
Colour: Fleshtone; yellow hair
Issued: 1942-1955

Colourways	Backstamp	Price U.S. $	Price Can. $	U.K. £
Fleshtone	Black	1,000.00	1,350.00	600.00

RW3382
THE LETTER

Modeller: Eileen Soper
Height: 4 ½", 11.9 cm
Colour: 1. Mother: Blue skirt; red top; white apron with red trim; brown hair
Child: White dress with blue dots; yellow hair
2. White
Issued: 1941-by 1953
Series: Wartime

Colourways	Backstamp	Price U.S. $	Price Can. $	U.K. £
1. Blue/red/white	Puce	3,750.00	5,000.00	2,200.00
2. White	Puce	800.00	1,000.00	400.00

*Photograph not
available
at press time*

RW3388
SOUTHWIND

Modeller: Agnes Pinder-Davis
Height: 7 ¼", 18.4 cm
Colour: Unknown
Issued: 1942

Colourways	Backstamp	Price U.S. $	Price Can. $	U.K. £
Unknown	Puce		Extremely rare	

RW3396
WESTWIND

Modeller: Agnes Pinder-Davis
Height: 7", 17.8 cm
Colour: Unknown
Issued: 1944

Colourways	Backstamp	U.S. $	Price Can. $	U.K. £
Unknown	Puce		Extremely rare	

Photograph not available at press time

RW3397
CHINOISERIE FIGURE (Male, kneeling) /THE GREETING

Modeller: Agnes Pinder-Davis
Height: 6", 15.0 cm
Colour: **Chinoiserie Figure (Male, kneeling)**
1. Black and green tunic; white base
2. Blue and pink tunic, yellow pants; white base
The Greeting
White; gold-lined base
Issued: **Chinoiserie Figure (Male, kneeling):** 1944
The Greeting: 1982-1985
Series: **Chinoiserie Figure (Male, kneeling):** Chinoiserie Figures
The Greeting: Art Deco

Description	Backstamp	U.S. $	Price Can. $	U.K. £
1. Chinoiserie Figure (male)	Black	500.00	625.00	280.00
2. The Greeting	Black	200.00	275.00	120.00

RW3398
CHINOISERIE FIGURE (Female, kneeling) / THE FAN

Modeller:	Agnes Pinder-Davis
Height:	5 ¼", 13.3 cm
Colour:	**Chinoiserie Figure (Female, kneeling)**
	1. Black and green tunic; white base
	2. Blue and pink tunic; yellow pants; white base
	The Fan
	White; gold lined base
Issued:	**Chinoiserie Figure (Female, kneeling)**: 1944
	The Fan: 1982-1985
Series:	**Chinoiserie Figure (Female, kneeling)**: Chinoiserie Figures
	The Fan: Art Deco

			Price	
Description	Backstamp	U.S. $	Can. $	U.K. £
1. Chinoiserie Figure (Female)	Black	500.00	625.00	280.00
2. The Fan	Black	200.00	275.00	100.00

RW3399
CHINOISERIE FIGURE (Male, standing)

Modeller:	Agnes Pinder-Davis
Height:	8 ½", 21.6 cm
Colour:	1. Black, green and purple; white base
	2. Blue tunic; pink pants; white base
Issued:	1944-by 1958
Series:	Chinoiserie Figures

			Price	
Colourways	Backstamp	U.S. $	Can. $	U.K. £
Coloured (as above)	Black	950.00	1,250.00	550.00

RW3400
CHINOISERIE FIGURE (Female, standing)

Modeller:	Agnes Pinder-Davis
Height:	7 ½", 19.1 cm
Colour:	1. Green tunic; black skirt; white base
	2. Pink tunic; yellow skirt; white base
Issued:	1944
Series:	Chinoiserie Figures

			Price	
Colourways	Backstamp	U.S. $	Can. $	U.K. £
Coloured (as above)	Black	950.00	1,250.00	550.00

RW3402
WATTEAU FIGURE (Male, standing)

Modeller: Agnes Pinder-Davis
Height: 8", 20.3 cm
Colour: Sage green vest; grey sleeves; yellow collar; pink pants;
            white hat with blue band
Issued: 1946-1953
Series: Watteau Figures

Colourways	Backstamp	Price U.S. $	Can. $	U.K. £
Sage green/grey/yellow/pink	Black	1,000.00	1,350.00	600.00

RW3403
WATTEAU FIGURE (Female, standing)

Modeller: Agnes Pinder-Davis
Height: 7 ½", 19.1 cm
Colour: Grey, pink and turquoise dress; brown basket of yellow flowers
Issued: 1946-1953
Series: Watteau Figures

Colourways	Backstamp	Price U.S. $	Can. $	U.K. £
Grey/pink/turquoise	Black	1,000.00	1,350.00	600.00

RW3404
WATTEAU FIGURE (Male, seated)

Modeller: Agnes Pinder-Davis
Height: 6", 15.0 cm
Colour: Grey shirt; pink vest; turquoise pants; yellow collar and bow;
            tan hat; white and brown dog
Issued: 1946-1953
Series: Watteau Figures

Colourways	Backstamp	Price U.S. $	Can. $	U.K. £
Grey/pink/turquoise	Black	1,000.00	1,350.00	600.00

RW3405
WATTEAU FIGURE (Female, seated)

Modeller:	Agnes Pinder-Davis
Height:	6", 15.0 cm
Colour:	Grey, turquoise and pink dress; brown basket of apples
Issued:	1946-1953
Series:	Watteau Figures

		Price		
Colourways	*Backstamp*	*U.S. $*	*Can. $*	*U.K. £*
Grey/turquoise/pink	Black	1,000.00	1,350.00	600.00

RW3414
REGENCY LADY

Modeller:	Agnes Pinder-Davis
Height:	10", 25.4 cm
Colour:	1. Pink dress with blue and green design; blue belt and edging; green shawl
	2. White dress; light blue belt and edging; light blue shawl
Issued:	1947-by 1953

		Price		
Colourways	*Backstamp*	*U.S. $*	*Can. $*	*U.K. £*
Coloured (as above)	Black	1,000.00	1,350.00	600.00

RW3415
REGENCY LADY WITH SHAWL IN HAND

Modeller:	Agnes Pinder-Davis
Height:	10", 25.4 cm
Colour:	1. Turquoise dress with red flowers; green ribbons; yellow shawl
	2. White dress; light blue ribbons and shawl; white and blue base
Issued:	1947-by 1953

		Price		
Colourways	*Backstamp*	*U.S. $*	*Can. $*	*U.K. £*
Coloured (as above)	Black	1,000.00	1,350.00	600.00

RW3416
APRIL

Modeller: Freda Doughty
Height: 6", 15.0 cm
Colour: Yellow bodice; white skirt with yellow and lavender stripes; white lamb with brown markings; green base with yellow and white flowers
Issued: 1947-1985
Series: Months of the Year

Colourways	Backstamp	U.S. $	Price Can. $	U.K. £
Yellow/white/lavender	Black	400.00	525.00	240.00

Note: See also miniature version RW4168 Springtime.

RW3417
OCTOBER

Modeller: Freda Doughty
Height: 8", 20.3 cm
Colour: Yellow sweater with blue bands; blue shorts; brown hair; brown squirrels; green base
Issued: 1951-1985
Series: Months of the Year

Colourways	Backstamp	U.S. $	Price Can. $	U.K. £
Yellow/blue	Black	400.00	525.00	240.00

Note: See also miniature version RW4157 Woodland Walk.

RW3418
NOVEMBER

Modeller: Freda Doughty
Height: 7 ½", 19.1 cm
Colour: Lavender coat with cream highlights; orange hat and leggings; four white doves
Issued: c.1950-1985
Varieties: RW3760 Fantails
Series: Months of the Year

Colourways	Backstamp	U.S. $	Price Can. $	U.K. £
Lavender/cream/orange	Black	450.00	575.00	260.00

Note: See also miniature version RW4167 Peace.

RW3419
CHINESE FIGURE WITH SHORT TUNIC (Female)

Modeller: Agnes Pinder-Davis
Height: 11", 27.9 cm
Colour: 1. Biscuit
2. Bronze tunic with gilt leaves; claret lining, flower and scarf
3. Green and black
4. Green, yellow and pink
5. Shaded grey robe; cream cuffs; apricot skirt; yellow scarf
Issued: 1947

| | | | Price | |
Colourways	Backstamp	U.S. $	Can. $	U.K. £
1. Coloured (as above)	Gold	825.00	1,050.00	475.00
2. Coloured (as above)	Black	750.00	950.00	425.00

RW3420
CHINESE FIGURE WITH LONG TUNIC (Female)

Modeller: Agnes Pinder-Davis
Height: 11", 27.9 cm
Colour: 1. Biscuit
2. Bronze tunic with gilt leaves; claret lining, flower and scarf
3. Green and black
4. Green, yellow and pink
5. Shaded grey robe; cream cuffs; apricot skirt; yellow scarf
Issued: 1947

| | | | Price | |
Colourways	Backstamp	U.S. $	Can. $	U.K. £
1. Coloured (as above)	Gold	825.00	1,050.00	475.00
2. Coloured (as above)	Black	750.00	950.00	425.00

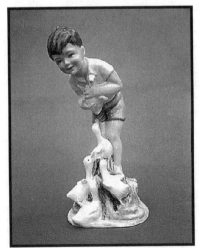

RW3433
JOHNNIE / FARMER'S BOY

Modeller: Freda Doughty
Height: 6 ½", 16.5 cm
Colour: **Johnnie**
White shirt; green shorts; dark brown hair; five yellow ducklings
Farmer's Boy
White shirt; blue shorts; brown hair; five white ducklings
Issued: **Johnnie:** 1947-1955
Farmer's Boy: 1947-1983
Varieties: Also called "Young Farmer"

| | | | Price | |
Description	Backstamp	U.S. $	Can. $	U.K. £
1. Johnnie	Black	450.00	575.00	260.00
2. Farmer's Boy	Black	375.00	500.00	220.00
3. Young Farmer	Black	375.00	500.00	220.00

RW3434
H.R.H. PRINCESS ELIZABETH ON "TOMMY"

Modeller: Doris Lindner
Height: With plinth: 15", 38.1 cm
Colour: 1. Black jacket and cap; mustard skirt; chestnut horse
        2. White
Issued: 1948 in a limited edition of 100

Colourways	Backstamp	U.S. $	Price Can. $	U.K. £
1. Black/mustard/chestnut	Black	7,000.00	9,000.00	4,000.00
2. White (classic)	Unknown		Very rare	

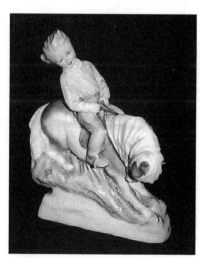

RW3435
HAPPY DAYS

Modeller: Freda Doughty
Height: 7 ½", 19.1 cm
Colour: Light green shirt; blue-grey trousers; yellow hair; cream
       and brown pony; cream base
Issued: 1948-by 1955

Colourways	Backstamp	U.S. $	Price Can. $	U.K. £
Light green/blue-grey	Black	1,900.00	2,500.00	1,100.00

RW3440
JULY

Modeller: Freda Doughty
Height: 7", 17.8 cm
Colour: Pink bathing suit; brown hair; blue and white base
Issued: c.1950-1985
Series: Months of the Year

Colourways	Backstamp	U.S. $	Price Can. $	U.K. £
Pink/blue/white	Black	425.00	550.00	250.00

Note: See also miniature version RW4190 At The Seaside.

RW3441
AUGUST

Modeller:	Freda Doughty
Height:	5", 12.7 cm
Colour:	Fleshtones; brown hair; blue base with white highlights; multicoloured fish
Issued:	c.1950-1985
Series:	Months of the Year

Colourways	Backstamp	U.S. $	Price Can. $	U.K. £
Fleshtones/blue	Black	425.00	525.00	240.00

Note: See also miniature version RW4191 Little Mermaid.

RW3446
CHINOISERIE FIGURE HOLDING BIRD (Female)

Modeller:	Agnes Pinder-Davis
Height:	13", 33.0 cm
Colour:	1. Bronze coat; fawn-pink sleeves; darker bronze and salmon dress; salmon hat; bronze bird
	2 Shot gold on black coat; purple dress with gold trim; turquoise hat and bird
	3. White glazed
Issued:	1949-c.1960
Series:	Chinoiserie Figures

Colourways	Backstamp	U.S. $	Price Can. $	U.K. £
1. Coloured (as above)	Gold	1,300.00	1,675.00	750.00
2. Coloured (as above)	Black	1,250.00	1,575.00	750.00
3. White glazed	Black	500.00	700.00	250.00

RW3447
CHINOISERIE FIGURE HOLDING BIRD (Male)

Modeller:	Agnes Pinder-Davis
Height:	13", 33.0 cm
Colour:	1. Bronze coat, hat and bird; pink sleeves; yellow pantaloons
	2. Shot gold on black, purple and white; white and green hat; green bird
	3. White glazed
Issued:	1949-c.1960
Series:	Chinoiserie Figures

Colourways	Backstamp	U.S. $	Price Can. $	U.K. £
1. Coloured (as above)	Gold	1,300.00	1,675.00	750.00
2. Coloured (as above)	Black	1,250.00	1,575.00	750.00
3. White glazed	Black	500.00	700.00	250.00

RW3452
JANUARY

Modeller:	Freda Doughty
Height:	6", 15.0 cm
Colour:	Burgundy coat; beige leggings; brown shoes; green scarf; yellow hair
Issued:	c.1950-1985
Series:	Months of the Year

		Price		
Colourways	Backstamp	U.S. $	Can. $	U.K. £
Burgundy/beige	Black	400.00	500.00	225.00

Note: See also miniature version RW4189 The Slide.

RW3453
FEBRUARY

Modeller:	Freda Doughty
Height:	6 ¼", 15.9 cm
Colour:	1. Blue raincoat; black hat and wellingtons; brown and white base
	2. Green raincoat; black hat and wellingtons; brown and white base
Issued:	c.1950-1985
Series:	Months of the Year

		Price		
Colourways	Backstamp	U.S. $	Can. $	U.K. £
Coloured (as above)	Black	450.00	550.00	250.00

Note: See also miniature version RW4165 Fisherman.

RW3454
MARCH

Modeller:	Freda Doughty
Height:	6", 15.0 cm
Colour:	Pink dress; blue hat; yellow hair; yellow shoes; green and beige base
Issued:	1947-1949
Series:	Months of the Year

		Price		
Colourways	Backstamp	U.S. $	Can. $	U.K. £
Pink	Black	425.00	550.00	240.00

Note: See also miniature version RW4202 Windy.

RW3455
MAY

Modeller:	Freda Doughty
Height:	5", 12.7 cm
Colour:	Blue dress; yellow hair; white daisies on a green base
Issued:	c.1950-1985
Series:	Months of the Year

		Price		
Colourways	Backstamp	U.S. $	Can. $	U.K. £
Blue	Black	450.00	575.00	260.00

Note: See also miniature version RW4203 Daisy Chain.

RW3456
JUNE
Style Two

Modeller:	Freda Doughty
Height:	6 ½", 16.5 cm
Colour:	White shirt; yellow shorts; multicoloured tie and belt; yellow hair; brown dog; grey and green base
Issued:	c.1950-1985
Series:	Months of the Year

		Price		
Colourways	Backstamp	U.S. $	Can. $	U.K. £
White/yellow	Black	425.00	550.00	240.00

Note: See also miniature version RW4204 Musical Moments.

RW3457
SEPTEMBER / SNOWY

Modeller:	Freda Doughty
Height:	4 ¾", 12.1 cm
Colour:	**September:** White shirt; blue tie, shorts, shoes and hat; white cat; green and beige base **Snowy:** White shirt; brown tie and shorts; red shoes; white hat with red band; white cat
Issued:	**September:** c.1950-1985 **Snowy:** c.1950-1983
Series:	**September:** Months of the Year

		Price		
Description	Backstamp	U.S. $	Can. $	U.K. £
1. September	Black	450.00	575.00	260.00
2. Snowy	Black	450.00	575.00	260.00

Note: See also miniature version RW4156 Christopher.

RW3458
DECEMBER

Modeller: Freda Doughty
Height: 6 ½", 16.5 cm
Colour: Creamy yellow coat and hat trimmed with burgundy; burgundy
mittens and shoes
Issued: c.1950-1985
Series: Months of the Year

Colourways	Backstamp	U.S. $	Price Can. $	U.K. £
Creamy-yellow/burgundy	Black	475.00	625.00	280.00

Note: See also miniature version RW4166 Snowball.

RRW3471
BATTLEDORE

Modeller: Freda Doughty
Height: Unknown
Colour: Unknown
Issued: 1951-1951

Colourways	Backstamp	U.S. $	Price Can. $	U.K. £
Unknown	Black		Extremely rare	

RW3472
SHUTTLECOCK

Modeller: Freda Doughty
Height: Unknown
Colour: Unknown
Issued: 1951-1951

Colourways	Backstamp	U.S. $	Price Can. $	U.K. £
Unknown	Black		Extremely rare	

RW3473
BALINESE DANCER
Style One

Modeller: Agnes Pinder-Davis
Height: 17", 43.2 cm
Colour: Unknown
Issued: 1951 in a limited edition of 25

		Price		
Colourways	*Backstamp*	*U.S. $*	*Can. $*	*U.K. £*
Unknown	Black	2,600.00	3,375.00	1,500.00

RW3474
SIAMESE DANCER
Style One

Modeller: Agnes Pinder-Davis
Height: 21", 53.3 cm
Colour: Gold
Issued: 1951 in a limited edition of 25

		Price		
Colourways	*Backstamp*	*U.S. $*	*Can. $*	*U.K. £*
Gold	Black	2.600.00	3,375.00	1,500.00

RW3479
PAUL

Modeller: Freda Doughty
Height: Unknown
Colour: Unknown
Issued: 1952-1952

		Price		
Colourways	*Backstamp*	*U.S. $*	*Can. $*	*U.K. £*
Unknown	Black		Extremely rare	

RW3480
PRISCILLA

Modeller:	Freda Doughty
Height:	Unknown
Colour:	Unknown
Issued:	1952-1952

			Price	
Colourways	*Backstamp*	*U.S. $*	*Can. $*	*U.K. £*
Unknown	Black		Extremely rare	

RW3481
CHINESE GODDESS (Arms crossed)

Modeller:	Agnes Pinder-Davis
Height:	12 ¼", 31.1 cm
Colour:	Gold lustre
Issued:	1952

			Price	
Colourways	*Backstamp*	*U.S. $*	*Can. $*	*U.K. £*
Gold lustre	Gold		Extremely rare	

RW3482
CHINESE GODDESS (With flower)

Modeller:	Agnes Pinder-Davis
Height:	12 ¼", 31.1 cm
Colour:	Burnished gilt robe; green dress; red necklace; grey base
Issued:	1952

			Price	
Colourways	*Backstamp*	*U.S. $*	*Can. $*	*U.K. £*
Gilt/green	Gold		Extremely rare	

*Photograph not
available
at press time*

RW3483
JESTER
Style Two

Modeller:	Miss M. J. Stevens
Height:	Unknown
Colour:	Unknown
Issued:	1952-by 1955

		Price		
Colourways	Backstamp	U.S. $	Can. $	U.K. £
Yellow	Black	1,650.00	2,150.00	950.00

RW3488
PUNCH

Modeller:	Freda Doughty
Height:	5 ½", 14.0 cm
Colour:	Yellow shirt; white collar; blue shorts; pink belt; ginger hair
Issued:	1952-1959

		Price		
Colourways	Backstamp	U.S. $	Can. $	U.K. £
Yellow/white/blue	Black	1,000.00	1,350.00	600.00

RW3489
JUDY

Modeller:	Freda Doughty
Height:	6", 15.0 cm
Colour:	Blue dress with white frills and purple highlights; yellow hair
Issued:	1952-1959

		Price		
Colourways	Backstamp	U.S. $	Can. $	U.K. £
Blue	Black	1,000.00	1,350.00	600.00

RW3491
SEA SCOUT

Modeller: Agnes Pinder-Davis
Height: 5 ½", 14.0 cm
Colour: 1. Green seahorse; yellow vest; blonde hair
       2. White seahorse with blue trim; blue vest; brown hair
Issued: 1953- by 1957
Series: Chinoiserie Sayings

Colourways	Backstamp	U.S. $	Price Can. $	U.K. £
Coloured (as above)	Black	775.00	1,000.00	450.00

RW3492
LUCKY SPIDER

Modeller: Agnes Pinder-Davis
Height: 5 ½", 14.0 cm
Colour: 1. Black and white
       2. Cream dress; green jacket; brown hair; brown spider
       3. White glazed
Issued: 1953- by 1957
Series: Chinoiserie Sayings

Colourways	Backstamp	U.S. $	Price Can. $	U.K. £
1. Coloured (as above)	Black	775.00	1,000.00	450.00
2. White glazed	Black	250.00	375.00	125.00

RW3493
FUNNY FISH

Modeller: Agnes Pinder-Davis
Height: 5 ½", 14.0 cm
Colour: 1. Black and white
       2. Blue and white suit; red shoes; white fish with blue
          highlights; white and blue rock
       3. White glazed
Issued: 1953- by 1957
Series: Chinoiserie Sayings

Colourways	Backstamp	U.S. $	Price Can. $	U.K. £
1. Coloured (as above)	Black	775.00	1,000.00	450.00
2. White glazed	Black	250.00	375.00	125.00

RW3494
DON'T LET THE CAT OUT OF THE BAG

Modeller:	Agnes Pinder-Davis
Height:	5 ½", 14.0 cm
Colour:	1. Black and white
	2. Bright colours
	3. White glazed
Issued:	1953-by 1957
Series:	Chinoiserie Sayings

		Price		
Colourways	Backstamp	U.S. $	Can. $	U.K. £
1. Coloured (as above)	Black	775.00	1,000.00	450.00
2. White glazed	Black	250.00	375.00	125.00

RW3495
SLOW COACH

Modeller:	Agnes Pinder-Davis
Height:	5 ½", 14.0 cm
Colour:	1. Black and white
	2. Green trousers; red vest; pink shoes; brown turtle
	3. White glazed
Issued:	1953-by 1957
Series:	Chinoiserie Sayings

		Price		
Colourways	Backstamp	U.S. $	Can. $	U.K. £
1. Coloured (as above)	Black	875.00	1,125.00	500.00
2. White glazed	Black	300.00	450.00	150.00

RW3496
JOY RIDE

Modeller:	Agnes Pinder-Davis
Height:	5 ½", 14.0 cm
Colour:	1. Beige fish; flesh coloured child; green base
	2. Black and white
	3. Blue fish; flesh coloured child; blue and white base
	4. White glazed
Issued:	1953-by 1957
Series:	Chinoiserie Sayings

		Price		
Colourways	Backstamp	U.S. $	Can. $	U.K. £
1. Coloured (as above)	Black	950.00	1,225.00	550.00
2. White glazed	Black	300.00	450.00	150.00

RW3497
APPLE OF YOUR EYE

Modeller: Agnes Pinder-Davis
Height: 5 ½", 14.0 cm
Colour: 1. Black and white
        2. Blue top edged with white; yellow trousers; red apples and
           shoes
        3. White glazed
Issued: 1953-by 1957
Series: Chinoiserie Sayings

Colourways	Backstamp	U.S. $	Price Can. $	U.K. £
1. Coloured (as above)	Black	725.00	950.00	420.00
2. White glazed	Black	250.00	400.00	125.00

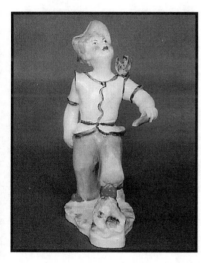

RW3498
EARLY BIRD

Modeller: Agnes Pinder-Davis
Height: 5 ½", 14.0 cm
Colour: 1. Black and white
        2. Green trousers; white blouse with blue trim; yellow hair;
           red shoes; brown bird
        3. White glazed
Issued: 1953-by 1957
Series: Chinoiserie Sayings

Colourways	Backstamp	U.S. $	Price Can. $	U.K. £
1. Coloured (as above)	Black	725.00	950.00	420.00
2. White glazed	Black	250.00	375.00	125.00

RW3499
TWO'S COMPANY, THREE'S NONE

Modeller: Agnes Pinder-Davis
Height: 5", 12.7 cm
Colour: 1. Black and white
        2. Green tunic; light pink trousers; red slippers; yellow hat
        3. White tunic with blue flowers; blue trousers; red slippers
Issued: 1953-by 1957
Series: Chinoiserie Sayings

Colourways	Backstamp	U.S. $	Price Can. $	U.K. £
Coloured (as above)	Black	775.00	1,000.00	450.00

RW3500
WISE AS AN OWL

Modeller: Agnes Pinder-Davis
Height: 5 ½", 14.0 cm
Colour: 1. Black and white
   2. Dark blue dress; white skirt with blue flowers; blue owl
   3 Green dress with white collar; cream trousers; red shoes; blonde hair; taupe owl
   4. White glazed
Issued: 1953-by 1957
Series: Chinoiserie Sayings

Colourways	Backstamp	U.S. $	Price Can. $	U.K. £
1. Coloured (as above)	Black	725.00	950.00	420.00
2. White glazed	Black	250.00	375.00	125.00

RW3501
HEN PARTY

Modeller: Agnes Pinder-Davis
Height: 5 ½", 14.0 cm
Colour: 1. Black and white
   2. Turquoise top with white collar; light blue trousers; red shoes; white hen with brown highlights
   3. White glazed
Issued: 1953-by 1957
Series: Chinoiserie Sayings

Colourways	Backstamp	U.S. $	Price Can. $	U.K. £
1. Coloured (as above)	Black	775.00	1,000.00	450.00
2. White glazed	Black	250.00	400.00	125.00

RW3502
MAD AS A HATTER

Modeller: Agnes Pinder-Davis
Height: 5 ½", 14.0 cm
Colour: 1. Black and white
   2. Blue trousers; white and blue top; blue hat; red shoes white hare with blue flecks
   3. White glazed
Issued: 1953-by 1957
Varieties: Also called "Mad as a March Hare"
Series: Chinoiserie Sayings

Colourways	Backstamp	U.S. $	Price Can. $	U.K. £
1. Coloured (as above)	Black	775.00	1,000.00	450.00
2. White glazed	Black	250.00	400.00	125.00

RW3510
RED RIDING HOOD

Modeller: Miss M. J. Stevens
Height: 8", 20.3 cm
Colour: Patterned dress
Issued: 1954

Colourways	Backstamp	U.S. $	Price Can. $	U.K. £
Patterned dress	Black		Extremely rare	

Photograph not available at press time

RW3511
WOLF

Modeller: Miss M. J. Stevens
Height: 8", 20.3 cm
Colour: Brown wolf; greenish-yellow dress; mauve shawl; white base
Issued: 1954

Colourways	Backstamp	U.S. $	Price Can. $	U.K. £
Brown/green-yellow/mauve	Black		Extremely rare	

RW3518
SUNDAY'S CHILD (Girl)

Modeller: Freda Doughty
Height: 7", 17.8 cm
Colour: Blue bodice; white skirt with red dots and hem; turquoise hat; blue shoes; yellow hair; green and white base
Issued: See below
Series: The Days of the Week

Issued	Colourway	Backstamp	U.S. $	Price Can. $	U.K. £
1938 to 1942	As above	Blue	475.00	700.00	240.00
1943 to 1961	As above	Black	350.00	525.00	180.00
1962 to 1984	As above	Black, circle	300.00	450.00	160.00
1996 to date	As above	Black, diamond	—	225.00	100.00

Note: Earlier models of Sunday's Child held a porcelain windmill.
See also miniature version RW4161 Let's Run.

RW3519
MONDAY'S CHILD (Boy) / ALL MINE

Modeller:	Freda Doughty
Height:	7 ¼", 19.1 cm
Colour:	**Monday's Child:** Blue shirt, shorts and shoes; blonde hair
	All Mine: Yellow shirt, green shorts, white shoes
Issued:	See below
Series:	**Monday's Child:** The Days of the Week

				Price	
Issued	*Colourway*	*Backstamp*	*U.S. $*	*Can. $*	*U.K. £*
Monday's Child					
1938 to 1942	As above	Blue	475.00	700.00	240.00
1943 to 1961	As above	Black	350.00	525.00	180.00
1962 to 1984	As above	Black, circle	300.00	450.00	160.00
1996 to date	As above	Black, diamond	—	225.00	100.00
All Mine					
1982 to 1983	As above	Black, circle	Very rare		

Note: See also miniature version RW4158 Three's Company.

RW3521
WEDNESDAY'S CHILD (Boy)

Modeller:	Freda Doughty
Height:	7", 17.8 cm
Colour:	Green top; orange shorts; red hair; grey teddy bear; orange and white base
Issued:	See below
Series:	The Days of the Week

				Price	
Issued	*Colourway*	*Backstamp*	*U.S. $*	*Can. $*	*U.K. £*
1938 to 1942	As above	Blue	475.00	700.00	240.00
1943 to 1961	As above	Black	350.00	525.00	180.00
1962 to 1984	As above	Black, circle	300.00	450.00	160.00
1996 to date	As above	Black, diamond	—	225.00	100.00

Note: See also miniature version RW4195 Poor Teddy.

RW3522
THURSDAY'S CHILD (Girl)

Modeller:	Freda Doughty
Height:	7", 17.8 cm
Colour:	Turquoise dress with white collar and cuffs; pink belt; turquoise and pink hat; brown shoes; green, beige and white base
Issued:	See below
Series:	The Days of the Week

				Price	
Issued	*Colourway*	*Backstamp*	*U.S. $*	*Can. $*	*U.K. £*
1938 to 1942	As above	Blue	475.00	700.00	240.00
1943 to 1961	As above	Black	350.00	525.00	180.00
1962 to 1984	As above	Black, circle	300.00	450.00	160.00
1996 to date	As above	Black, diamond	—	225.00	100.00

Note: See also miniature version RW4159 Hometime.

RW3523
FRIDAY'S CHILD (Girl)

Modeller:	Freda Doughty	
Height:	6", 15.0 cm	
Colour:	Yellow dungarees; brown bird; green base	
Issued:	See below	
Series:	The Days of the Week	

				Price	
Issued	Colourway	Backstamp	U.S. $	Can. $	U.K. £
1938 to 1942	As above	Blue	475.00	700.00	240.00
1943 to 1961	As above	Black	350.00	525.00	180.00
1962 to 1984	As above	Black, circle	300.00	450.00	160.00
1996 to date	As above	Black, diamond	—	225.00	100.00

Note: See also miniature version RW4160 Teatime.

RW3524
SATURDAY'S CHILD (Boy)

Modeller:	Freda Doughty	
Height:	6", 15.0 cm	
Colour:	Blue overalls; white shirt and hat; brown and grey spade; brown and green base	
Issued:	See below	
Series:	The Days of the Week	

				Price	
Issued	Colourway	Backstamp	U.S. $	Can. $	U.K. £
1938 to 1942	As above	Blue	475.00	700.00	240.00
1943 to 1961	As above	Black	350.00	525.00	180.00
1962 to 1984	As above	Black, circle	300.00	450.00	160.00
1996 to date	As above	Black, diamond	—	225.00	100.00

Note: See also miniature version RW4192 Gardener.

RW3534
TUESDAY'S CHILD (Boy)

Modeller:	Freda Doughty	
Height:	6", 15.0 cm	
Colour:	Yellow sweater and hat with red stripes; blue trousers; brown skates; pale blue and white base	
Issued:	See below	
Series:	The Days of the Week	

				Price	
Issued	Colourway	Backstamp	U.S. $	Can. $	U.K. £
1938 to 1942	As above	Blue	475.00	700.00	240.00
1943 to 1961	As above	Black	350.00	525.00	180.00
1962 to 1984	As above	Black, circle	300.00	450.00	160.00
1996 to date	As above	Black, diamond	—	225.00	100.00

Note: See also miniature version RW4199 Skating.

RW3535
OFFICER OF THE 29TH FOOT (WORCESTERSHIRE REGIMENT) 1812

Modeller: Frederick M. Gertner
Height: 12", 30.5 cm
Colour: Red military jacket; white trousers; black boots, hat and base
Issued: 1954-c.1975
Series: Historical Military Figures

Colourways	Backstamp	Price U.S. $	Can. $	U.K. £
Red/white/black	Black	950.00	1,250.00	550.00

RW3538
ISABELLA

Modeller: Miss Mitchell-Smith
Height: Unknown
Colour: Unknown
Issued: 1955

Colourways	Backstamp	U.S. $	Price Can. $	U.K. £
Unknown	Black		Extremely rare	

*Possibly not
put into
production*

RW3541
ROSE
Style Two

Modeller: Agnes Pinder-Davis
Height: Unknown
Colour: Unknown
Issued: 1955
Series: The Cries of London

Colourways	Backstamp	U.S. $	Price Can. $	U.K. £
Unknown	Black		Extremely rare	

RW3542
VIOLET

Modeller:	Agnes Pinder-Davis
Height:	Unknown
Colour:	Unknown
Issued:	1955
Series:	The Cries of London

Colourways	Backstamp	U.S. $	Price Can. $	U.K. £
Unknown	Black		Extremely rare	

Note: If you have any information on *The Cries of London Series* that you wish to share, please call or write; the phone number and address are on page iii.

RW3543
HEATHER

Modeller:	Agnes Pinder-Davis
Height:	Unknown
Colour:	Unknown
Issued:	1955
Series:	The Cries of London

Colourways	Backstamp	U.S. $	Price Can. $	U.K. £
Unknown	Black		Extremely rare	

RW3546
SPRING MORNING / SPRING MORN / RACHEL (Style One)
First Version - 6"

Modeller:	Freda Doughty
Height:	6", 15.0 cm
Colour:	**Spring Morning**

1. Green dress with white collar and cuffs; pink sash; dark green hat; yellow flowers in light brown basket
2. Red dress with white collar and cuffs; turquoise sash; blue hat

Spring Morn
Green dress; white apron with yellow flowered design; yellow hat
Rachel
Peach dress; white collar, cuffs and apron; straw basket of yellow flowers

Issued:	**Spring Morning:** 1955-1962
	Spring Morn: 1982-c.1985
	Rachel (Style One): 1988-1991
Series:	**Spring Morn:** Age of Romance, Series One
	Rachel: Age of Romance, Series One

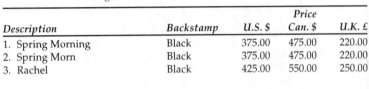

			Price	
Description	Backstamp	U.S. $	Can. $	U.K. £
1. Spring Morning	Black	375.00	475.00	220.00
2. Spring Morn	Black	375.00	475.00	220.00
3. Rachel	Black	425.00	550.00	250.00

Second Version - 9"

Modeller:	Freda Doughty
Height:	9", 22.5 cm
Colour:	**Spring Morning**

Orange dress with white collar and cuffs; green sash; green hat; yellow daffodils in light brown basket

Issued:	1955-1962

			Price	
Colourways	Backstamp	U.S. $	Can. $	U.K. £
Orange/green	Black	475.00	625.00	280.00

RW3547
SUMMER DAY / SUMMER'S DAY / SARAH (Style One)
First Version - 7½"

Modeller: Freda Doughty
Height: 7 ½", 19.1 cm
Colour: **Summer Day**
Red dress; white collar and underskirt; blue ribbon;
straw basket of flowers
Summer's Day
Blue bodice and underskirt; white overskirt with pink flowers;
blue ribbon; straw basket of flowers
Sarah (Style One)
Pink dress; white overskirt with pink flowers; pink ribbon;
straw basket of flowers
Issued: **Summer Day:** 1955-1958
Summer's Day: 1982-c.1985
Sarah (Style One): 1988-1991
Series: **Summer's Day:** Age of Romance, Series One
Sarah: Age of Romance, Series One

Description	Backstamp	Price U.S. $	Can. $	U.K. £
1. Summer Day	Black	425.00	550.00	250.00
2. Summer's Day	Black	425.00	550.00	250.00
3. Sarah (Style One)	Black	425.00	550.00	250.00

Second Version - 9½"

Modeller: Freda Doughty
Height: 9 ½", 24.1 cm
Colour: **Summer Day**
1. Red dress with white collar and underdress; blue
sash; blue hat with yellow band; yellow shoe
2. Rose-pink dress with white collar, cuffs and
underdress; green sash and shoes
Issued: 1955-1958

Colourways	Backstamp	Price U.S. $	Can. $	U.K. £
Coloured (as above)	Black	650.00	850.00	380.00

RW3550
BALINESE DANCER
Style Two
Modeller: Agnes Pinder-Davis
Height: 6", 15.0 cm
Colour: 1. Coloured
             2. Gold
Issued: 1955

Colourways	Backstamp	Price		
		U.S. $	Can. $	U.K. £
1. Coloured	Black	Extremely rare		
2. Gold	Black	1,400.00	1,750.00	800.00

Note: Model RW3550 was available with or without a base.

RW3551
SIAMESE DANCER
Style Two
Modeller: Agnes Pinder-Davis
Height: 6", 15.0 cm
Colour: 1. Coloured
             2. Gold
Issued: 1955

Colourways	Backstamp	Price		
		U.S. $	Can. $	U.K. £
1. Coloured	Black	Extremely rare		
2. Gold	Black	1,400.00	1,750.00	800.00

Note: Model RW3551 was available with or without a base.

*Possibly not
put into
production*

RW3557
PHILLIP
Modeller: Miss Mitchell-Smith
Height: Unknown
Colour: Unknown
Issued: 1955

Colourways	Backstamp	Price		
		U.S. $	Can. $	U.K. £
Unknown	Black	Extremely rare		

RW3558
WHITE BOY

Modeller: Unknown
Height: Unknown
Colour: Unknown
Issued: 1955

Colourways	Backstamp	U.S. $	Price Can. $	U.K. £
Unknown	Black		Extremely rare	

RW3559
PICKANINNY

Modeller: Unknown
Height: Unknown
Colour: Unknown
Issued: 1955

Colourways	Backstamp	U.S. $	Price Can. $	U.K. £
Unknown	Black		Extremely rare	

RW3560
DAISY
Style One

Modeller: Agnes Pinder-Davis
Height: Unknown
Colour: Unknown
Issued: 1955
Series: The Cries of London

Colourways	Backstamp	U.S. $	Price Can. $	U.K. £
Unknown	Black		Extremely rare	

*Possibly not
put into
production*

RW3569
THE SEAMSTRESS
First Version - 6"

Modeller:	Freda Doughty
Height:	6", 15.0 cm
Colour:	1. Lemon dress; cream patterned fabrics
	2. Red dress; multicoloured fabrics
	3. Turquoise dress; blue and rose fabrics
Issued:	1956-1959

		Price		
Colourways	Backstamp	U.S. $	Can. $	U.K. £
Coloured (as above)	Black	600.00	775.00	350.00

Second Version - 9"

Modeller:	Freda Doughty
Height:	9", 22.9 cm
Colour:	1. Red
	2. Mauve
Issued:	1956-1959

		Price		
Colourways	Backstamp	U.S. $	Can. $	U.K. £
Coloured (as above)	Black	775.00	1,000.00	450.00

RW3580
TROOPER OF THE SWISS GUARD OF HIS HOLINESS THE POPE

Modeller:	Frederick M. Gertner
Height:	15", 38.1 cm
Colour:	Orange, blue and red striped uniform; platinum and red helmet; brown and platinum staff
Issued:	1956 in a limited edition of 150
Series:	Papal Guard

		Price		
Colourways	Backstamp	U.S. $	Can. $	U.K. £
Orange/blue/red	Gold	850.00	1,100.00	480.00

Note: Each model is numbered and comes with a certificate of authenticity.

RW3585
LE PANIER

Modeller:	A. Azori
Height:	11 ¼", 28.5 cm
Colour:	1. Glazed cream (Wallbody)
	2. Glazed white (Bone china)
Issued:	1956
Series:	Bisque Figures

Description	Backstamp	U.S. $	Price Can. $	U.K. £
1. Cream (Wallbody)	Black	500.00	625.00	280.00
2. White (Bone china)	Black	200.00	300.00	100.00

RW3586
LA FLEUR

Modeller:	A. Azori
Height:	11 ¼", 28.5 cm
Colour:	1. Glazed cream (Wallbody)
	2. Glazed white (Bone china)
Issued:	1956
Series:	Bisque Figures

Description	Backstamp	U.S. $	Price Can. $	U.K. £
1. Cream (Wallbody)	Black	500.00	625.00	280.00
2. White (Bone china)	Black	200.00	300.00	100.00

RW3587
L'OISEAU

Modeller:	A. Azori
Height:	11 ¼", 28.5 cm
Colour:	1. Glazed cream (Wallbody)
	2. Glazed white (Bone china)
Issued:	1956
Series:	Bisque Figures

Description	Backstamp	U.S. $	Price Can. $	U.K. £
1. Cream (Wallbody)	Black	500.00	625.00	280.00
2. White (Bone china)	Black	200.00	300.00	100.00

RW3588
LE MIROIR

Modeller:	A. Azori
Height:	11 ¼", 28.5 cm
Colour:	1. Glazed cream (Wallbody)
	2. Glazed white (Bone china)
Issued:	1956
Series:	Bisque Figures

		Price		
Description	Backstamp	U.S. $	Can. $	U.K. £
1. Cream (Wallbody)	Black	500.00	625.00	280.00
2. White (Bone china)	Black	200.00	300.00	100.00

RW3589
THE PRIVY CHAMBERLAIN OF THE SWORD AND CAPE TO THE POPE IN THE SPANISH COSTUME

Modeller:	Frederick M. Gertner
Height:	11", 27.9 cm
Colour:	Charcoal uniform with black trim; black hat and stockings; scarlet sash; white ruff
Issued:	1956 in a limited edition of 150
Series:	Papal Guard

		Price		
Colourways	Backstamp	U.S. $	Can. $	U.K. £
Charcoal/black/scarlet/white	Gold	850.00	1,100.00	480.00

Note: Each model is numbered and comes with a certificate of authenticity.

RW3594
COLONEL OF THE NOBLE GUARD IN GALA UNIFORM

Modeller:	Neal French
Height:	12", 30.5 cm
Colour:	Red jacket with gold decoration; white trousers; long black boots
Issued:	1956 in a limited edition of 150
Series:	Papal Guard

		Price		
Colourways	Backstamp	U.S. $	Can. $	U.K. £
Red/white/black	Gold	850.00	1,100.00	480.00

RW3595
AN OFFICER OF THE PALATINE GUARD

Modeller: Neal French
Height: 12", 30.5 cm
Colour: Black jacket with gold trim; blue trousers; black shoes;
black and gold hat with white plume
Issued: 1956 in a limited edition of 150
Series Papal Guard

Colourways	Backstamp	Price U.S. $	Can. $	U.K. £
Black/blue/gold	Gold	850.00	1,100.00	480.00

Note: Each model is numbered and comes with a certificate of authenticity.

RW3596
PAPAL GENDARME

Modeller: Neal French
Height: 12", 30.5 cm
Colour: Indigo tunic; white trousers; black helmet with red plume;
black boots
Issued: 1956 in a limited edition of 150
Series: Papal Guard

Colourways	Backstamp	Price U.S. $	Can. $	U.K. £
Indigo/white/black	Gold	850.00	1,100.00	480.00

Note: Each model is numbered and comes with a certificate of authenticity.

RW3607
CLARISSA

Modeller: Neal French
Height: 7", 17.8 cm
Colour: Light green dress with leaf pattern; apricot underskirt, bustle;
black, white and gold base
Issued: 1956-by 1959

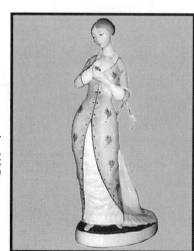

Colourways	Backstamp	Price U.S. $	Can. $	U.K. £
Light green	Black	425.00	550.00	250.00

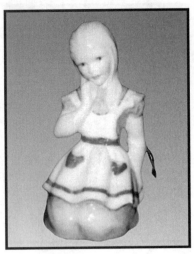

RW3608
ALICE
Style One

Modeller:	Freda Doughty
Height:	4", 10.1 cm
Colour:	Pale blue dress; white apron edged with pink; yellow hair
Issued:	1957-1959
Series:	Alice in Wonderland

Colourways	Backstamp	U.S. $	Price Can. $	U.K. £
Pale blue/white/pink	Black	875.00	1,125.00	500.00

RW3609
CHESHIRE CAT

Modeller:	Freda Doughty
Height:	4", 10.1 cm
Colour:	Grey with white markings
Issued:	1957-1959
Series:	Alice in Wonderland

Colourways	Backstamp	U.S. $	Price Can. $	U.K. £
Grey	Black	1,000.00	1,350.00	600.00

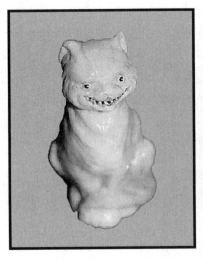

RW3610
MOCK TURTLE

Modeller:	Freda Doughty
Height:	3 ¼", 8.3 cm
Colour:	Brown head; green flippers; yellow shell
Issued:	1957-1959
Series:	Alice in Wonderland

Colourways	Backstamp	U.S. $	Price Can. $	U.K. £
Brown/green/yellow	Black	875.00	1,125.00	500.00

Note: The Mock Turtle is a hollow-based figure and not a candle-snuffer.

RW3611
WHITE RABBIT

Modeller:	Freda Doughty
Height:	4", 10.1 cm
Colour:	Red coat; yellow waistcoat; black buttons; black bow-tie; white gloves
Issued:	1957-1959
Series:	Alice in Wonderland

Colourways	Backstamp	Price U.S. $	Can. $	U.K. £
Red/yellow	Black	1,125.00	1,450.00	650.00

RW3612
THE DUCHESS

Modeller:	Freda Doughty
Height:	4", 10.1 cm
Colour:	Purple robe edged in yellow; yellow dress; purple headdress; white veil
Issued:	1957-1959
Series:	Alice in Wonderland

Colourways	Backstamp	Price U.S. $	Can. $	U.K. £
Purple/yellow/white	Black	775.00	1,000.00	450.00

RW3613
THE DODO

Modeller:	Freda Doughty
Height:	4", 10.1 cm
Colour:	1. Brown back; yellow breast; cream and yellow face; red eyes, beak and feet; brown cane
	2. Pale brown back; yellow breast; pale green and yellow face; blue cuffs; pink eyes, beak and feet; pale brown cane
Issued:	1957-1959
Series:	Alice in Wonderland

Colourways	Backstamp	Price U.S. $	Can. $	U.K. £
Coloured (as above)	Black	850.00	1,100.00	480.00

Note: The Dodo is a hollow-based figure and not a candle-snuffer.

148

RW3614
OLD FATHER WILLIAM

Modeller:	Freda Doughty
Height:	3 ¼", 8.3 cm
Colour:	Blue coat; yellow waistcoat with blue buttons; brown trousers; red cravat; white hair and pipe
Issued:	1957-1959
Series:	Alice in Wonderland

		Price		
Colourways	*Backstamp*	*U.S. $*	*Can. $*	*U.K. £*
Blue/yellow/brown	Black	1,000.00	1,300.00	580.00

Note: Old Father William is a hollow-based figure and not a candle-snuffer.

RW3620
AMANDA

Modeller:	Neal French
Height:	7", 17.8 cm
Colour:	1. Beige overdress; blue underskirt; green edging
	2. Light blue overdress; cream underskirt; green and white base
	3. White dress with claret rose pattern; claret and white striped bodice; black, white and gold base
Issued:	1957-by 1959

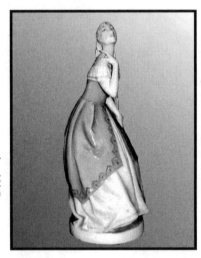

		Price		
Colourways	*Backstamp*	*U.S. $*	*Can. $*	*U.K. £*
Coloured (as above)	Black	500.00	625.00	280.00

RW3622
OFFICER OF THE LIFE GUARDS

Modeller:	Doris Lindner
Height:	9", 22.9 cm
Colour:	Red, white and black
Issued:	1957 in a limited edition of 150

		Price		
Colourways	*Backstamp*	*U.S. $*	*Can. $*	*U.K. £*
Red/white/black	Black	975.00	1,250.00	550.00

RW3623
OFFICER OF THE BLUES

Modeller:	Doris Lindner
Height:	9", 22.9 cm
Colour:	Blue, white and black
Issued:	1957 in a limited edition of 150

Colourways	Backstamp	U.S. $	Price Can. $	U.K. £
Blue/white/black	Black	975.00	1,250.00	550.00

RW3629
FIRST DANCE
Style One

Modeller:	Freda Doughty
Height:	7", 17.8 cm
Colour:	1. Cream dress; burgundy stole with black fringe
	2. Green dress with yellow highlights; yellow stole with gold fringe
	3. Mauve dress; pink stole with yellow and blue edging and black fringe
Issued:	1957-1983
Reissued:	1990-1996

Colourways	Backstamp	U.S. $	Price Can. $	U.K. £
Coloured (as above)	Black	200.00	275.00	120.00

RW3630
SWEET ANNE

Modeller:	Freda Doughty
Height:	7", 17.8 cm
Colour:	1. Blue dress with white cuffs and underskirt; light brown hair; green fan (gloss)
	2. Mottled green and lilac dress (gloss)
	3. Pale green dress with white cuffs and underskirt; multicoloured fan; light brown hair (matt)
Issued:	1957-1983

Colourways	Backstamp	U.S. $	Price Can. $	U.K. £
Coloured (as above)	Black	200.00	275.00	125.00

RW3642
LISETTE

Modeller:	Ruth Van Ruyckevelt
Height:	6 ½", 16.5 cm
Colour:	Turquoise jacket and muff edged with white; yellow and white skirt; lavender underskirt with ruffled edges; pink shoe
Issued:	1958 in a limited edition of 500
Series:	Victorian Ladies

		Price		
Colourways	Backstamp	U.S. $	Can. $	U.K. £
Turquoise/yellow/white	Black	775.00	1,000.00	450.00

RW3643
PENELOPE

Modeller:	Ruth Van Ruyckevelt
Height:	6 ½", 16.5 cm
Colour:	Pale orange dress; yellow overskirt trimmed with white; brown hair; green shoe; yellow and white bouquet
Issued:	1958 in a limited edition of 500
Series:	Victorian Ladies

		Price		
Colourways	Backstamp	U.S. $	Can. $	U.K. £
Pale orange/yellow	Black	775.00	1,000.00	450.00

RW3655
SURPRISE

Modeller:	Freda Doughty
Height:	7 ½", 19.1 cm
Colour:	Yellow dress; pink and green sash; brown hair
Issued:	1958-1958

		Price		
Colourways	Backstamp	U.S. $	Can. $	U.K. £
Yellow	Black	1,000.00	1,350.00	600.00

RW3656
MAYFLOWER
First Version (Hat and telescope on base)

Modeller: Freda Doughty
Height: 7 ½", 19.1 cm
Colour: 1. Blue jacket; yellow epaulettes and buttons; cream waistcoat; light brown breeches; brown bow, shoes and hat; dark brown ship with cream sails
2. Red jacket; yellow epaulettes and buttons; yellow waistcoat; pale green breeches; black bow, shoes and hat; light brown ship with yellow sails
Issued: 1958-1958
Varieties: RW3761

| Colourways | Backstamp | Price | | |
		U.S. $	Can. $	U.K. £
Coloured (as above)	Black	1,000.00	1,350.00	600.00

RW3662
SISTER, THE LONDON HOSPITAL

Modeller: Ruth Van Ruyckevelt
Height: 6 ¾", 17.2 cm
Colour: Blue uniform with white cuffs, buttons, collar and cap; brown shoes; white and blue patterned chair with wooden frame; white and gold base
Issued: 1958 in a limited edition of 500
Series: Nursing Sisters

| Colourways | Backstamp | Price | | |
		U.S. $	Can. $	U.K. £
Blue	Black	950.00	1,250.00	550.00

RW3663
SISTER, NIGHTINGALE TRAINING SCHOOL
ST. THOMAS' HOSPITAL (LONDON)

Modeller: Ruth Van Ruyckevelt
Height: 7", 17.8 cm
Colour: Dark blue uniform with white cuffs; white apron and cap; black shoes; white and mauve striped chair; white and gold base
Issued: 1958 in a limited edition of 500
Series: Nursing Sisters

| Colourways | Backstamp | Price | | |
		U.S. $	Can. $	U.K. £
Dark blue/white	Black	950.00	1,250.00	550.00

RW3667
THE WINNER WITH JOCKEY AND STABLE BOY

Modeller: Doris Lindner
Height: 11 ¼", 28.5 cm
Colour: 1. Grey
        2. Brown
Issued: 1959-1959

Colourways	Backstamp	U.S. $	Price Can. $	U.K. £
Coloured (as above)	Black		Extremely rare	

RW3671
THE WINNER

Modeller: Doris Lindner
Height: 11 ¼", 28.5 cm
Colour: Rider: Red and purple silks; white jodhpurs; black hat and boots;
        Horse: Bay
Issued: 1959-by 1980

Colourways	Backstamp	U.S. $	Price Can. $	U.K. £
Red/purple/white/bay	Black	1,500.00	1,800.00	800.00

Note: To make production more practical, the stable boy was eliminated from model RW3667 and the plinth was shortened slightly. Although the jockey came painted in the Queen's racing colours, for an extra fee the colours could be customised.

Photograph not available at press time

RW3675
OFFICER OF THE COLDSTREAM GUARDS
Third Version

Modeller: Frederick M. Gertner
Height: 11 ¾", 29.8 cm
Colour: Red tunic; white trousers; black hat and boots; gold decoration
Issued: 1959-c.1979
Variations: RW2635 (First Version), RW2676 (Second Version)
Series: Historical Military Figures

Colourways	Backstamp	U.S. $	Price Can. $	U.K. £
Red/white/black/gold	Black	775.00	1,000.00	450.00

Note: Commissioned by Aspreys, London, England.

RW3677
OFFICER OF THE SCOTS GUARDS

Modeller:	Frederick M. Gertner
Height:	11 ¼", 28.5 cm
Colour:	Red jacket with gold epaulettes; green, blue and turquoise kilt; black bearskin
Issued:	1959-c.1979
Varieties:	Also called RW2657 "Seaforth Highlander Officer"
Series:	Historical Military Figures

			Price	
Colourways	Backstamp	U.S. $	Can. $	U.K. £
Red/white/bay	Black	775.00	1,000.00	450.00

Photograph not available at press time

Note: Commissioned by Aspreys, London, England.

RW3678
FOXHUNTER AND LIEUT.-COL. H.M. LLEWELLYN, C.B.E.

Modeller:	Doris Lindner
Height:	12", 30.5 cm
Colour:	Rider: Red jacket; white jodhpurs; black boots and hat
	Horse: Bay with black lower legs and tail
Issued:	1959 in a limited edition of 500

			Price	
Colourways	Backstamp	U.S. $	Can. $	U.K. £
Red/white/bay	Black	975.00	1,250.00	550.00

Note: There are 100 signed and 400 unsigned pieces.

RW3679
MERLIN

Modeller:	Freda Doughty
Height:	7", 17.8 cm
Colour:	Cream shirt; beige and maroon doublet; brown shoes; dark brown and golden merlin
Issued:	1959-1959
Varieties:	Also called "The Falconer"

			Price	
Colourways	Backstamp	U.S. $	Can. $	U.K. £
Cream/beige/maroon	Black	1,400.00	1,800.00	800.00

RW3681
BEATRICE

Modeller:	Ruth Van Ruyckevelt
Height:	7 ½", 19.1 cm
Colour:	Lavender
Issued:	1959 in a limited edition of 500
Series:	Victorian Ladies

		Price		
Colourways	*Backstamp*	*U.S. $*	*Can. $*	*U.K. £*
Lavender	Black	775.00	1,000.00	450.00

RW3682
CAROLINE
Style One

Modeller:	Ruth Van Ruyckevelt
Height:	7 ½", 19.1 cm
Colour:	Light blue skirt with white flowers and trim; red striped bodice; white fan; black gloves; brown hair
Issued:	1959 in a limited edition of 500
Series:	Victorian Ladies

		Price		
Colourways	*Backstamp*	*U.S. $*	*Can. $*	*U.K. £*
Light blue/white/red	Black	775.00	1,000.00	450.00

RW3687
REBECCA
Style One

Modeller:	Ruth Van Ruyckevelt
Height:	8 ¼", 21.0 cm
Colour:	1. Green bodice; multicoloured ruffled skirt; black and purple bow; cream and yellow lattice chair 2. Pink and blue crinoline
Issued:	1959 in a limited edition of 500
Series:	Victorian Ladies

		Price		
Colourways	*Backstamp*	*U.S. $*	*Can. $*	*U.K. £*
Coloured (as above)	Black	875.00	1,125.00	500.00

RW3688
LOUISA

Modeller:	Ruth Van Ruyckevelt
Height:	7 ¾", 19.7 cm
Colour:	White, pink and lavender
Issued:	1959 in a limited edition of 500
Series:	Victorian Ladies

			Price	
Colourways	Backstamp	U.S. $	Can. $	U.K. £
White/pink/lavender	Black	775.00	1,000.00	450.00

RW3698
INVITATION
Style One

Modeller:	Freda Doughty
Height:	8 ¾", 22.2 cm
Colour:	Pale green-yellow dress; red and green neck bow; yellow hair
Issued:	1960

			Price	
Colourways	Backstamp	U.S. $	Can. $	U.K. £
Pale green-yellow	Black	1,650.00	2,150.00	950.00

RW3699
RED RIBBONS

Modeller:	Freda Doughty
Height:	8", 20.3 cm
Colour:	Multicoloured
Issued:	1960-1960

			Price	
Colourways	Backstamp	U.S. $	Can. $	U.K. £
Multi-coloured	Black	1,650.00	2,150.00	950.00

RW3700
THE TEA PARTY

Modeller:	Ruth Van Ruyckevelt
Height:	8", 20.3 cm
Colour:	Standing lady: Mustard dress, white trim; pink feather in brown hat and feather
	Seated lady: Light blue-grey dress with white trim; purple hat and feather and parasol
	Girl: Light blue and white patterned dress; straw hat
	Dog: White and brown
Issued:	1960 in a limited edition of 250
Series:	Victorian Figures

Colourways	Backstamp	Price U.S. $	Can. $	U.K. £
Coloured (as above)	Black	2,175.00	2,800.00	1,250.00

RW3720
WILL YOU, WON'T YOU?

Modeller:	Freda Doughty
Height:	Unknown
Colour:	Unknown
Issued:	1961-1961

Colourways	Backstamp	Price U.S. $	Can. $	U.K. £
Unknown	Black		Extremely rare	

RW3745
CAPTAIN RAIMONDO D'INZEO ON MERANO

Modeller:	Doris Lindner
Height:	11", 27.9 cm
Colour:	Rider: Olive jacket and cap; white jodhpurs; black boots
	Horse: Chestnut
Issued:	1962 in a limited edition of 500

Colourways	Backstamp	Price U.S. $	Can. $	U.K. £
Olive/white/chestnut	Black	1,200.00	1,675.00	750.00

RW3747
YOUNG ENGLAND

Modeller: Neal French
Height: 5", 12.7 cm
Colour: Dark green jersey; white shorts; brown ball and football (soccer)
boots; light brown shoes
Issued: 1962
Series: Playtime Series

Colourways	Backstamp	U.S. $	Price Can. $	U.K. £
Green/white/brown	Black	775.00	1,000.00	450.00

RW3748
TREASURE TROVE

Modeller: Neal French
Height: 5", 12.7cm
Colour: Light green dress; pink headband; brown hair;
beige box with red lining
Issued: 1962
Series: Playtime Series

Colourways	Backstamp	U.S. $	Price Can. $	U.K. £
Light green	Black	875.00	1,125.00	500.00

RW3749
MELANIE

Modeller: Ruth Van Ruyckevelt
Height: 8 ¼", 21.0 cm
Colour: Unknown
Issued: 1962 in a limited edition of 500
Series: Victorian Ladies

Colourways	Backstamp	U.S. $	Price Can. $	U.K. £
Unknown	Black	775.00	1,000.00	450.00

RW3750
ROSALIND

Modeller:	Ruth Van Ruyckevelt
Height:	8", 20.3 cm
Colour:	Cream dress with pink trim; light grey dotted skirt; black neck bow; black hair
Issued:	1962 in a limited edition of 500
Series:	Victorian Ladies

		Price		
Colourways	Backstamp	U.S. $	Can. $	U.K. £
Cream/pink/grey	Black	775.00	1,000.00	450.00

RW3754
POUPÉE

Modeller:	Neal French
Height:	5", 12.7 cm
Colour:	Dark blue bodice; white collar, cuffs and skirt; red belt and shoes; blonde hair; doll dressed in red
Issued:	1962
Series:	Playtime Series

		Price		
Colourways	Backstamp	U.S. $	Can. $	U.K. £
Dark blue/white/red	Black	775.00	1,000.00	450.00

RW3755
MASTER MARINER

Modeller:	Neal French
Height:	5", 12.7 cm
Colour:	Cream T-shirt; blue trousers; green boat with white sails
Issued:	1962
Series:	Playtime Series

		Price		
Colourways	Backstamp	U.S. $	Can. $	U.K. £
Cream/blue	Black	775.00	1,000.00	450.00

RW3756
FIRST AID

Modeller: Neal French
Height: 5", 12.7 cm
Colour: Blue and white uniform; white cap with red cross; black shoes;
           golden bear
Issued: 1962
Series: Playtime Series

Colourways	Backstamp	U.S. $	Price Can. $	U.K. £
Blue/white	Black	875.00	1,125.00	500.00

RW3757
SHERIFF

Modeller: Neal French
Height: 5", 12.7 cm
Colour: Light blue jersey; light brown shorts; black cowboy boots;
           dark brown hat
Issued: 1962
Series: Playtime Series

Colourways	Backstamp	U.S. $	Price Can. $	U.K. £
Light blue/brown/black	Black	775.00	1,000.00	450.00

RW3760
FANTAILS

Modeller: Freda Doughty
Height: 7 ¼", 18.4 cm
Colour: White coat with lilac highlights; blue leggings; blue cap trimmed
           with white; three white doves
Issued: 1962-c.1982
Varieties: Also called RW3418 November

Colourways	Backstamp	U.S. $	Price Can. $	U.K. £
White/lilac/blue	Black	400.00	500.00	225.00

RW3761
MAYFLOWER
Second Version (Without hat and telescope)

Modeller: Freda Doughty
Height: 7 ½", 19.0 cm
Colour: Blue jacket; yellow epaulettes, buttons and waistcoat; beige breeches; black bow and shoes; brown ship with white sails
Issued: 1963-1963
Varieties: RW3656

Colourways	Backstamp	Price U.S. $	Can. $	U.K. £
Blue/yellow/beige	Black	1,300.00	1,650.00	750.00

RW3771
SISTER, THE UNIVERSITY COLLEGE HOSPITAL, LONDON

Modeller: Ruth Van Ruyckevelt
Height: 9", 22.9 cm
Colour: Black and white uniform; grey cap; black shoes; grey clipboard
Issued: 1964 in a limited edition of 500
Series: Nursing Sisters

Colourways	Backstamp	Price U.S. $	Can. $	U.K. £
Black/white/grey	Black	600.00	775.00	350.00

RW3774
ELIZABETH
Style One

Modeller: Ruth Van Ruyckevelt
Height: 8 ½", 21.6 cm
Colour: Grey-black bodice; white skirt and sleeves with black dots; scarlet umbrella
Issued: 1964 in a limited edition of 500
Series: Victorian Ladies

Colourways	Backstamp	Price U.S. $	Can. $	U.K. £
Grey-black/white	Black	775.00	1,000.00	450.00

RW3775
MADELAINE

Modeller: Ruth Van Ruyckevelt
Height: 8 ½", 21.6 cm
Colour: Ivory dress; lilac bow and plume in hair
Issued: 1964 in a limited edition of 500
Series: Victorian Ladies

Colourways	Backstamp	Price U.S. $	Can. $	U.K. £
Ivory/lilac	Black	775.00	1,000.00	450.00

RW3803
MARION

Modeller: Ruth Van Ruyckevelt
Height: 7 ½", 19.1 cm
Colour: Navy skirt with white trim; light blue and white blouse; red and white striped tie and hat band; straw hat
Issued: 1965 in a limited edition of 500
Series: Victorian Ladies

Colourways	Backstamp	Price U.S. $	Can. $	U.K. £
Navy/light blue/white	Black	775.00	1,000.00	450.00

RW3804
CHARLOTTE AND JANE

Modeller: Ruth Van Ruyckevelt
Height: 6 ½", 16.5 cm
Colour: Lady: Green dress with white ruffles; green hat with white and yellow flowers; dark red handbag
Girl: Lilac and white dress; white stockings; black shoes; red hair
Issued: 1965 in a limited edition of 500
Series: Victorian Ladies

Colourways	Backstamp	Price U.S. $	Can. $	U.K. £
Green/white/lilac	Black	1,125.00	1,450.00	650.00

RW3805
ROYAL CANADIAN MOUNTED POLICE

Modeller: Doris Lindner
Height: 12 ¼", 31.1 cm
Colour: Red jacket; black trousers; brown hat and boots; black horse
Issued: 1967 in a limited edition of 500

| | | | Price | |
Description	Backstamp	U.S. $	Can. $	U.K. £
1. With 1967 symbol	Black	2,100.00	2,750.00	1,200.00
2. Without 1967 symbol	Black	2,100.00	2,750.00	1,200.00

Note: The first 100 models issued bore the Canadian Centennial Symbol for 1967.

RW3809
BOY WITH HAT (ANTHONY)

Modeller: Ronald Van Ruyckevelt
Height: Unknown
Colour: Unknown
Issued: 1966

| | | | Price | |
Colourways	Backstamp	U.S. $	Can. $	U.K. £
Unknown	Black		Extremely rare	

*Photograph not
available
at press time*

RW3810
GIRL WITH HAT (SARAH JANE)

Modeller: Ronald Van Ruyckevelt
Height: Unknown
Colour: Unknown
Issued: 1966

| | | | Price | |
Colourways	Backstamp	U.S. $	Can. $	U.K. £
Unknown	Black		Extremely rare	

RW3841
EMILY
Style One

Modeller:	Ruth Van Ruyckevelt
Height:	7 ¾", 19.7 cm
Colour:	White skirt; red jacket trimmed with black; black hat; brown and cream muff
Issued:	1967 in a limited edition of 500
Series:	Victorian Ladies

			Price		
Colourways	Backstamp	U.S. $	Can. $	U.K. £
White/red/black	Black	775.00	1,000.00	450.00

RW3842
BRIDGET

Modeller:	Ruth Van Ruyckevelt
Height:	7 ½", 19.1 cm
Colour:	White dress; yellow hat with blue trim; red ball
Issued:	1967 in a limited edition of 500
Series:	Victorian Ladies

			Price		
Colourways	Backstamp	U.S. $	Can. $	U.K. £
White/yellow	Black	850.00	1,075.00	480.00

RW3846
H.R.H. THE DUKE OF EDINBURGH ON HIS POLO PONY

Modeller:	Doris Lindner
Height:	15 ¾", 40.0 cm
Colour:	Dark grey shirt; white jodhpurs; black hat; bay horse
Issued:	1968 in a limited edition of 750

			Price		
Colourways	Backstamp	U.S. $	Can. $	U.K. £
Dark grey/white/bay	Black	1,125.00	1,450.00	650.00

RW3860
NAPOLEON BONAPARTE

Modeller: Bernard Winskill
Height: 16 ¼", 41.2 cm
Colour: 1. Bone china: Red cape; dark blue coat, hat, boots and
saddlecloth; cream breeches and gloves; white horse; gold reins
2. Bronze metal
Issued: 1. Bone china: 1968 in a limited edition of 750
2. Bronze metal: 1968 in a limited edition of 15
Series: Military Commanders

			Pric	
Description	Backstamp	U.S. $	Can. $	U.K. £
1. Bone china	Black	3,500.00	4,500.00	2,000.00
2. Bronze metal	R-W	5,000.00	7,000.00	3,000.00

RW3861
BRITISH RED CROSS V.A.D. MEMBER

Modeller: Ruth Van Ruyckevelt
Height: 8 ½", 21.6 cm
Colour: Blue uniform; white apron with red cross on bib;
white cap; black bag
Issued: 1968 in a limited edition of 750

		Price		
Colourways	Backstamp	U.S. $	Can. $	U.K. £
Blue/white	Black	650.00	850.00	380.00

RW3864
19TH CENTURY CIGAR STORE INDIAN

Modeller: Peter Ewence
Height: 9", 22.9 cm
Colour: Green wrap; red-brown headdress; dark brown leggings;
black hair
Issued: 1968 in a limited edition of 500

			Price	
Colourways	Backstamp	U.S. $	Can. $	U.K. £
Green/brown	Black	775.00	1,000.00	450.00

Note: This model was produced exclusively for Rothmans of Pall Mall.

RW3870
THE DUKE OF WELLINGTON

Modeller: Bernard Winskill
Height: 16", 40.6 cm
Colour: 1. Bone china: Rider: Red jacket with blue sash; white jodhpurs;
black boots; Horse: Brown
2. Bronze metal
Issued: 1. Bone china: 1968 in a limited edition of 750
2. Bronze metal: 1968 in a limited edition of 15
Series: Military Commanders

Description	Backstamp	U.S. $	Price Can. $	U.K. £
1. Bone china	Black	4,000.00	5,000.00	2,300.00
2. Bronze metal	R-W	6,000.00	8,000.00	3,500.00

RW3872
STROLLER AND MARION COAKES

Modeller: Doris Lindner
Height: 11 ¼", 28.5 cm
Colour: Rider: Black jacket and boots; white jodhpurs
Horse: Light brown
Issued: 1968 in a limited edition of 750

Colourways	Backstamp	U.S. $	Price Can. $	U.K. £
Black/white/brown	Black	1,225.00	1,575.00	700.00

RW3877
ELAINE

Modeller: Ruth Van Ruyckevelt
Height: 5 ¾", 14.6 cm
Colour: Orange patterned dress with white upper bodice; black hair;
brown guitar
Issued: 1971 in a limited edition of 750
Series: Victorian Ladies

Colourways	Backstamp	U.S. $	Price Can. $	U.K. £
Orange/white	Black	600.00	775.00	350.00

RW3878
FELICITY

Modeller:	Ruth Van Ruyckevelt
Height:	6 ¾", 17.2 cm
Colour:	White dress with blue design; blue hat; golden brown retriever
Issued:	1971 in a limited edition of 750
Series:	Victorian Ladies

		Price		
Colourways	Backstamp	U.S. $	Can. $	U.K. £
White/blue	Black	725.00	950.00	420.00

RW3881
PICNIC (The)

Modeller:	Ruth Van Ruyckevelt
Height:	6 ½", 16.5 cm
Colour:	Lady kneeling: Green dress with white trim; straw hat
	Lady seated: White dress with pink flowers and trim
Issued:	1969 in a limited edition of 250
Series:	Victorian Ladies

		Price		
Colourways	Backstamp	U.S. $	Can. $	U.K. £
Green/white/pink	Black	2,350.00	3,000.00	1,350.00

RW3887
ALICE
Style Two

Modeller:	Ruth Van Ruyckevelt
Height:	8 ½", 21.6 cm
Colour:	Blue dress; white underskirt; black hat with pink roses
Issued:	1969 in a limited edition of 750
Series:	Victorian Ladies

		Price		
Colourways	Backstamp	U.S. $	Can. $	U.K. £
Blue/white/black	Black	850.00	1,100.00	480.00

RW3892
CECILIA

Modeller: Ruth Van Ruyckevelt
Height: 7 ½", 19.1 cm
Colour: Royal blue dress with white trim
Issued: 1969 in a limited edition of 750
Series: Victorian Ladies

Colourways	Backstamp	U.S. $	Price Can. $	U.K. £
Royal blue/white	Black	725.00	950.00	420.00

RW3897
WASHINGTON (George)

Modeller: Bernard Winskill
Height: 18", 45.7 cm
Colour: 1. Bone china: Navy jacket with gold trim; black boots; white jodhpurs; grey horse
2. Bronze metal
Issued: 1. Bone china: 1972 in a limited edition of 750
2. Bronze metal: 1975 in a limited edition of 15
Series: Military Commanders

Description	Backstamp	U.S. $	Price Can. $	U.K. £
1. Bone china	Black	4,000.00	5,000.00	2,300.00
2. Bronze metal	R-W	6,000.00	8,000.00	3,500.00

RW3912
H.R.H. PRINCESS ANNE AND DOUBLET

Modeller: Doris Lindner
Height: 13", 33.0 cm
Colour: Rider: Blue jersey; cream jodhpurs; black hat
Horse: Brown
Issued: 1972 in a limited edition of 750

Colourways	Backstamp	U.S. $	Price Can. $	U.K. £
Blue/cream/brown	Black	1,225.00	1,575.00	700.00

RW3914
DUKE OF MARLBOROUGH, THE

Modeller: Bernard Winskill
Height: 18", 45.7 cm
Colour: 1. Bone china: Red jacket; blue sash and trim; grey horse
2. Bronze metal
Issued: 1. Bone china: 1973 in a limited edition of 350
2. Bronze metal: 1973 in a limited edition of 15
Sereis: Military Commanders

Description	Backstamp	Price U.S. $	Can. $	U.K. £
1. Bone china	Black	3,500.00	4,500.00	2,000.00
2. Bronze metal	R-W	5,000.00	7,000.00	3,000.00

RW3934
MAN AND WOMAN

Modeller: Cecil Michaelis
Height: 12", 30.5 cm
Colour: 1. Bronze metal
2. Glazed bone china
Issued: 1. Bronze metal: 1973 in a limited edition of 15
2. Glazed bone china: 1973 in a limited edition of 100

Description	Backstamp	Price U.S. $	Can. $	U.K. £
1. Bronze metal	R-W	1,400.00	1,750.00	800.00
2. Glazed bone china	Black	600.00	775.00	350.00

RW3936
QUEEN MARY I

Modeller: Ronald Van Ruyckevelt
Height: 9", 22.9 cm
Colour: Dark blue and grey-green
Issued: 1973 in a limited edition of 250
Series: Queens Regnant

Colourways	Backstamp	Price U.S. $	Can. $	U.K. £
Dark blue/grey-green	Black	950.00	1,225.00	550.00

Note: A base of elm burr with solid rosewood coping and ceramic tile on top accompanied this piece.

RW3937
QUEEN ELIZABETH I
Style Two

Modeller:	Ronald Van Ruyckevelt
Height:	12 ½", 31.7 cm
Colour:	Gold and white dress
Issued:	1973 in a limited edition of 250
Series:	Queens Regnant

		Price		
Colourways	Backstamp	U.S. $	Can. $	U.K. £
Gold/white	Black	1,475.00	1,900.00	850.00

RW3938
QUEEN ANNE

Modeller:	Ronald Van Ruyckevelt
Height:	Unknown
Colour:	Yellow dress with light grey highlights
Issued:	1973 in a limited edition of 250
Series:	Queens Regnant

		Price		
Colourways	Backstamp	U.S. $	Can. $	U.K. £
Yellow/light grey	Black	1,125.00	1,450.00	650.00

RW3939
QUEEN MARY II

Modeller:	Ronald Van Ruyckevelt
Height:	12", 30.5 cm
Colour:	Yellow dress; green and cream cape
Issued:	1973 in a limited edition of 250
Series:	Queens Regnant

		Pric		
Colourways	Backstamp	U.S. $	Can. $	U.K. £
Yellow/green/cream	Black	1,125.00	1,450.00	650.00

RW3940
QUEEN VICTORIA
Style One

Modeller:	Ronald Van Ruyckevelt
Height:	9", 22.9 cm
Colour:	Light grey and white skirt edged with white frill; black top and veil
Issued:	1973 in a limited edition of 250
Series:	Queens Regnant

		Price		
Colourways	*Backstamp*	*U.S. $*	*Can. $*	*U.K. £*
Light grey/white/black	Black	1,475.00	1,900.00	850.00

RW3941
QUEEN ELIZABETH II
Style One

Modeller:	Ronald Van Ruyckevelt, Kenneth Potts
Height:	14 ¾", 37.5 cm
Colour:	White dress; royal blue cloak with white lining and bows; royal blue hat with white plume; white gloves; red sash
Issued:	1973 in a limited edition of 250
Series:	Queens Regnant

		Price		
Colourways	*Backstamp*	*U.S. $*	*Can. $*	*U.K. £*
White/royal blue	Black	1,125.00	1,425.00	650.00

Note: Commissioned by Compton & Woodhouse.

RW3943
RICHARD MEADE AND LAURISTON

Modeller:	Doris Lindner
Height:	13", 33.0 cm
Colour:	Rider: Cream riding outfit; black hat Horse: Black
Issued:	1974 in a limited edition of 500

		Price		
Colourways	*Backstamp*	*U.S. $*	*Can. $*	*U.K. £*
Cream/black	Black	1,300.00	1,675.00	750.00

RW3945
PREFERENCE

Modeller: Cecil Michaelis
Height: 13 ½", 34.3 cm
Colour: 1. Bronze metal
        2. Glazed bone china
Issued: 1. Bronze metal: 1975 in a limited edition of 15
        2. Glazed bone china: 1975 in a limited edition of 100
Series: Sur la Plage

Colourways	Backstamp	U.S. $	Price Can. $	U.K. £
1. Bronze metal	R-W	1,700.00	2,125.00	950.00
2. Glazed bone china	Black	600.00	775.00	350.00

RW3946
PLONGUER

Modeller: Cecil Michaelis
Height: Unknown
Colour: 1. Bronze metal
        2. Glazed bone china
Issued: 1. Bronze metal: 1974 in a limited edition of 15
        2. Glazed bone china: 1974 in a limited edition of 100
Series: Sur la Plage

Description	Backstamp	U.S. $	Price Can. $	U.K. £
1. Bronze metal	R-W	1,700.00	2,125.00	950.00
2. Glazed bone china	Black	600.00	775.00	350.00

RW3947
BAIGNEUSE (La Plongée Attendue)

Modeller: Cecil Michaelis
Height: Unknown
Colour: 1. Bronze metal
        2. Glazed bone china
Issued: 1. Bronze metal: 1974 in a limited edition of 15
        2. Glazed bone china: 1974 in a limited edition of 100
Series: Sur la Plage

Description	Backstamp	U.S. $	Price Can. $	U.K. £
1. Bronze metal	R-W	1,700.00	2,125.00	950.00
2. Glazed bone china	Black	600.00	775.00	350.00

RW3948
BY A SHORT HEAD

Modeller:	Bernard Winskill
Height:	Unknown
Colour:	1. Bone china: Riders: Yellow and white silks; blue and white silks Horses: Chestnut
	2. Bronze metal
Issued:	1. Bone china: 1974 in a limited edition of 100
	2. Bronze metal: 1974 in a limited edition of 15
Series:	Racing Studies

			Price	
Description	Backstamp	U.S. $	Can. $	U.K. £
1. Bone china	Black	4,375.00	5,625.00	2,500.00
2. Bronze metal	R-W	6,000.00	9,000.00	4,000.00

RW3950
JEUX DE PLAGE

Modeller:	Cecil Michaelis
Height:	14 ¾", 37.5 cm
Colour:	1. Bronze metal
	2. Glazed bone china
Issued:	1. Bronze metal: 1974 in a limited edition of 15
	2. Glazed bone china: 1974 in a limited edition of 100
Series:	Sur la Plage

			Price	
Description	Backstamp	U.S. $	Can. $	U.K. £
1. Bronze metal	R-W	1,700.00	2,125.00	950.00
2. Glazed bone china	Black	600.00	775.00	350.00

RW3952
CHELTENHAM

Modeller:	Bernard Winskill
Height:	Unknown
Colour:	1. Bone china: Rider One: Green, pink and white silks; black boots Rider Two: Lilac, grey and white silks; black boots Horses: Grey
	2. Bronze metal
Issued:	1. Bone china: 1978 in a limited edition of 100
	2. Bronze metal: 1978 in a limited edition of 15
Series:	Racing Studies

			Price	
Description	Backstamp	U.S. $	Can. $	U.K. £
1. Bone china	Black	4,375.00	5,625.00	2,500.00
2. Bronze metal	R-W	6,000.00	9,000.00	4,000.00

RW3953
L'IMPETUEUX

Modeller: Cecil Michaelis
Height: 11 ¾", 29.8 cm
Colour: 1. Bronze metal
           2. Glazed bone china
Issued: 1. Bronze metal: 1974 in a limited edition of 15
           2. Glazed bone china: 1974 in a limited edition of 100
Series: Sur la Plage

Description	Backstamp	U.S. $	Price Can. $	U.K. £
1. Bronze metal	R-W	1,700.00	2,125.00	950.00
2. Glazed bone china	Black	600.00	775.00	350.00

RW3954
LEÇON À LA MER

Modeller: Cecil Michaelis
Height: Unknown
Colour: 1. Bronze metal
           2. Glazed bone china
Issued: 1. Bronze metal: 1974 in a limited edition of 15
           2. Glazed bone china: 1974 in a limited edition of 100
Series: Sur la Plage

Description	Backstamp	U.S. $	Price Can. $	U.K. £
1. Bronze metal	R-W	1,700.00	2,125.00	950.00
2. Glazed bone china	Black	600.00	775.00	350.00

RW3956
ALEXANDER (The Great)

Modeller: Bernard Winskill
Height: 19", 48.3 cm
Colour: 1. Bone china: Fleshtone; white toga; brown horse
           2. Bronze metal
Issued: 1. Bone china: 1975 in a limited edition of 250
           2. Bronze metal: 1975 in a limited edition 15
Series: Military Commanders

Description	Backstamp	U.S. $	Price Can. $	U.K. £
1. Bone china	Black	3,750.00	4,950.00	2,200.00
2. Bronze metal	R-W	6,000.00	8,000.00	3,500.00

RW3959A
AT THE START
Style One (No. 4)

Modeller: Bernard Winskill
Height: Unknown
Colour: 1. Bone china: Rider: Gold and black silks; white jodhpurs;
               black and gold boots; Horse: Brown
           2. Bronze metal
Issued: 1. Bone china: 1975 in a limited edition of 100
           2. Bronze metal: 1975 in a limited edition of 15
Series: Racing Studies

| | | Price | | |
Description	Backstamp	U.S. $	Can. $	U.K. £
1. Bone china	Black	1,300.00	1,675.00	750.00
2. Bronze metal	R-W	2,500.00	3,750.00	1,750.00

RW3959B
AT THE START
Style Two (No. 6)

Modeller: Bernard Winskill
Height: Unknown
Colour: Rider: Red silks; white jodhpurs; black boots
           Horse: Brown
Issued: 1975 in a limited edition of 100
Series: Racing Studies

| | | Price | | |
Colourways	Backstamp	U.S. $	Can. $	U.K. £
Red/white/brown	Black	1,300.00	1,675.00	750.00

RW3982
GRUNDY WITH PAT EDDERY UP

Modeller: Doris Lindner
Height: 11 ½", 29.2 cm
Colour: Jockey: Blue, white and yellow silks
           Horse: Chestnut
Issued: 1976 in a limited edition of 500
Series: Racing Studies

| | | Price | | |
Colourways	Backstamp	U.S. $	Can. $	U.K. £
Blue/white/yellow/chestnut	Black	1,300.00	1,675.00	750.00

RW3984
DELETTANTE

Modeller: Kenneth Potts
Height: 10", 25.4 cm
Colour: Green frock coat with gold highlights; brown and white dog
Issued: 1977 in a limited edition of 500
Series: The Age of Elegance, Series One

Colourways	Backstamp	Price U.S. $	Can. $	U.K. £
White/gold/brown	Black	600.00	775.00	350.00

RW3985
INNOCENCE

Modeller: Kenneth Potts
Height: 10", 25.4 cm
Colour: Pink and white dress, parasol and shoes; gold highlights
Issued: 1977 in a limited edition of 500
Series: The Age of Elegance, Series One

Colourways	Backstamp	Price U.S. $	Can. $	U.K. £
Pink/white/gold	Black	600.00	775.00	350.00

RW3986
THE DANDY

Modeller: Kenneth Potts
Height: 10", 25.4 cm
Colour: Unknown
Issued: 1977 in a limited edition of 500
Series: The Age of Elegance, Series One

Colourways	Backstamp	Price U.S. $	Can. $	U.K. £
Unknown	Black	600.00	775.00	350.00

RW3987
THE PARAMOUR

Modeller: Kenneth Potts
Height: 10", 25.4 cm
Colour: Unknown
Issued: 1977 in a limited edition of 500
Series: The Age of Elegance, Series One

Colourways	Backstamp	Price U.S. $	Price Can. $	Price U.K. £
Unknown	Black	600.00	775.00	350.00

RW4011
GRACE
Style One

Modeller: Kenneth Potts
Height: 10", 25.4 cm
Colour: Lemon dress
Issued: 1977 in a limited edition of 500
Series: The Age of Elegance, Series One

Colourways	Backstamp	Price U.S. $	Price Can. $	Price U.K. £
Lemon	Black	600.00	750.00	350.00

RW4012
PHILANDERER

Modeller: Kenneth Potts
Height: 10", 25.4 cm
Colour: Black frock coat
Issued: 1977 in a limited edition of 500
Series: The Age of Elegance, Series One

Colourways	Backstamp	Price U.S. $	Price Can. $	Price U.K. £
Black	Black	600.00	750.00	350.00

RW4013
GIRL WITH SETTER

Modeller: Kenneth Potts
Height: Unknown
Colour: Unknown
Issued: 1. Bone china: 1977
2. Bronze metal: 1977 in a limited edition of 25

Description	Backstamp	U.S. $	Price Can. $	U.K. £
1. Bone china	Black		Rare	
2. Bronze metal	R-W		Very rare	

RW4015
MISTRAL AND LESTER PIGGOT

Modeller: Bernard Winskill
Height: 16", 40.6 cm
Colour: Rider: Blue, green and white silks; white jodhpurs
Horse: Chestnut
Issued: 1. Bronze metal: 1978 in a limited edition of 25
2. Glazed bone china: 1978 in a limited edition of 150
Series: Racing Studies

Description	Backstamp	U.S. $	Price Can. $	U.K. £
1. Bronze metal	R-W	4,275.00	5,600.00	2,500.00
2. Bone china	Black	2,650.00	3,375.00	1,500.00

RW4017
DUNFERMLINE

Modeller: Bernard Winskill
Height: Unknown
Colour: Bronze metal
Issued: In a limited edition of 25

Description	Backstamp	U.S. $	Price Can. $	U.K. £
Bronze metal	R-W		Rare	

Photograph not available at press time

RW4023
MORNING WALK

Modeller:	Donald Brindley
Height:	6", 15.0 cm
Colour:	1. White dress with blue design on bodice
	2. White dress with red dots on sleeves, red sash and ribbons
Issued:	1979-1984
Varieties:	Also called "Red Ribbons"
Series:	Age of Romance, Series Two

			Price	
Colourways	Backstamp	U.S. $	Can. $	U.K. £
Coloured (as above)	Black	165.00	210.00	95.00

RW4024
SPRING FAIR

Modeller:	Donald Brindley
Height:	6", 15.0 cm
Colour:	1. White skirt with pink design; white bodice, apron and frills; basket of yellow flowers
	2. Yellow skirt; white bodice and apron; basket of pink flowers
Issued:	1979-1980
Series:	Age of Romance, Series Two

			Price	
Colourways	Backstamp	U.S. $	Can. $	U.K. £
Coloured (as above)	Black	165.00	200.00	95.00

RW4025
WEDDING DAY (Girl)

Modeller:	Donald Brindley
Height:	4", 10.1 cm
Colour:	White dress and veil; pink flowers attached to veil; white posy
Issued:	1979-1980
Series:	Age of Romance, Series Two

			Price	
Colourways	Backstamp	U.S. $	Can. $	U.K. £
White/pink	Black	130.00	165.00	75.00

RW4026
WEDDING DAY (Boy)

Modeller: Donald Brindley
Height: 4", 10.1 cm
Colour: White jacket, shirt and top hat; blue shorts; pink tie
Issued: 1979-1980
Series: Age of Romance, Series Two

Colourways	Backstamp	Price U.S. $	Can. $	U.K. £
White/blue/pink	Black	130.00	165.00	75.00

RW4031
H.R.H. PRINCE CHARLES ON PANS FOLLY

Modeller: Lorne McKean
Height: 16", 40.6 cm
Colour: 1. Bone china: Green shirt; white jodhpurs; brown boots;
        black hat; brown horse
        2. Bronze metal
Issued: 1. Bone china: 1978 in a limited edition of 250
        2. Bronze metal: 1978 in a limited edition of 15

Description	Backstamp	Price U.S. $	Can. $	U.K. £
1. Bone china	Black	1,650.00	2,125.00	950.00
2. Bronze metal	R-W	3,500.00	4,500.00	2,000.00

RW4032
CRINOLINE LADY

Modeller: Donald Brindley
Height: 6", 15.0 cm
Colour: 1. Lilac patterned dress, white frills, deep lilac bow and ribbons;
        straw hat with deep lilac ribbon and bow
        2. White dress with lemon highlights; yellow bow and ribbons;
        straw hat with yellow ribbon and bow
Issued: 1979-1980
Series: Age of Romance, Series Two

Colourways	Backstamp	Price U.S. $	Can. $	U.K. £
Coloured (as above)	Black	165.00	200.00	95.00

RW4033
WINTER WALTZ

Modeller:	Donald Brindley
Height:	6", 15.0 cm
Colour:	1. Red skirt; white coat with brown fur trim and buttons; red ruff at neck; brown fur muff and hat
	2. White skirt; yellow coat with brown fur trim and buttons; yellow ruff at neck; brown fur hat and muff
Issued:	1979-1980
Series:	Age of Romance, Series Two

		Price		
Colourways	*Backstamp*	*U.S. $*	*Can. $*	*U.K. £*
Coloured (as above)	Black	165.00	200.00	95.00

RW4034
RICHARD COEUR DE LION

Modeller:	Bernard Winskill
Height:	15 ½", 39.4 cm
Colour:	1. Bone china: Red cape and reins; grey tunic and horse
	2. Bronze metal
Issued:	1. Bone china: 1978 in a limited edition of 250
	2. Bronze metal: 1978 in a limited edition of 15
Series:	Military Commanders

		Price		
Description	*Backstamp*	*U.S. $*	*Can. $*	*U.K. £*
1. Bone china	Black	4,375.00	5,600.00	2,500.00
2. Bronze metal	R-W	6,000.00	9,000.00	4,000.00

RW4038
INVITATION
Style Two

Modeller:	Donald Brindley
Height:	6", 15.0 cm
Colour:	1. Lemon dress; pink roses on skirt; lemon fan
	2. White dress; patterned blue underskirt and fan
Issued:	1979-1984
Series:	Age of Romance, Series Two

		Price		
Colourways	*Backstamp*	*U.S. $*	*Can. $*	*U.K. £*
Coloured (as above)	Black	165.00	200.00	95.00

RW4039
FRAGRANCE

Modeller: Donald Brindley
Height: 6", 15.0 cm
Colour: 1. Pink dress; white jacket
2. Yellow dress; white jacket
Issued: 1979-1984
Series: Age of Romance, Series Two

Colourways	Backstamp	Price U.S. $	Can. $	U.K. £
Coloured (as above)	Black	165.00	200.00	95.00

RW4041
SUNDAY MORNING

Modeller: Donald Brindley
Height: 6", 15.0 cm
Colour: 1. Green skirt and hat; dark green jacket and umbrella
2. Pale brown skirt; dark brown jacket and hat; yellow umbrella
Issued: 1979-1984
Series: Age of Romance, Series Two

Colourways	Backstamp	Price U.S. $	Can. $	U.K. £
Coloured (as above)	Black	165.00	200.00	95.00

RW4044
CHARITY

Modeller: Donald Brindley
Height: 6", 15.0 cm
Colour: 1. Cream dress with brown flowers; golden ribbons
2. Salmon pink; rust ribbons
Issued: 1980-1984
Series: Age of Romance, Series Two

Colourways	Backstamp	Price U.S. $	Can. $	U.K. £
Coloured (as above)	Black	165.00	200.00	95.00

RW4055
EUGENE DE BEAUHARNAIS / CHASSEUR AND CHAVAL

Modeller: Bernard Winskill
Height: Unknown
Colour: 1. Red and black jacket; cream jodhpurs; black saddle pad; brown horse
2. Red and yellow jacket; white jodhpurs; cream and gold saddle pad; light brown horse
Issued: 1980 in a limited edition of 250
Series: **Eugene de Beauharnais:** Military Commanders

Colourways	Backstamp	U.S. $	Price Can. $	U.K. £
Coloured (as above)	Black	4,375.00	5,600.00	2,000.00

RW4058
SUMMERTIME

Modeller: Donald Brindley
Height: 6", 15.0 cm
Colour: 1. White dress with blue flowers and ribbon; blue hat and ribbon
2. White dress with lemon shading; yellow hat with cream ribbon
Issued: 1980-1985
Series: Age of Romance, Series Two

Colourways	Backstamp	U.S. $	Price Can. $	U.K. £
Coloured (as above)	Black	165.00	200.00	95.00

RW4059
SAVED

Modeller: Kenneth Potts
Height: 8", 20.3 cm
Colour: Black uniform; gold helmet; light grey dress
Issued: 1979

Colourways	Backstamp	U.S. $	Price Can. $	U.K. £
Black/gold/grey	Black	950.00	1,225.00	550.00

Note: Commissioned by Phoenix World.

RW4062
SINCERITY

Modeller:	Donald Brindley
Height:	6", 15.0 cm
Colour:	1. Lilac
	2. Spring green
Issued:	1980-1985
Series:	Age of Romance, Series Two

			Price	
Colourways	Backstamp	U.S. $	Can. $	U.K. £
Coloured (as above)	Black	165.00	200.00	95.00

RW4064
COMING OF AGE

Modeller:	Donald Brindley
Height:	6", 15.0 cm
Colour:	1. White, green trim
	2. White, maroon trim
	3. Red
Issued:	1980-1984
Series:	Age of Romance, Series Two

			Price	
Colourways	Backstamp	U.S. $	Can. $	U.K. £
Coloured (as above)	Black	165.00	200.00	95.00

RW4065
FLIRTATION
Style One

Modeller:	Donald Brindley
Height:	6", 15.0 cm
Colour:	1. Light blue dress
	2. Pink dress
Issued:	1980-1984
Series:	Age of Romance, Series Two

			Price	
Colourways	Backstamp	U.S. $	Can. $	U.K. £
Coloured (as above)	Black	165.00	200.00	95.00

RW4066
EQUESTRIENNE

Modeller:	Donald Brindley
Height:	6", 15.0 cm
Colour:	1. Red riding jacket; grey skirt; black hat
	2. Blue riding jacket and hat; peach skirt
Issued:	1980-1985
Series:	Age of Romance, Series Two

			Price	
Colourways	Backstamp	U.S. $	Can. $	U.K. £
Coloured (as above)	Black	165.00	200.00	95.00

RW4067
WILLIAM THE CONQUEROR

Modeller:	Bernard Winskill
Height:	Unknown
Colour:	1. Bone china: Dark brown, tan and blue;
	2. Bronze metal
Issued:	1. Bone china: 1980 in a limited edition of 250
	2. Bronze metal: 1980 in a limited edition of 15
Series:	Military Commanders

			Price	
Description	Backstamp	U.S. $	Can. $	U.K. £
1. Bone china	Black	4,375.00	5,600.00	2,500.00
2. Bronze metal	R-W	6,000.00	9,000.00	4,000.00

RW4072
GERMAINE

Modeller:	Kenneth Potts
Height:	8 ¾", 22.2 cm
Colour:	Pink, blue and yellow skirt; yellow and blue blouse and hat; pink and blue umbrella
Issued:	1979 in a limited edition of 500
Series:	The World of the Impressionists

			Price	
Colourways	Backstamp	U.S. $	Can. $	U.K. £
Pink/blue/yellow	Blue	600.00	775.00	350.00

RW4073
JEANNE

Modeller: Kenneth Potts
Height: 8 ¼", 21.0 cm
Colour: White dress shaded in lilac, yellow and blue; dark blue
bows and underskirt
Issued: 1979 in a limited edition of 500
Series: The World of the Impressionists

Colourways	Backstamp	U.S. $	Price Can. $	U.K. £
White/lilac/yellow	Blue	600.00	775.00	350.00

RW4076
SIMON BOLIVAR

Modeller: Bernard Winskill
Height: 15 ½", 39.4 cm
Colour: Rider: Navy jacket with gold epaulettes; white jodhpurs
Horse: Grey
Issued: 1979 in a limited edition of 250
Series: Military Commanders

Colourways	Backstamp	U.S. $	Price Can. $	U.K. £
Navy/white/grey	Black	3,500.00	4,500.00	2,000.00

RW4079
BELLE OF THE BALL (Style One) / EMILY (Style Two)

Modeller: Donald Brindley
Height: 7 ¾", 19.7 cm
Colour: 1. **Belle of the Ball:** White dress with pink flowers, green trim
2. **Emily:** Lilac and white dress
Issued: 1. **Belle of the Ball:** 1979-1991
2. **Emily:** 1988-1991
Series: Age of Romance, Series Two

Description	Backstamp	U.S. $	Price Can. $	U.K. £
1. Belle of the Ball (Style One)	Black	165.00	200.00	95.00
2. Emily (Style Two)	Black	165.00	200.00	95.00

RW4080
EASTER PARADE

Modeller: Donald Brindley
Height: Unknown
Colour: Unknown
Issued: 1979

Colourways	Backstamp	U.S. $	Price Can. $	U.K. £
Unknown	Black		Rare	

RW4083
REBECCA (Style Two) / WINTER'S MORN

Modeller: Donald Brindley
Height: 7 ¾", 19.7 cm
Colour: 1. **Rebecca:** Blue jacket and hat; yellow and blue skirt; fur trim
2. **Winter's Morn:** Blue jacket and hat; pale yellow and white skirt; fur trim
Issued: 1. **Rebecca:** 1988-1991
2. **Winter's Morn:** 1979-1991
Series: Age of Romance, Series Two

Description	Backstamp	U.S. $	Price Can. $	U.K. £
1. Rebecca (Style Two)	Black	165.00	200.00	95.00
2. Winter's Morn	Black	165.00	200.00	95.00

RW4084
CAMILLE

Modeller: Kenneth Potts
Height: 8 ½", 21.6 cm
Colour: Pink dress with blue shading; navy shawl with white trim; straw hat with navy ribbon; pale blue umbrella
Issued: 1979 in a limited edition of 500
Series: The World of the Impressionists

Colourways	Backstamp	U.S. $	Price Can. $	U.K. £
Pink/blue	Blue	600.00	775.00	350.00

187

RW4085
ALPHONSINE

Modeller: Kenneth Potts
Height: 7", 17.8 cm
Colour: Burgundy skirt; white top with yellow and red design;
           yellow straw hat with blue bow
Issued: 1979 in a limited edition of 500
Series: The World of the Impressionists

Colourways	Backstamp	U.S. $	Price Can. $	U.K. £
Burgundy/white	Blue	600.00	775.00	350.00

RW4086
MODESTY

Modeller: Donald Brindley
Height: 5", 12.7 cm
Colour: Pink dress with white frills; bouquet of red roses
Issued: 1981-1984
Series: Age of Romance Miniatures

Colourways	Backstamp	U.S. $	Price Can. $	U.K. £
Pink/white	Black	130.00	165.00	75.00

RW4087
AUTUMN SONG

Modeller: Donald Brindley
Height: 6", 15.0 cm
Colour: 1. Pale blue skirt, darker blue jacket and hat
           2. Pale brown skirt, darker brown jacket and hat
Issued: 1980-1984
Series: Age of Romance, Series Two

Colourways	Backstamp	U.S. $	Price Can. $	U.K. £
Coloured (as above)	Black	165.00	200.00	95.00

RW4088
MARGUERITE AND DON PEDRO

Modeller:	Kenneth Potts
Height:	8 ½", 21.6 cm
Colour:	Marguerite: Shaded pink, blue and yellow dress; dark blue collar, bows and underskirt
	Don Pedro: Yellow trousers; blue jacket, hat and tie; white shirt
Issued:	1980 in a limited edition of 500
Series:	The World of the Impressionists

		Price		
Colourways	Backstamp	U.S. $	Can. $	U.K. £
Pink/blue/yellow	Blue	775.00	1,000.00	450.00

RW4089
NORBERT

Modeller:	Kenneth Potts
Height:	8 ¼", 21.0 cm
Colour:	Dark blue suit; white shirt; dark yellow tie; light yellow hat
Issued:	1980 in a limited edition of 500
Series:	The World of the Impressionists

		Price		
Colourways	Backstamp	U.S. $	Can. $	U.K. £
Blue/white/yellow	Blue	600.00	775.00	350.00

RW4090
DEBUTANTE / DIANA (Style One)

Modeller:	Donald Brindley
Height:	7 ¾", 19.7 cm
Colour:	1. **Debutante:** White skirt; green and white top
	2. **Diana:** Pink dress with white trim
Issued:	1. **Debutante:** 1980-1991
	2. **Diana:** 1988-1991
Series:	Age of Romance, Series Two

		Price		
Description	Backstamp	U.S. $	Can. $	U.K. £
1. Debutante	Black	165.00	200.00	95.00
2. Diana (Style One)	Black	165.00	200.00	95.00

RW4091
COQUETTE
Style Two

Modeller: Donald Brindley
Height: 5", 12.7 cm
Colour: Pale blue dress, white underskirt and bow
Issued: 1981-1984
Series: Age of Romance Miniatures

Colourways	Backstamp	Price U.S. $	Can. $	U.K. £
Blue/white	Black	130.00	165.00	75.00

RW4097
PARTY DRESS

Modeller: Donald Brindley
Height: 4", 10.1 cm
Colour: Yellow dress
Issued: 1981-1984
Series: Age of Romance Miniatures

Colourways	Backstamp	Price U.S. $	Can. $	U.K. £
Yellow	Black	130.00	165.00	75.00

RW4098
MARY MARY

Modeller: Donald Brindley
Height: 5", 12.7 cm
Colour: Rose-pink pinafore; white dress and cap; yellow watering can
Issued: 1981-1984
Series: Age of Romance Miniatures

Colourways	Backstamp	Price U.S. $	Can. $	U.K. £
Rose-pink/white	Black	130.00	165.00	75.00

RW4100
LA MIDINETTE

Modeller: Kenneth Potts
Height: 8", 20.3 cm
Colour: Mottled green and blue dress; yellow basket, blue contents
Issued: 1980 in a limited edition of 500
Series: The World of the Impressionists

Colourways	Backstamp	U.S. $	Price Can. $	U.K. £
Mottled green/blue	Blue	600.00	775.00	350.00

RW4109
CURTSEY (Style Two) / LITTLE MAID

Modeller: Donald Brindley
Height: 4", 10.1 cm
Colour: Orange dress; white apron, cuffs and petticoat;
            brown hair
Issued: 1980

Colourways	Backstamp	U.S. $	Price Can. $	U.K. £
Brown-orange	Black	Only a few trial pieces made		

RW4112
RENDEZVOUS

Modeller: Donald Brindley
Height: 6", 15.0 cm
Colour: Brown-orange dress
Issued: 1981-1984
Series: Age of Romance Miniatures

Colourways	Backstamp	U.S. $	Price Can. $	U.K. £
Brown-orange	Black	165.00	200.00	95.00

RW4113
AFFECTION

Modeller: Donald Brindley
Height: 5", 12.7 cm
Colour: Pale green dress with dark green trim
Issued: 1981-1984
Series: Age of Romance Miniatures

Colourways	Backstamp	U.S. $	Price Can. $	U.K. £
Yellow	Black	130.00	165.00	75.00

RW4114
EVENING ENGAGEMENT

Modeller: Donald Brindley
Height: 6", 15.0 cm
Colour: White dress with pink trim; brown cape and hat trimmed
            with yellow; blue lining
Issued: 1981-1984
Series: Age of Romance Miniatures

Colourways	Backstamp	U.S. $	Price Can. $	U.K. £
White/brown	Black	165.00	200.00	95.00

RW4115
MARCH WINDS

Modeller: Donald Brindley
Height: 4", 10.1 cm
Colour: Pale green and yellow
Issued: 1981-1984
Series: Age of Romance Miniatures

Colourways	Backstamp	U.S. $	Price Can. $	U.K. £
Pale green/yellow	Black	130.00	165.00	75.00

RW4119
THE BRIDE

Modeller:	Donald Brindley
Height:	6", 15.0 cm
Colour:	White dress and veil; pink rose; green leaves; pale blue ribbon
Issued:	1981-1984
Series:	Age of Romance, Series Two

		Price		
Colourways	Backstamp	U.S. $	Can. $	U.K. £
White	Black	165.00	200.00	95.00

RW4124
BALLET MASTER

Modeller:	Kenneth Potts
Height:	9", 22.9 cm
Colour:	Green-gray jacket; brown-green trousers; white shirt; red neck tie
Issued:	1982 in a limited edition of 500
Series:	The World of the Impressionists

		Price		
Colourways	Backstamp	U.S. $	Can. $	U.K. £
Green-grey/brown-green/red	Blue	600.00	775.00	350.00

RW4126
LA LEÇON

Modeller:	Kenneth Potts
Height:	7", 17.8 cm
Colour:	White dress with yellow highlights; black sash and bow; pink ballet slippers
Issued:	1980 in a limited edition of 500
Series:	The World of the Impressionists

		Price		
Colourways	Backstamp	U.S. $	Can. $	U.K. £
White/yellow	Blue	600.00	775.00	350.00

RW4127
L'ÉTUDE

Modeller: Kenneth Potts
Height: 6", 15.0 cm
Colour: Mottled blue and pink dress; pink ballet slippers
Issued: 1982 in a limited edition of 500
Series: The World of the Impressionists

Colourways	Backstamp	U.S. $	Price Can. $	U.K. £
Mottled blue/pink	Blue	600.00	775.00	350.00

RW4129
POPE JOHN PAUL II (Bust on plinth)

Designer: Donald Brindley
Height: 11 ½", 29.2 cm
Colour: Cream; gilding; pink flowers in mitre (matte)
Issued: c.1980 in a limited edition of 250

Colourways	Backstamp	U.S. $	Price Can. $	U.K. £
Cream/gilding	Black	875.00	1,250.00	500.00

RW4139
EN REPOSE (1926)

Modeller: Kenneth Potts
Height: Unknown
Colour: White jacket with blue stripes; rust and blue trim; light blue shirt and trousers; burgundy couch
Issued: 1981 in a limited edition of 500
Series: À La Mode

Colourways	Backstamp	U.S. $	Price Can. $	U.K. £
White/blue/burgundy	Black	600.00	775.00	350.00

RW4140
SOIREE (1926)

Modeller:	Kenneth Potts
Height:	Unknown
Colour:	Green coat, striped scarf; yellow hair
Issued:	1981 in a limited edition of 500
Series:	À la Mode

		Price		
Colourways	Backstamp	U.S. $	Can. $	U.K. £
Green	Black	600.00	775.00	350.00

RW4148
SKATER

Modeller:	Donald Brindley
Height:	Unknown
Colour:	Unknown
Issued:	1982
Series:	Age of Romance

		Price		
Colourways	Backstamp	U.S. $	Can. $	U.K. £
Unknown	Possibly not put into production			

RW4149
MASQUERADE
Style Two

Modeller:	Donald Brindley
Height:	6", 15.0 cm
Colour:	Light blue overcoat; pale pink skirt; light blue hat with pink feather; black mask
Issued:	1982
Series:	Age of Romance, Series Two

		Price		
Colourways	Backstamp	U.S. $	Can. $	U.K. £
Light blue/pale pink	Black	165.00	200.00	95.00

RW4150
CHIC (1933)

Modeller:	Kenneth Potts
Height:	Unknown
Colour:	Peach dress, white collar, gold buttons and shoes; yellow dog; peach flowered hat
Issued:	1981 in a limited edition of 500
Series:	À La Mode

Colourways	Backstamp	U.S. $	Price Can. $	U.K. £
Peach	Black	600.00	775.00	350.00

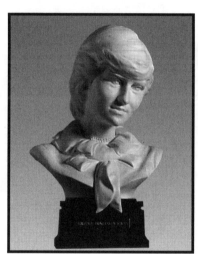

RW4152
DIANA, PRINCESS OF WALES (Bust on plinth)

Modeller:	Donald Brindley
Height:	Unknown
Colour:	Cream (Wallbody)
Issued:	1982

Colourways	Backstamp	U.S. $	Price Can. $	U.K. £
Cream	Black	700.00	900.00	400.00

RW4153
PROMENADE (1922)

Modeller:	Kenneth Potts
Height:	Unknown
Colour:	Green dress and hat with red edging; white greyhound
Issued:	1982 in a limited edition of 500
Series:	À la Mode

Colourways	Backstamp	U.S. $	Price Can. $	U.K. £
Green/red/white	Black	725.00	925.00	420.00

RW4154
KATIE
Style One

Modeller:	Freda Doughty
Height:	3", 7.6 cm
Colour:	Blue dress; yellow hair
Issued:	1982-1985
Series:	The Worcester Children

Colourways	Backstamp	U.S. $	Price Can. $	U.K. £
Blue	Black	215.00	275.00	125.00

RW4155
LITTLE GRANDMOTHER'S DRESS

Modeller:	Freda Doughty
Height:	3", 7.6 cm
Colour:	1. Green dress; yellow hair
	2. Yellow dress; brown hair
Issued:	1982-1985
Series:	The Worcester Children

Colourways	Backstamp	U.S. $	Price Can. $	U.K. £
Coloured (as above)	Black	215.00	275.00	125.00

Note: See also RW4155 Grandmother's Dress.

RW4156
CHRISTOPHER

Modeller:	Freda Doughty
Height:	3", 7.6 cm
Colour:	Yellow shirt; brown shorts; green shoes; yellow hat
Issued:	1982-by 1985
Series:	The Worcester Children

Colourways	Backstamp	U.S. $	Price Can. $	U.K. £
Yellow/brown	Black	325.00	425.00	190.00

Note: See also RW3457 September / Snowy.

RW4157
WOODLAND WALK

Modeller: Freda Doughty
Height: 3", 7.6 cm
Colour: Grey-blue
Issued: 1982-by 1985
Series: The Worcester Children

| | | | Price | |
Colourways	Backstamp	U.S. $	Can. $	U.K. £
Grey-blue	Black	260.00	335.00	150.00

Note: See also RW3417 October.

RW4158
THREE'S COMPANY

Modeller: Freda Doughty
Height: 3", 7.6 cm
Colour: Brown shorts and hair
Issued: 1982-by 1985
Series: The Worcester Children

| | | | Price | |
Colourways	Backstamp	U.S. $	Can. $	U.K. £
Brown	Black	275.00	350.00	160.00

Note: See also RW3519 Monday's Child (Boy) / All Mine.

RW4159
HOMETIME

Modeller: Freda Doughty
Height: 3", 7.6 cm
Colour: Blue coat and shoes
Issued: 1982-by 1985
Series: The Worcester Children

| | | | Price | |
Colourways	Backstamp	U.S. $	Can. $	U.K. £
Blue	Black	260.00	335.00	150.00

Note: See also RW3522 Thursday's Child (Girl).

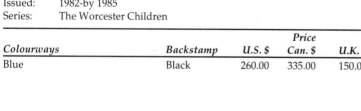

RW4160
TEATIME
Style One

Modeller:	Freda Doughty
Height:	3", 7.6 cm
Colour:	Blue dungarees; yellow hair; brown bird
Issued:	1982-by 1985
Series:	The Worcester Children

		Price		
Colourways	Backstamp	U.S. $	Can. $	U.K. £
Blue	Black	325.00	400.00	180.00

Note: See also RW3523 Friday's Child (Girl).

RW4161
LET'S RUN

Modeller:	Freda Doughty
Height:	3", 7.6 cm
Colour:	Red dress and shoes; white hat with red band; metal windmill
Issued:	1982-by 1985
Series:	The Worcester Children

		Price		
Colourways	Backstamp	U.S. $	Can. $	U.K. £
Red	Black	425.00	550.00	250.00

Note: See also RW3518 Sunday's Child (Girl).

RW4163
LITTLE PARAKEET BOY

Modeller:	Freda Doughty
Height:	3", 7.6 cm
Colour:	Green suit; yellow hair
Issued:	1982-1985
Series:	The Worcester Children

		Price		
Colourways	Backstamp	U.S. $	Can. $	U.K. £
Green	Black	210.00	275.00	125.00

Note: See also RW3087 Boy With Parakeet.

RW4164
SUNSHINE DAYS

Modeller: Freda Doughty
Height: 3", 7.6 cm
Colour: Blue outfit; blonde hair; red ball;
yellow sandy base
Issued: 1982-1985
Series: The Worcester Children

Colourways	Backstamp	U.S. $	Price Can. $	U.K. £
Blue	Black	210.00	275.00	125.00

Note: See also RW3256 Sunday's Child (Boy).

RW4165
FISHERMAN

Modeller: Freda Doughty
Height: 3", 7.6 cm
Colour: Yellow raincoat; green hat; black wellingtons
Issued: 1982-by 1985
Series: The Worcester Children

Colourways	Backstamp	U.S. $	Price Can. $	U.K. £
Yellow	Black	275.00	350.00	160.00

Note: See also RW3453 February.

RW4166
SNOWBALL

Modeller: Freda Doughty
Height: 3", 7.6 cm
Colour: Red coat with white trim
Issued: 1982-by 1985
Series: The Worcester Children

Colourways	Backstamp	U.S. $	Price Can. $	U.K. £
Red	Black	375.00	475.00	220.00

Note: See also RW3458 December.

RW4167
PEACE

Modeller: Freda Doughty
Height: 3", 7.6 cm
Colour: Pink hat and coat; brown shoes
Issued: 1982-by 1985
Series: The Worcester Children

Colourways	Backstamp	U.S. $	Price Can. $	U.K. £
Pink	Black	350.00	450.00	200.00

Note: See also RW3418 November.

RW4168A
SPRINGTIME

Modeller: Freda Doughty
Height: 3", 7.6 cm
Colour: White bodice, green skirt; yellow hair
Issued: 1982-by 1985
Series: The Worcester Children

Colourways	Backstamp	U.S. $	Price Can. $	U.K. £
White/yellow	Black	250.00	335.00	150.00

Note: See also RW3416 April.

RW4168B
SPRING
Style Four

Modeller: Kenneth Potts
Height: 9", 22.9 cm
Colour: Pink and silver dress; gilt mounts
Issued: 1982
Series: The Four Seasons, Series Three

Colourways	Backstamp	U.S. $	Price Can. $	U.K. £
Pink/silver	Black	550.00	750.00	300.00

RW4188
BALLERINA

Modeller: Freda Doughty
Height: 3", 7.6 cm
Colour: Pink tutu; yellow hair
Issued: 1983-1985
Series: The Worcester Children

Colourways	Backstamp	U.S. $	Price Can. $	U.K. £
Pink	Black	250.00	335.00	150.00

Note: See also RW3258 Tuesday's Child (Girl) / Red Shoes.

RW4189
THE SLIDE

Modeller: Freda Doughty
Height: 3", 7.6 cm
Colour: Light brown coat; dark brown shoes; blue scarf; yellow hair
Issued: 1982-1988
Series: The Worcester Children

Colourways	Backstamp	U.S. $	Price Can. $	U.K. £
Light brown	Black	190.00	250.00	110.00

Note: See also RW3452 January.

RW4190
AT THE SEASIDE

Modeller: Freda Doughty
Height: 3", 7.6 cm
Colour: Yellow bathing suit; brown hair
Issued: 1982-by 1985
Series: The Worcester Children

Colourways	Backstamp	U.S. $	Price Can. $	U.K. £
Yellow	Black	300.00	400.00	180.00

Note: See also RW3440 July.

RW4191
LITTLE MERMAID

Modeller: Freda Doughty
Height: 3", 7.6 cm
Colour: Fleshtones; blue base
Issued: 1982-by 1985
Series: The Worcester Children

Colourways	Backstamp	U.S. $	Price Can. $	U.K. £
Fleshtones	Black	275.00	350.00	160.00

Note: See also RW3441 August.

RW4192
GARDENER

Modeller: Freda Doughty
Height: 3", 7.6 cm
Colour: Green dungarees; yellow hair
Issued: 1982-by 1985
Series: The Worcester Children

Colourways	Backstamp	U.S. $	Price Can. $	U.K. £
Green	Black	275.00	350.00	160.00

Note: See also RW3524 Saturday's Child (Boy).

RW4193
OLD FRIENDS

Modeller: Freda Doughty
Height: 3", 7.6 cm
Colour: Blue top; dark blue shorts; yellow hair
Issued: 1982-1985
Series: The Worcester Children

Colourways	Backstamp	U.S. $	Price Can. $	U.K. £
Blue	Black	225.00	290.00	130.00

Note: See also RW3261 Friday's Child (Boy)/ My Pet.

RW4194
BIRTHDAY GIRL

Modeller:	Freda Doughty
Height:	3", 7.6 cm
Colour:	White dress with blue bow and trim; yellow hair
Issued:	1982-1985
Series:	The Worcester Children

Colourways	Backstamp	U.S. $	Price Can. $	U.K. £
White/blue	Black	210.00	275.00	125.00

Note: See also RW3257 Monday's Child (Girl) / Susie.

RW4195
POOR TEDDY

Modeller:	Freda Doughty
Height:	3", 7.6 cm
Colour:	Yellow smock; brown hair
Issued:	1982-by 1985
Series:	The Worcester Children

Colourways	Backstamp	U.S. $	Price Can. $	U.K. £
Yellow	Black	275.00	350.00	160.00

Note: See also RW3521 Wednesday's Child (Boy).

RW4199
SKATING

Modeller:	Freda Doughty
Height:	3", 7.6 cm
Colour:	Red coat
Issued:	1982-by 1985
Series:	The Worcester Children

Colourways	Backstamp	U.S. $	Price Can. $	U.K. £
Red	Black	275.00	350.00	160.00

Note: See also RW3534 Tuesday's Child (Boy).

*Photograph not
available
at press time*

RW4200
LOST SLIPPER

Modeller: Freda Doughty
Height: 3", 7.6 cm
Colour: Blue dress; brown hair
Issued: 1982-1985
Series: The Worcester Children

Colourways	Backstamp	Price U.S. $	Can. $	U.K. £
Blue	Black	210.00	275.00	125.00

Note: See also RW3259 Wednesday's Child (Girl).

RW4201
COUNTRY BOY

Modeller: Freda Doughty
Height: 3", 7.6 cm
Colour: Blue coat; yellow hair
Issued: 1982-1985
Series: The Worcester Children

Colourways	Backstamp	Price U.S. $	Can. $	U.K. £
Blue	Black	210.00	275.00	125.00

*Photograph not
available
at press time*

Note: See also RW3260 Thursday's Child (Boy)/ Smiling Through.

*Photograph not
available
at press time*

RW4202
WINDY

Modeller: Freda Doughty
Height: 3", 7.6 cm
Colour: White dress trimmed in green; green belt; brown hat; brown hair
Issued: 1982-by 1985
Series: The Worcester Children

Colourways	Backstamp	Price U.S. $	Can. $	U.K. £
White/green/brown	Black	525.00	675.00	300.00

Note: See also RW3454 March.

RW4203
DAISY CHAIN

Modeller:	Freda Doughty
Height:	3", 7.6 cm
Colour:	Pink dress; brown hair; yellow flowers and base
Issued:	1982-by 1985
Series:	The Worcester Children

Colourways	Backstamp	U.S. $	Price Can. $	U.K. £
Pink	Black	475.00	600.00	275.00

Photograph not available at press time

Note: See also RW3455 May.

RW4204
MUSICAL MOMENTS

Modeller:	Freda Doughty
Height:	3", 7.6 cm
Colour:	Yellow shirt; blue shorts; yellow hair
Issued:	1982-by 1985
Series:	The Worcester Children

Colourways	Backstamp	U.S. $	Price Can. $	U.K. £
Yellow/blue	Black	275.00	350.00	160.00

Note: See also RW3456 June (Style Two).

RW4205
MOTHER'S HELPER / POLLY KETTLE

Modeller:	Freda Doughty
Height:	3", 7.6 cm
Colour:	Pink apron; gold kettle
Issued:	1982-1985
Series:	The Worcester Children

Colourways	Backstamp	U.S. $	Price Can. $	U.K. £
Pink/gold	Black	425.00	550.00	250.00

Photograph not available at press time

Note: See also RW3303 Polly Put the Kettle On.

Photograph not available at press time

RW4206
SOLITAIRE

Modeller:	Freda Doughty
Height:	3", 7.6 cm
Colour:	Yellow dress with an orange border; dark brown hair; yellow base
Issued:	1983-1985
Series:	The Worcester Children

		Price		
Colourways	Backstamp	U.S. $	Can. $	U.K. £
Yellow/orange	Black	525.00	67500	300.00

Note: See also RW3226 Only Me.

RW4207
WINTER
Style Three

Modeller:	Kenneth Potts
Height:	9", 22.9 cm
Colour:	Unknown; gilt mounts
Issued:	1983
Series:	The Four Seasons, Series Three

		Price		
Colourways	Backstamp	U.S. $	Can. $	U.K. £
Unknown	Black		Very few made	

Photograph not available at press time

RW4215
NINA LA LOGE

Modeller:	Kenneth Potts
Height:	Unknown
Colour:	Black and white striped dress
Issued:	1983 in a limited edition of 500
Series:	The World of the Impressionists

		Price		
Colourways	Backstamp	U.S. $	Can. $	U.K. £
Black/white	Black		Extremely rare	

Note: Possibly only prototype models available.

RW4216
CHA-U-KAU (Female clown)

Modeller: Kenneth Potts
Height: 8 ¾", 22.2 cm
Colour: Yellow tunic with white and red frills; black hair; blue shoes
Issued: 1983
Series: The World of the Impressionists

Colourways	Backstamp	U.S. $	Price Can. $	U.K. £
Yellow/black	Black	Only a handful of trial models produced		

RW4222
NYMPH WITH DAISY

Modeller: David Fryer
Height: 8 ½", 21.6 cm
Colour: Light blue dress; yellow hair and flowers; bronze leaves, stem and base
Issued: 1984-1988
Series: Sylvan Nymphs

Colourways	Backstamp	U.S. $	Price Can. $	U.K. £
Light blue/yellow	R-W	165.00	210.00	95.00

RW4223
NYMPH WITH WINTER JASMINE

Modeller: David Fryer
Height: 8 ½", 21.6 cm
Colour: Lemon dress; yellow flowers; bronze stem and base
Issued: 1984-1988
Series: Sylvan Nymphs

Colourways	Backstamp	U.S. $	Price Can. $	U.K. £
Lemon/yellow	R-W	165.00	210.00	95.00

RW4226
NYMPH WITH CONVOULVULUS

Modeller: David Fryer
Height: 8 ½", 21.6 cm
Colour: Pink flowers, dress and butterfly; ginger hair;
bronze stem, leaves and base
Issued: 1984-1988
Series: Sylvan Nymphs

Colourways	Backstamp	U.S. $	Price Can. $	U.K. £
Pink	R-W	165.00	210.00	95.00

RW4227
NYMPH WITH SNOWDROP

Modeller: David Fryer
Height: 8 ½", 21.6 cm
Colour: White flowers; white dress with green details; ginger hair;
bronze leaves, stem and base
Issued: 1984-1988
Series: Sylvan Nymphs

Colourways	Backstamp	U.S. $	Price Can. $	U.K. £
White/green	R-W	165.00	210.00	95.00

RW4228
NYMPH WITH HAIRBELL

Modeller: David Fryer
Height: 8 ½", 21.6 cm
Colour: Pink dress; pale lilac flowers; bronze stems, leaves and base
Issued: 1984-1988
Series: Sylvan Nymphs

Colourways	Backstamp	U.S. $	Price Can. $	U.K. £
Pink/lilac	R-W	165.00	210.00	95.00

RW4229
NYMPH WITH VIOLA

Modeller:	David Fryer
Height:	8 ½", 21.6 cm
Colour:	Lemon dress and flowers; bronze stems and base
Issued:	1984-1988
Series:	Sylvan Nymphs

		Price		
Colourways	Backstamp	U.S. $	Can. $	U.K. £
Lemon	R-W	165.00	210.00	95.00

RW4230
MARY CASSAT

Modeller:	Kenneth Potts
Height:	Unknown
Colour:	Brown dress, bonnet and bag
Issued:	1983
Series:	The World of the Impressionists

		Price		
Colourways	Backstamp	U.S. $	Can. $	U.K. £
Brown		Small number of trial models produced		

RW4231
LE CERCEAU

Modeller:	Kenneth Potts
Height:	6", 15.0 cm
Colour:	Dark blue and yellow
Issued:	1980
Series:	The World of the Impressionists

		Price		
Colourways	Backstamp	U.S. $	Can. $	U.K. £
Dark blue/yellow		Small number of trial models produced		

Note: This model comes with a hoop which is missing from this illustration.

RW4234
BLUE COAT SCHOOL (Boy)

Modeller: Kenneth Potts
Height: 6", 15.0 cm
Colour: Blue
Issued: 1983 in a limited edition of 200

Colourways	Backstamp	U.S. $	Price Can. $	U.K. £
Blue	Blue	260.00	335.00	150.00

RW4235
BLUE COAT SCHOOL (Girl)

Modeller: Kenneth Potts
Height: 6", 15.0 cm
Colour: Blue
Issued: 1983 in a limited edition of 200

Colourways	Backstamp	U.S. $	Price Can. $	U.K. £
Blue	Blue	260.00	335.00	150.00

RW4261
SUMMER
Style Three

Modeller: Kenneth Potts
Height: 9", 22.9 cm
Colour: Unknown; gilt mounts
Issued: 1984
Series: The Four Seasons, Series Three

Colourways	Backstamp	U.S. $	Price Can. $	U.K. £
Unknown	Black		Very few made	

RW4262
AUTUMN
Style Three

Modeller:	Kenneth Potts
Height:	9", 22.9 cm
Colour:	Unknown; gilt mounts
Issued:	1984
Series:	The Four Seasons, Series Three

Colourways	Backstamp	U.S. $	Price Can. $	U.K. £
Unknown	Black		Very few made	

RW4288
RICHMOND GIRL

Modeller:	Timothy Potts
Height:	8 ¼", 21.3 cm
Colour:	Pale blue dress and hat
Issued:	1988
Series:	English Girls

Colourways	Backstamp	U.S. $	Price Can. $	U.K. £
Pale blue	Black	210.00	275.00	120.00

RW4322
ROSIE PICKING APPLES

Modeller:	Sheila Mitchell
Height:	8 ½", 21.6 cm
Colour:	Peach skirt; blue blouse with yellow flowers, white collar and cuffs; white apron; blue cap; yellow basket of apples
Issued:	1986 in a limited edition of 9,500
Series:	Old Country Ways

Colourways	Backstamp	U.S. $	Price Can. $	U.K. £
Peach/blue/white	Black	165.00	210.00	95.00

Note: Commissioned by Compton & Woodhouse.

RW4323
LOVE

Modeller:	Sheila Mitchell
Height:	7", 17.8 cm
Colour:	Girl: Pale blue dress; brown bair
	Baby: Peach dress; white pinafore; blonde hair
Issued:	1989 in a limited edition of 9,500
Series:	NSPCC

			Price	
Colourways	Backstamp	U.S. $	Can. $	U.K. £
Pale blue/orange	Black	165.00	210.00	95.00

Note: Commissioned by Compton & Woodhouse.

RW4347
EMMA WOODHOUSE

Modeller:	Kenneth Potts
Height:	9", 22.9 cm
Colour:	Blue dress; yellow hat with blue ribbon
Issued:	1988-1991
Series:	Jane Austen Collection

			Price	
Colourways	Backstamp	U.S. $	Can. $	U.K. £
Blue	Blue	250.00	325.00	140.00

RW4348
ELIZABETH BENNET

Modeller:	Kenneth Potts
Height:	9", 22.9 cm
Colour:	Yellow and white dress; yellow hat
Issued:	1988-1991
Series:	Jane Austen Collection

			Price	
Colourways	Backstamp	U.S. $	Can. $	U.K. £
Yellow/white	Blue	250.00	325.00	140.00

RW4349
ANNE ELLIOT

Modeller: Kenneth Potts
Height: 9", 22.0 cm
Colour: Light blue dress; pink shawl and bow
Issued: 1988-1991
Series: Jane Austen Collection

Colourways	Backstamp	U.S. $	Price Can. $	U.K. £
Light blue/pink	Blue	250.00	325.00	140.00

---

*Photograph not
available
at press time*

RW4353
APHRODITE (La Tendresse)

Modeller: Unknown
Height: 32 ½", 82.55 cm
Colour: Gold
Issued: 1987 in a limited edition of 1,000

Colourways	Backstamp	U.S. $	Price Can. $	U.K. £
Gold	Black		Rare	

Note: Commissioned by Goldshieder.

RW4355
SAFE AT LAST

Modeller: Sheila Mitchell
Height: 5", 12.7 cm
Colour: White dress with blue design; pale blue pinafore; ginger cat
Issued: 1988 in a limited edition of 12,500

Colourways	Backstamp	U.S. $	Price Can. $	U.K. £
White/blue	Black	—	—	135.00

Note: Commissioned by Compton & Woodhouse.

214

RW4356
QUEEN ELIZABETH I
Style Three

Modeller:	Kenneth Potts
Height:	15 ½", 39.4 cm
Colour:	Creamy-white gown and cape; gold decoration; burgundy cap; grey horse; blue and gold saddle cloth
Issued:	1988 in a limited edition of 100

			Price	
Colourways	Backstamp	U.S. $	Can. $	U.K. £
Creamy-white/gold/grey/blue	Black	—	—	7,085.00

RW4357
LAUNDRY MAID

Designer:	Maureen Halson
Modeller:	Kenneth Potts
Height:	9 ¼", 23.5 cm
Colour:	Grey dress; white petticoats, apron and mob cap
Issued:	1987-c.1990
Series:	Upstairs, Downstairs

			Price	
Colourways	Backstamp	U.S. $	Can. $	U.K. £
Grey/white	Black	495.00	625.00	280.00

RW4361
FANNY PRICE

Modeller:	Kenneth Potts
Height:	9", 22.9 cm
Colour:	Pale green dress with yellow trim
Issued:	1988-1991
Series:	Jane Austen Collection

			Price	
Colourways	Backstamp	U.S. $	Can. $	U.K. £
Pale green/yellow	Blue	250.00	325.00	140.00

RW4362
CATHERINE MORLAND

Modeller:	Kenneth Potts
Height:	9", 22.9 cm
Colour:	Cream dress with peach shading
Issued:	1988-1991
Series:	Jane Austen Collection

		Price		
Colourways	Backstamp	U.S. $	Can. $	U.K. £
White/peach	Blue	250.00	325.00	140.00

RW4363
LADY SUSAN

Modeller:	Kenneth Potts
Height:	9", 22.5 cm
Colour:	Yellow dress; lilac coat, hat and parasol
Issued:	1988-1991
Series:	Jane Austen Collection

		Price		
Colourways	Backstamp	U.S. $	Can. $	U.K. £
Yellow/lilac	Blue	250.00	325.00	140.00

RW4368
CHAMBER MAID

Designer:	Maureen Halson
Modeller:	Timothy Potts
Height:	8", 20.3 cm
Colour:	Pink dress; white petticoats, collar, apron, towel and cap; white jug with pink flowers
Issued:	1989-1991
Series:	Upstairs, Downstairs

		Price		
Colourways	Backstamp	U.S. $	Can. $	U.K. £
Pink/white	Black	485.00	625.00	280.00

RW4369
PARLOUR MAID

Designer: Maureen Halson
Modeller: Timothy Potts
Height: 9 ¼", 23.5 cm
Colour: Blue dress; white apron, petticoats and cap; ginger cat
Issued: 1989-1991
Series: Upstairs, Downstairs

Colourways	Backstamp	U.S. $	Price Can. $	U.K. £
Blue/white	Black	485.00	625.00	280.00

RW4371
SCULLERY MAID

Designer: Maureen Halson
Modeller: Timothy Potts
Height: 8 ¾", 22.2 cm
Colour: Grey dress and coal scuttle; white pinafore and cap; ginger cats
Issued: 1988-c.1990
Series: Upstairs, Downstairs

Colourways	Backstamp	U.S. $	Price Can. $	U.K. £
Grey/white	Black	495.00	625.00	280.00

RW4372
REGENCY (The)

Modeller: Sandro Maggioni
Height: 9", 22.9 cm
Colour: Lilac coat and hat with pink trim
Issued: 1989 in a limited edition of 9,500
Series: Walking-Out Dresses of the 19th Century
                   (Victoria and Albert Museum)

Colourways	Backstamp	U.S. $	Price Can. $	U.K. £
Lilac/pink	Black	—	—	165.00

Note: Commissioned by Compton & Woodhouse.

RW4373
A FARMER'S WIFE

Modeller: Maureen Halson
Height: 8 ½", 21.6 cm
Colour: Lilac skirt; peach blouse; white apron; white scarf with lilac design; white chicken
Issued: 1988 in a limited edition of 9,500
Series: Old Country Ways

Colourways	Backstamp	Price U.S. $	Can. $	U.K. £
Lilac/peach/white	Black	165.00	210.00	95.00

Note: Commissioned by Compton & Woodhouse.

RW4385
COOK

Designer: Maureen Halson
Modeller: Kenneth Potts
Height: 8", 20.3 cm
Colour: Blue-grey dress, white apron and mobcap; pale yellow dog
Issued: 1989-1991
Series: Upstairs, Downstairs

Colourways	Backstamp	Price U.S. $	Can. $	U.K. £
Blue-grey/white	Black	495.00	625.00	280.00

RW4408
SWEET DREAMS

Modeller: Maureen Halson
Height: 8 ¼", 21.0 cm
Colour: Cream (Wallbody)
Issued: 1989-2000
Series: Mother's Love

Colourways	Backstamp	Price U.S. $	Can. $	U.K. £
Cream	Black	—	—	99.00

Note: Commissioned by Compton & Woodhouse.

RW4409
ROMANTIC (The)
Style One

Modeller: Sandro Maggioni
Height: 9", 22.9 cm
Colour: White dress with blue flower pattern; white shoulder cape
and gloves; beige bonnet with pink roses
Issued: 1990 in a limited edition of 9,500
Series: Walking-Out Dresses of the 19th Century
(Victoria and Albert Museum)

Colourways	Backstamp	U.S. $	Price Can. $	U.K. £
White/blue	Black	250.00	325.00	140.00

Note: Commissioned by Compton & Woodhouse.

RW4411
MAYFAIR GIRL

Modeller: Timothy Potts
Height: 8 ¼", 21.0 cm
Colour: Orange dress; dark brown coat
Issued: 1988
Series: English Girls

Colourways	Backstamp	U.S. $	Price Can. $	U.K. £
Orange/dark brown	Black	210.00	275.00	120.00

RW4412
COUNTRY GIRL

Modeller: Timothy Potts
Height: 8 ¼", 21.0 cm
Colour: Blue shirt, darker blue collar; blue denim skirt;
white shoes with pink laces
Issued: 1988
Series: English Girls

Colourways	Backstamp	U.S. $	Price Can. $	U.K. £
Blue	Black	210.00	275.00	120.00

RW4413
WEST END GIRL

Modeller: Timothy Potts
Height: 8 ½", 21.6 cm
Colour: Red-brown skirt and jacket; beige shirt; brown shoes and bag; yellow-beige hat
Issued: 1988
Series: English Girls

Colourways	Backstamp	U.S. $	Price Can. $	U.K. £
Red-brown	Black	210.00	275.00	120.00

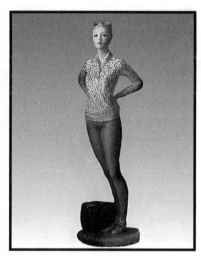

RW4414
WEEKEND GIRL

Modeller: Timothy Potts
Height: 8 ¼", 21.0 cm
Colour: Cream shirt with green, red and blue design; blue trousers
Issued: 1988
Series: English Girls

Colourways	Backstamp	U.S. $	Price Can. $	U.K. £
Cream/green/red/blue	Black	210.00	275.00	120.00

RW4415
LADY OF THE HOUSE

Modeller: Glenis Devereaux
Height: 9 ¾", 24.7 cm
Colour: Pale blue dress; white fan; pink rose and gloves
Issued: 1989-1991
Series: Upstairs, Downstairs

Colourways	Backstamp	U.S. $	Price Can. $	U.K. £
Pale blue/white	Black	495.00	625.00	280.00

RW4422
CRINOLINE (The)

Modeller:	Sandro Maggioni
Height:	9", 22.9 cm
Colour:	Pink dress and hat with white shading; lilac parasol and ribbons
Issued:	1990 in a limited edition of 9,500
Series:	Walking-Out Dresses of the 19th Century (Victoria and Albert Musuem)

			Price	
Colourways	Backstamp	U.S. $	Can. $	U.K. £
Pink/white/lilac	Black	—	—	165.00

Note: Commissioned by Compton & Woodhouse.

RW4423
CITY GIRL

Modeller:	Timothy Potts
Height:	8 ¼", 21.0 cm
Colour:	Navy suit; stocks and shares newspaper
Issued:	1988
Series:	English Girls

			Price	
Colourways	Backstamp	U.S. $	Can. $	U.K. £
Navy	Black	210.00	275.00	120.00

RW4428
GENTLEMAN OF THE HOUSE

Modeller:	Glenis Devereaux
Height:	9 ¾", 24.7 cm
Colour:	Black evening suit, bowtie, cape, and shoes; white shirt and gloves; blue waistcoat
Issued:	1989-1991
Series:	Upstairs, Downstairs

			Price	
Colourways	Backstamp	U.S. $	Can. $	U.K. £
Black/white	Black	495.00	625.00	280.00

RW4440
DAUGHTER OF THE HOUSE

Modeller: Glenis Devereaux
Height: 8", 20.3 cm
Colour: Cream dress; rose-pink belt and hair ribbon
Issued: 1990-1991
Series: Upstairs, Downstairs

Colourways	Backstamp	U.S. $	Price Can. $	U.K. £
Cream/rose-pink	Black	495.00	625.00	280.00

RW4441
SHEPHERDESS (The)
Style Two

Modeller: Maureen Halson
Height: 8 ½", 21.6 cm
Colour: Pale blue skirt and cap; peach bodice; white apron and lambs
Issued: 1990 in a limited edition of 9,500
Series: Old Country Ways

Colourways	Backstamp	U.S. $	Price Can. $	U.K. £
Pale blue/peach/white	Black	165.00	210.00	95.00

Note: Commissioned by Compton & Woodhouse.

RW4442
LULLABY

Modeller: Sheila Mitchell
Height: 7", 17.8 cm
Colour: Lilac nightdress with white frills
Issued: 1988 in a limited edition of 9,500
Series: NSPCC

Colourways	Backstamp	U.S. $	Price Can. $	U.K. £
Lilac/white	Black	—	—	135.00

Note: Commissioned by Compton & Woodhouse.

RW4446
GOVERNESS AND CHILD

Modeller:	Glenis Devereaux
Height:	8", 20.3 cm
Colour:	Governess: Blue dress; white apron and cap; brown book
	Child: Lemon dress with pink sash
Issued:	1990-1991
Series:	Upstairs, Downstairs

		Price		
Colourways	Backstamp	U.S. $	Can. $	U.K. £
Blue/white/lemon/pink	Black	495.00	625.00	280.00

RW4454
BUSTLE (The)

Modeller:	John Bromley
Height:	9", 22.9 cm
Colour:	Blue dress with white shading; rose-pink gloves, shoe and hat ribbon; yellow hat
Issued:	1990 in a limited edition of 9,500
Series:	Walking-Out Dresses of the 19th Century (Victoria and Albert Museum)

		Price		
Colourways	Backstamp	U.S. $	Can. $	U.K. £
Blue	Black	—	—	165.00

Note: Commissioned by Compton & Woodhouse.

RW4458
MILKMAID (The)

Modeller:	Maureen Halson
Height:	8 ½", 21.6 cm
Colour:	Blue skirt, bonnet and ribbons; yellow blouse with red design and white frills; white apron; brown bucket and kitten
Issued:	1989 in a limited edition of 9,500
Series:	Old Country Ways

		Price		
Colourways	Backstamp	U.S. $	Can. $	U.K. £
Blue/yellow/white	Black	165.00	210.00	95.00

Note: Commissioned by Compton & Woodhouse.

RW4459
FIRST STEPS

Modeller: Glenis Devereaux
Height: 8 ¼", 21.0 cm
Colour: Cream (Wallbody)
Issued: 1989-2000
Series: Mother's Love

Colourways	Backstamp	U.S. $	Price Can. $	U.K. £
Cream	Black	—	—	100.00

Note: Commissioned by Compton & Woodhouse.

RW4464
QUEEN MOTHER

Modeller: Kenneth Potts
Height: 9", 22.9 cm
Colour: Pink dress; blue sash
Issued: 1989 in a limited edition of 9,000

Colourways	Backstamp	U.S. $	Price Can. $	U.K. £
Pink/blue	Black	165.00	210.00	95.00

Note: Commissioned by Mulberry Hall, York.

RW4466
BATH TIME

Modeller: Glenis Devereaux
Height: 6 ¾", 17.2 cm
Colour: Pink towel; white cap; rag doll has yellow hair and blue trousers
Issued: 1994-1999
Series: Katie's Day

Colourways	Backstamp	U.S. $	Price Can. $	U.K. £
Pink/white	Black	210.00	275.00	120.00

RW4468
ONCE UPON A TIME
Modeller: Glenis Devereaux
Height: 8 ¼", 21.0 cmcm
Colour: Cream (Wallbody)
Issued: 1990-2000
Series: Mother's Love

Colourways	Backstamp	U.S. $	Price Can. $	U.K. £
Cream	Black	—	—	100.00

Note: Commissioned by Compton & Woodhouse.

RW4472
SCHOOL TIME
Modeller: Glenis Devereaux
Height: 6 ¼", 15.9 cm
Colour: Light grey pinafore and hat; white blouse; yellow sash
              and ribbons; black shoes; beige satchel
Issued: 1989-1999
Series: Katie's Day

Colourways	Backstamp	U.S. $	Price Can. $	U.K. £
Grey/white/black	Black	210.00	270.00	120.00

RW4473
BED TIME
Modeller: Glenis Devereaux
Height: 4 ½", 11.9 cm
Colour: Pale blue nightdress; rag doll has blue dress and yellow hair
Issued: 1989-1999
Series: Katie's Day

Colourways	Backstamp	U.S. $	Price Can. $	U.K. £
Pale blue	Black	210.00	275.00	120.00

RW4474
TEA TIME
Style Two

Modeller:	Glenis Devereaux
Height:	5 ¾", 14.6 cm
Colour:	Yellow dress and bow; white socks; blue shoes
Issued:	1989-1999
Series:	Katie's Day

		Price		
Colourways	Backstamp	U.S. $	Can. $	U.K. £
Yellow	Black	210.00	275.00	120.00

RW4482
GRANDMOTHER'S BONNET

Modeller:	Sheila Mitchell
Height:	7 ¾", 19.7 cm
Colour:	Pale blue dress
Issued:	1990 in a limited edition of 9,500

		Price		
Colourways	Backstamp	U.S. $	Can. $	U.K. £
Pale blue	Black	—	—	135.00

Note: Commissioned by Compton & Woodhouse.

RW4483
STORY TIME

Modeller:	Glenis Devereaux
Height:	4 ¼", 10.8 cm
Colour:	Blue dressing gown, bow and slippers; pale blue nightdress; doll wears blue dress; brown teddy bear
Issued:	1989-1999
Series:	Katie's Day

		Price		
Colourways	Backstamp	U.S. $	Can. $	U.K. £
Blue	Black	210.00	275.00	120.00

RW4484
PLAY TIME

Modeller:	Glenis Devereaux
Height:	5 ¾", 14.6 cm
Colour:	Blue-grey dungarees; white blouse; rag doll with yellow hair
Issued:	1990-1999
Series:	Katie's Day

Colourways	Backstamp	U.S. $	Price Can. $	U.K. £
Blue-grey/white	Black	250.00	325.00	140.00

RW4487
WEDNESDAY'S CHILD

Modeller:	Carol Gladman
Height:	5", 12.7 cm
Colour:	Pink dress with white collar; brown hair; brown dog; grey rock; green and yellow base
Issued:	1990

Colourways	Backstamp	U.S. $	Price Can. $	U.K. £
Unknown	Black		Rare	

RW4488
NEW ARRIVAL
Style One

Modeller:	Maureen Halson
Height:	8 ¼", 21.0 cm
Colour:	Cream (Wallbody)
Issued:	1990-2000
Series:	Mother's Love

Colourways	Backstamp	U.S. $	Price Can. $	U.K. £
Cream	Black	—	—	100.00

Note: Commissioned by Compton & Woodhouse.

COMPTON & WOODHOUSE COMMISSIONS

The Flirtation, Style Two

The Golden Jubilee Ball

The Last Waltz

A Royal Presentation

UPSTAIRS, DOWNSTAIRS COLLECTION

Cook

Chamber Maid

Laundry Maid

JANE AUSTEN COLLECTION

Fanny Price

Anne Elliot

Catherine Morland

VICTORIAN LADIES

Caroline, Style One

Lisette

Charlotte and Jane

Elaine

MODERN LADIES
Large Size

Amy, Style One

Ladies Day

Reflection, Style One

Wedding Day, Style Two

MODERN LADIES
Small Size

Emily, Style Three

Kate

Joanne

Nicola

THE WORLD OF THE IMPRESSIONISTS

Norbert

Marguerite and Don Pedro

Jeanne

Germaine

FREDA DOUGHTY'S "CHILDREN"

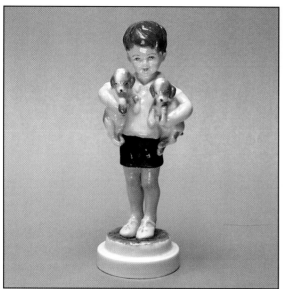

All Mine

Fantails

The Curtsey, Style One and The Bow

Grandmother's Dress and Boy with Parakeet

WILLIAM THE CONQUEROR

RW4498
KING HENRY VIII
Style Two

Modeller:	Kenneth Potts
Height:	15 ½", 39.4 cm
Colour:	Burgundy cape; grey tunic; white stockings; bay horse; green reins and riding cloth
Issued:	1991 in a limited edition of 75

Colourways	Backstamp	U.S. $	Price Can. $	U.K. £
Burgundy/grey/white/bay	Black	—	—	8,105.00

Note: Issued to commemorate the 500th anniversary of the birth of Henry VIII (1491).

RW4499
A POSY FOR MOTHER

Modeller:	Maureen Halson
Height:	7", 17.8 cm
Colour:	Pale blue dress, shawl and hat; shawl and hat trimmed with purple; white apron with pink trim; posy of pink flowers
Issued:	1990 in a limited edition of 7,500
Series:	NSPCC

Colourways	Backstamp	U.S. $	Price Can. $	U.K. £
Pale blue/white	Black	165.00	210.00	95.00

Note: Commissioned by Compton & Woodhouse.

RW4503
SCARF OF THE DANCE

Modeller:	Maureen Halson
Height:	10", 25.4 cm
Colour:	Cream (Wallbody) with pearl lustre
Issued:	1991 in a limited edition of 5,000
Series:	Spirit of the Dance

Colourways	Backstamp	U.S. $	Price Can. $	U.K. £
Cream/lustre	Black	155.00	200.00	90.00

Note: Commissioned by Compton & Woodhouse.

RW4504
SPRING
Style Five

Modeller:	Maureen Halson
Height:	9", 22.9 cm
Colour:	Pink skirt; deeper pink bodice; white apron, underskirt and gloves; cream sleeves and neckline; yellow straw hat; yellow flowers
Issued:	1992 in a limited edition of 7,500
Series:	The Four Seasons, Series Four

			Price	
Colourways	Backstamp	U.S. $	Can. $	U.K. £
Pink/white	Black	—	—	165.00

Note: Commissioned by Compton & Woodhouse.

RW4507
MASQUERADE BEGINS (The)

Modeller:	Nigel Stevens
Height:	8 ¼", 21.6 cm
Colour:	Pink gown decorated with deeper pink roses and ribbons; gold necklace and bracelets
Issued:	1991 in a limited edition of 12,500
Series:	Enchanted Evenings

			Price	
Colourways	Backstamp	U.S. $	Can. $	U.K. £
Pink	Black	165.00	210.00	95.00

Note: Commissioned by Compton & Woodhouse.

RW4508
BALLET

Modeller:	Glenis Devereaux
Height:	4 ½", 11.4 cm
Colour:	Pink ballet dress and slippers
Issued:	1992-1999
Series:	Boys and Girls Come Out to Play

			Price	
Colourways	Backstamp	U.S. $	Can. $	U.K. £
Pink	Black	210.00	275.00	120.00

RW4509
DRESSING UP

Modeller: Glenis Devereaux
Height: 6 ¾", 17.2 cm
Colour: Blue dress and hat; black sandal
Issued: 1992-1999
Series: Boys and Girls Come Out to Play

Colourways	Backstamp	U.S. $	Price Can. $	U.K. £
Blue	Black	210.00	275.00	120.00

RW4510
SUMMER
Style Four

Modeller: Maureen Halson
Height: 9", 22.9 cm
Colour: Pale lilac dress; tan boots; yellow straw hat
Issued: 1992 in a limited edition of 7,500
Series: The Four Seasons, Series Four

Colourways	Backstamp	U.S. $	Price Can. $	U.K. £
Lilac	Black	—	—	165.00

Note: Commissioned by Compton & Woodhouse.

RW4511
LEGAL EAGLE

Modeller: David Fryer and Peter Ewence
Height: Unknown
Colour: Unknown
Issued: 1992

Colourways	Backstamp	U.S. $	Price Can. $	U.K. £
Unknown	Black	325.00	450.00	200.00

*Photograph not
available
at press time*

Note: Commissioned by the Law Society.

RW4512
DIANA (1921)
Style Two

Modeller:	Nigel Stevens
Height:	8 ½", 21.6 cm
Colour:	1. Cream (Wallbody)
	2. Coloured
Issued:	1. Cream: 1992
	2. Coloured: 1992
Series:	1. The Roaring Twenties
	2. The 1920s Vogue Collection

		Price		
Colourways	Backstamp	U.S. $	Can. $	U.K. £
Coloured (as above)	Black	165.00	210.00	95.00

Note: Commissioned by Compton & Woodhouse.

RW4514
CLARA (1925)

Modeller:	Nigel Stevens
Height:	8", 20.3 cm
Colour:	1. Cream (Wallbody)
	2. Pale green dress with white and blue trim; white hat with blue trim; brown and white dog
Issued:	1. Cream: 1992
	2. Pale green: 1992
Series:	1. The Roaring Twenties
	2. The 1920s Vogue Collection

		Price		
Colourways	Backstamp	U.S. $	Can. $	U.K. £
Coloured (as above)	Black	165.00	210.00	95.00

Note: Commissioned by Compton & Woodhouse.

RW4515
SEE-SAW

Modeller:	Glenis Devereaux
Height:	6 ¼", 15.9 cm
Colour:	Blue shorts; white shirt; yellow dress; brown see-saw
Issued:	1992-1999
Series:	Boys and Girls Come Out to Play

		Price		
Colourways	Backstamp	U.S. $	Can. $	U.K. £
Blue/white/yellow-green	Black	375.00	495.00	220.00

RW4517
FIRST FLIGHT

Modeller: Glenis Devereux
Height: 6 ½", 16.5 cm
Colour: Blue trousers; green sweater and cap; yellow scarf and pom-pom
Issued: 1992-1999
Series: Boys and Girls Come Out to Play

Colourways	Backstamp	U.S. $	Price Can. $	U.K. £
Blue/green/yellow	Black	210.00	275.00	120.00

RW4518
AUTUMN
Style Four

Modeller: Maureen Halson
Height: 9", 22.9 cm
Colour: Mauve dress; white apron, collar and underskirt; tan
           shawl and straw hat; brown basket with purple flowers
Issued: 1992 in a limited edition of 7,500
Series: The Four Seasons, Series Four

Colourways	Backstamp	U.S. $	Price Can. $	U.K. £
Mauve/white	Black	—	—	165.00

Note: Commissioned by Compton & Woodhouse.

RW4519
DAISY (1922)
Style Two

Modeller: Nigel Stevens
Height: 8 ¼", 21.0 cm
Colour: 1. Cream (Wallbody)
           2. Pink dress; cream sash; pink and cream hat
Issued: 1. Cream: 1992
           2. Pink and Lilac: 1992
Series: 1. The Roaring Twenties
           2. The 1920s Vogue Collection

Colourways	Backstamp	U.S. $	Price Can. $	U.K. £
Coloured (as above)	Black	165.00	210.00	95.00

Note: Commissioned by Compton & Woodhouse.

RW4520
MILLIE (1926)
Style One

Modeller:	Nigel Stevens
Height:	8 ¼", 21.0 cm
Colour:	1. Cream (Wallbody)
	2. Pale blue with pale turquoise trim
Issued:	1. Cream: 1992
	2. Pale blue: 1992
Series:	1. The Roaring Twenties
	2. The 1920s Vogue Collection

		Price		
Colourways	Backstamp	U.S. $	Can. $	U.K. £
Coloured (as above)	Black	165.00	210.00	95.00

Note: Commissioned by Compton & Woodhouse.

RW4521
POPPY (1924)

Modeller:	Nigel Stevens
Height:	8", 20.3 cm
Colour:	1. Cream (Wallbody)
	2. Pale yellow dress; blue headband and shoes
Issued:	1. Cream: 1992
	2. Pale yellow: 1992
Series:	1. The Roaring Twenties
	2. The 1920s Vogue Collection

		Price		
Colourways	Backstamp	U.S. $	Can. $	U.K. £
Coloured (as above)	Black	165.00	210.00	95.00

Note: Commissioned by Compton & Woodhouse.

RW4522
FIRST PRIZE

Modeller:	Glenis Devereaux
Height:	7 ¼", 18.4 cm
Colour:	White shirt; yellow jodhpurs; black hat and boots; brown saddle
Issued:	1992-1999
Series:	Boys and Girls Come Out to Play

		Price		
Colourways	Backstamp	U.S. $	Can. $	U.K. £
White/yellow/black	Black	210.00	275.00	120.00

RW4523
WINTER
Style Four

Modeller:	Maureen Halson
Height:	9", 22.9 cm
Colour:	Pale brown jacket, skirt and boots; pink scarf and hat; brown muff; brown basket of holly
Issued:	1992 in a limited edition of 7,500
Series:	The Four Seasons, Series Four

Colourways	Backstamp	U.S. $	Price Can. $	U.K. £
Brown/pink	Black	—	—	165.00

Note: Commissioned by Compton & Woodhouse.

RW4524
LAST WALTZ (The)

Modeller:	Nigel Stevens
Height:	8 ¼", 21.0 cm
Colour:	Lilac gown with deeper lilac and gold design
Issued:	1992 in a limited edition of 12,500
Series:	Enchanted Evenings

Colourways	Backstamp	U.S. $	Price Can. $	U.K. £
Lilac	Black	165.00	210.00	95.00

Note: Commissioned by Compton & Woodhouse.

RW4527
MOLLY

Modeller:	Nigel Stevens
Height:	8 ½", 21.6 cm
Colour:	1. Cream (Wallbody)
	2. Coloured
Issued:	1. Cream: 1992
	2. Coloured: 1992
Series:	1. The Roaring Twenties
	2. The 1920s Vogue Collection

Photograph not available at press time

Colourways	Backstamp	U.S. $	Price Can. $	U.K. £
Coloured (as above)	Black	165.00	210.00	95.00

Note: Commissioned by Compton & Woodhouse.

RW4529
QUEEN OF THE MAY (The)

Modeller:	Maureen Halson
Height:	8", 20.3 cm
Colour:	Pink dress with pale green overdress; basket of red roses; red rose crown in her hair
Issued:	1992 in a limited edition of 9,500
Series:	Festive Country Days

		Price		
Colourways	Backstamp	U.S. $	Can. $	U.K. £
Pink/pale green	Black	165.00	210.00	95.00

Note: Commissioned by Compton & Woodhouse.

RW4532
QUEEN OF HEARTS

Designer:	Nigel Stevens
Modeller:	John Bromley
Height:	8 ¼", 21.0 cm
Colour:	Turquoise gown with deeper pink roses and gold highlights
Issued:	1992 in a limited edition of 12,500
Series:	Enchanted Evenings

		Price		
Colourways	Backstamp	U.S. $	Can. $	U.K. £
Turquoise/pink	Black	175.00	225.00	100.00

Note: Commissioned by Compton & Woodhouse.

RW4533
JOY
Style Two

Modeller:	Maureen Halson
Height:	9", 22.9 cm
Colour:	1. Cream (Wallbody)
	2. Pale blue
Issued:	1. Cream: 1992 in a limited edition of 5,000
	2. Pale Blue: 1992 in a limited edition of 5,000

		Price		
Colourways	Backstamp	U.S. $	Can. $	U.K. £
Coloured (as above)	Black	220.00	275.00	125.00

Note: Commissioned by Compton & Woodhouse.

RW4537
KITTY (1928)

Designer: Nigel Stevens
Modeller: John Bromley
Height: 8 ¼", 21.0 cm
Colour: 1. Cream (Wallbody)
            2. Pale yellow dress and hat trimmed with red; red shoes
Issued: 1. Cream: 1992
            2. Pale yellow: 1992
Series: 1. The Roaring Twenties
            2. The 1920s Vogue Collection

Colourways	Backstamp	U.S. $	Price Can. $	U.K. £
Coloured (as above)	Black	165.00	210.00	95.00

Note: Commissioned by Compton & Woodhouse.

RW4538
FIRST QUADRILLE (The) [Henrietta]

Modeller: Nigel Stevens
Height: 8 ¼", 21.0 cm
Colour: Pale blue dress with deeper blue shading;
            pink roses, gold highlights
Issued: 1992 in a limited edition of 12,500
Series: Enchanted Evenings

Colourways	Backstamp	U.S. $	Price Can. $	U.K. £
Pale blue/deep blue	Black	—	—	165.00

Note: Commissioned by Compton & Woodhouse.

RW4539
NOELLE

Modeller: Maureen Halson
Height: 8 ½", 21.6 cm
Colour: Pink dress with red flowered trim; red shoulder cape
            with pink lining
Issued: 1992 in a limited edition of 9,500
Series: Festive Country Days

Colourways	Backstamp	U.S. $	Price Can. $	U.K. £
Pink/red	Black	265.00	350.00	150.00

236

RW4540
ELLEN

Modeller:	Nigel Stevens
Height:	8 ½", 21.6 cm
Colour:	1. Coloured
	2. Cream (Wallbody)
Issued:	1. Coloured: 1992
	2. Cream: 1992
Series:	1. The Roaring Twenties
	2. The 1920s Vogue Collection

			Price	
Colourways	Backstamp	U.S. $	Can. $	U.K. £
Coloured (as above)	Black	165.00	210.00	95.00

Note: Commissioned by Compton & Woodhouse.

RW4543
ANNIE (1927)

Modeller:	Nigel Stevens
Height:	8 ¾", 22.2 cm
Colour:	1. Cream (Wallbody)
	2. Lilac with maroon trim
Issued:	1. Cream: 1992
	2. Lilac: 1992
Series:	1. The Roaring Twenties
	2. The 1920s Vogue Collection

			Price	
Colourways	Backstamp	U.S. $	Can. $	U.K. £
Coloured (as above)	Black	165.00	210.00	95.00

Note: Commissioned by Compton & Woodhouse.

RW4544
MINNIE (1929)

Modeller:	Nigel Stevens
Height:	8 ¼", 21.0 cm
Colour:	1. Cream (Wallbody)
	2. Pale pink dress and hat; iron red sash and shoes
Issued:	1. Cream: 1992
	2. Pale pink: 1992
Series:	1. The Roaring Twenties
	2. The 1920s Vogue Collection

			Price	
Colourways	Backstamp	U.S. $	Can. $	U.K. £
Coloured (as above)	Black	165.00	210.00	95.00

Note: Commissioned by Compton & Woodhouse.

RW4545
CHRISTENING (The)

Modeller:	Maureen Halson	
Height:	9", 22.9 cm	
Colour:	Cream (Wallbody)	
Issued:	1993 in a limited edition of 9,500	
Series:	Our Cherished Moments	

Colourways	Backstamp	U.S. $	Price Can. $	U.K. £
Cream	Black	140.00	175.00	80.00

Note: Commissioned by Compton & Woodhouse.

RW4546
ARAB STALLION (and Rider)

Modeller:	Kenneth Potts	
Height:	16", 40.6 cm	
Colour:	Rider: Multicoloured	
	Horse: Grey	
Issued:	1993 in a limited edition of 50	

Colourways	Backstamp	U.S. $	Price Can. $	U.K. £
Multicoloured	Black	—	—	6,745.00

RW4547
FAIREST ROSE (The)

Modeller:	Nigel Stevens	
Height:	8 ¼", 21.0 cm	
Colour:	Pink gown; white frills; gold decoration	
Issued:	1993 in a limited edition of 12,500	
Series:	Enchanted Evenings	

Colourways	Backstamp	U.S. $	Price Can. $	U.K. £
Pink/white	Black	250.00	325.00	150.00

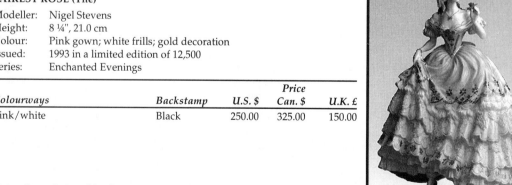

Note: Commissioned by Compton & Woodhouse.

RW4548
VILLAGE BRIDE (The)

Modeller:	Maureen Halson
Height:	8 ½", 21.6 cm
Colour:	Pale pink dress with deeper pink design, white frills and lilac ribbons; posy of yellow, red and purple flowers
Issued:	1993 in a limited edition of 9,500
Series:	Festive Country Days

Colourways	Backstamp	U.S. $	Price Can. $	U.K. £
Pink	Black	165.00	210.00	95.00

Note: Commissioned by Compton & Woodhouse.

RW4549
MARKET DAY

Modeller:	Maureen Halson
Height:	8 ½", 21.6 cm
Colour:	Peach dress; white apron; light blue shawl with white flower design; straw hat; tan basket of vegetables
Issued:	1993 in a limited edition of 5,000
Series:	Pastoral Collection

Colourways	Backstamp	U.S. $	Price Can. $	U.K. £
Peach/white/blue	Black	165.00	210.00	95.00

Note: Commissioned by Compton & Woodhouse.

RW4550
BEA (1922)

Modeller:	Nigel Stevens
Height:	8 ½", 21.6 cm
Colour:	1. Cream (Wallbody)
	2. Light pink dress and headband; lilac sash and shoes
Issued:	1. Cream: 1993
	2. Light pink: 1994
Series:	1. The Roaring Twenties
	2. The 1920s Vogue Collection

Colourways	Backstamp	U.S. $	Price Can. $	U.K. £
Coloured (as above)	Black	165.00	210.00	95.00

Note: Commissioned by Compton & Woodhouse.

RW4551
WEDDING DAY (The)
Style One

Modeller: Maureen Halson
Height: 9", 22.9 cm
Colour: Cream (Wallbody)
Issued: 1993 in a limited edition of 9,500
Series: Our Cherished Moments

Colourways	Backstamp	U.S. $	Price Can. $	U.K. £
Cream	Black	225.00	275.00	120.00

Note: Commissioned by Compton & Woodhouse.

RW4552
SWEETEST VALENTINE

Modeller: Nigel Stevens
Height: 8 ¼", 21.0 cm
Colour: Pink gown decorated with gold highlighted roses
Issued: 1993 in a limited edition of 12,500
Series: Enchanted Evenings

Colourways	Backstamp	U.S. $	Price Can. $	U.K. £
Pink/gold	Black	—	—	165.00

Note: Commissioned by Compton & Woodhouse.

RW4554
EVIE (1923)

Modeller: Nigel Stevens
Height: 8 ½", 21.6 cm
Colour: 1. Cream
2. Grey coat; grey and dark grey skirt; pink tie and cap
Issued: 1. Cream: 1994
2. Grey: 1992
Series: 1. The Roaring Twenties
2. The 1920s Vogue Collection

Colourways	Backstamp	U.S. $	Price Can. $	U.K. £
Coloured (as above)	Black	165.00	210.00	95.00

Note: Commissioned by Compton & Woodhouse.

RW4555
ELEANOR (1928)

Modeller:	Nigel Stevens
Height:	8 ¾", 22.2 cm
Colour:	1. Cream (Wallbody)
	2. Turquoise dress and hat; pink sash, bow and shoes
Issued:	1. Cream: 1994
	2. Turquoise: 1994
Series:	1. The Roaring Twenties
	2. The 1920s Vogue Collection

		Price		
Colourways	Backstamp	U.S. $	Can. $	U.K. £
Coloured (as above)	Black	165.00	210.00	95.00

Note: Commissioned by Compton & Woodhouse.

RW4556
SUMMER'S SWEET KISS

Modeller:	Nigel Stevens
Height:	8 ½", 21.6 cm
Colour:	White dress decorated with rose-pink roses; pink shawl; straw hat
Issued:	1995 in a limited edition of 4,900

		Price		
Colourways	Backstamp	U.S. $	Can. $	U.K. £
White/pink	Black	225.00	275.00	125.00

RW4557
SUNDAY BEST

Modeller:	Maureen Halson
Height:	8 ½", 21.6 cm
Colour:	Peach jacket; pale peach skirt and shawl with deeper peach design; straw hat; tan boots
Issued:	1993 in a limited edition of 9,500
Series:	Pastoral Collection

		Price		
Colourways	Backstamp	U.S. $	Can. $	U.K. £
Peach	Black	165.00	210.00	95.00

Note: Commissioned by Compton & Woodhouse.

RW4560
MOTHERING SUNDAY

Modeller:	Maureen Halson
Height:	9", 22.9 cm
Colour:	1. Cream (Wallbody)
	2. Mother: Blue and white dress
	Daughter: Pink dress, white petticoats
Issued:	1. 1994 in a limited edition of 9,500
	2. In a limited edition of 750
Series:	Our Cherished Moments

		Price		
Colourways	Backstamp	U.S. $	Can. $	U.K. £
1. Cream	Black	150.00	190.00	85.00
2. Blue/pink	Black	—	—	180.00

Note: Commissioned by Compton & Woodhouse.

RW4561
CONSTANCE (1924)

Modeller:	Nigel Stevens
Height:	8 ¼", 21.0 cm
Colour:	1. Cream (Wallbody)
	2. Lilac dress; white feather boa, fan and shoes
Issued:	1. Cream: 1994
	2. Lilac: 1992
Series:	1. The Roaring Twenties
	2. The 1920s Vogue Collection

		Price		
Colourways	Backstamp	U.S. $	Can. $	U.K. £
Coloured (as above)	Black	165.00	210.00	95.00

Note: Commissioned by Compton & Woodhouse.

RW4562
BELLE OF THE BALL
Style Two

Modeller:	Nigel Stevens
Height:	8 ¼", 21.0 cm
Colour:	Lilac and ecru gown; gold decoration
Issued:	1994 in a limited edition of 12,500
Series:	Enchanted Evenings

		Price		
Colourways	Backstamp	U.S. $	Can. $	U.K. £
Lilac/ecru	Black	165.00	225.00	95.00

Note: Commissioned by Compton & Woodhouse.

RW4565
A PRESENT FOR SANTA

Modeller: Maureen Halson
Height: 9", 22.9 cm
Colour: Cream (Wallbody)
Issued: 1995 in a limited edition of 9,500
Series: Our Cherished Moments

Colourways	Backstamp	Price U.S. $	Price Can. $	U.K. £
Cream	Black	140.00	180.00	80.00

Note: Commissioned by Compton & Woodhouse.

RW4566
GOOSE GIRL

Modeller: Maureen Halson
Height: 8 ½", 21.6 cm
Colour: Light blue skirt; white apron; peach and white top;
            straw basket of lilac flowers; white goose
Issued: 1994 in a limited edition of 5,000
Series: Pastoral Collection

Colourways	Backstamp	Price U.S. $	Price Can. $	U.K. £
Blue/white/peach	Black	165.00	210.00	95.00

Note: Commissioned by Compton & Woodhouse.

RW4567
IRENE (Miss 1920)

Modeller: Maureen Halson
Height: 8 ¼", 21.0 cm
Colour: 1. Cream (Wallbody)
            2. Pale pink dress; rose-pink sash and ribbon
Issued: 1. Cream: 1994
            2. Pale pink: 1994
Series: 1. The Roaring Twenties
            2. The 1920s Vogue Collection

Colourways	Backstamp	Price U.S. $	Price Can. $	U.K. £
Coloured (as above)	Black	165.00	210.00	95.00

RW4569
ROYAL DEBUT

Designer: Raymond Hughes
Modeller: John Bromley
Height: 8 ¼", 21.0 cm
Colour: White gown with pink frills, decorated with gold stars
Issued: 1994 in a limited edition of 12,500
Series: Enchanted Evenings

Colourways	Backstamp	U.S. $	Price Can. $	U.K. £
White/pink/gold	Black	175.00	225.00	100.00

Note: Commissioned by Compton & Woodhouse.

RW4571
OLIVIA
Style One

Modeller: David Lyttleton
Height: 9 ½", 24.0 cm
Colour: Tiger-striped black and orange dress; white wrap;
             feathered hat
Issued: 1995 in a limited edition of 12,500
Series: Hollywood Glamour

Colourways	Backstamp	U.S. $	Price Can. $	U.K. £
Black/orange/white	Black	165.00	210.00	95.00

Note: Commissioned by Compton & Woodhouse.

RW4572
FIRST TOUCH

Modeller: Maureen Halson
Height: 8 ¼", 21.0 cm
Colour: Cream (Wallbody)
Issued: 1994 in a limited edition of 7,500
Series: Tender Moments

Colourways	Backstamp	U.S. $	Price Can. $	U.K. £
Cream	Black	140.00	180.00	80.00

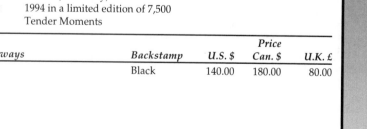

Note: Commissioned by Compton & Woodhouse.

RW4573
LIZ

Modeller:	David Lyttleton
Height:	9 ½", 24.0 cm
Colour:	Black and leopard print dress; leopard print gloves; white feather boa; black hat with gold feather
Issued:	1999 in a limited edition of 9,500
Series:	Hollywood Glamour

			Price	
Colourways	Backstamp	U.S. $	Can. $	U.K. £
Black/leopard print	Black	—	—	125.00

Note: Commissioned by Compton & Woodhouse.

RW4574
SWEET ROSE

Modeller:	David Lyttleton
Height:	6 ¾", 17.2 cm
Colour:	Pink bodice, shawl and hat; white skirt with pink roses and shading
Issued:	1995 in a limited edition of 9,500
Series:	Sweet Posy Collection

			Price	
Colourways	Backstamp	U.S. $	Can. $	U.K. £
Pink/white	Black	150.00	200.00	90.00

Note: Commissioned by Compton & Woodhouse.

RW4575
BETTE

Modeller:	David Lyttleton
Height:	9 ½", 24.0 cm
Colour:	Black spotted dress; fur and feather wrap; black feathered hat
Issued:	1995 in a limited edition of 9,500
Series:	Hollywood Glamour

			Price	
Colourways	Backstamp	U.S. $	Can. $	U.K. £
Black	Black	—	—	125.00

Note: Commissioned by Compton & Woodhouse.

RW4576
DOLLY

Modeller: Nigel Stevens
Height: 8 ¼", 21.0 cm
Colour: 1. Cream (Wallbody)
2. Mauve and white dress; ruby sash; mauve hat and gloves
Issued: 1. Cream: 1994
2. Mauve and white: 1992
Series: 1. The Roaring Twenties
2. The 1920s Vogue Collection

Colourways	Backstamp	U.S. $	Price Can. $	U.K. £
Coloured (as above)	Black	165.00	210.00	95.00

Note: Commissioned by Compton & Woodhouse.

RW4577
LADY VIOLET

Modeller: Jack Glynn
Height: 9 ½", 24.0 cm
Colour: Lilac dress and hat with mauve trim;
mauve and white parasol; gold highlights
Issued: 1996 in a limited edition of 9,500
Series: Fashion Figurine of the Year (1909)

Colourways	Backstamp	U.S. $	Price Can. $	U.K. £
Lilac/mauve/white	Black	175.00	225.00	100.00

Note: Commissioned by Compton & Woodhouse.

RW4579
PAINTING

Modeller: Maureen Halson
Height: 8 ¼", 22.2 cm
Colour: White underskirt with pink flowers; pale pink dress with white frills;
white shawl with pink design; gilt highlights
Issued: 1995 in a limited edition of 2,500
Series: The Graceful Arts

Colourways	Backstamp	U.S. $	Price Can. $	U.K. £
White/pink	Black	425.00	550.00	250.00

Note: Commissioned by Compton & Woodhouse.

RW4580
LADY EMMA
Style One

Modeller:	Richard Moore
Height:	5", 12.7 cm
Colour:	Rose-pink dress and hat; pink collar, frills and parasol
Issued:	1995 in a limited edition of 9,500
Series:	The Fashionable Victorians (Victoria and Albert Museum)

Colourways	Backstamp	U.S. $	Price Can. $	U.K. £
Rose-pink	Black	140.00	180.00	80.00

Note: Commissioned by Compton & Woodhouse.

RW4581
LADY ELIZABETH

Modeller:	David Lyttleton
Height:	5", 12.7 cm
Colour:	Crimson dress
Issued:	1995 in a limited edition of 9,500
Series:	The Fashionable Victorians (Victoria and Albert Museum)

Colourways	Backstamp	U.S. $	Price Can. $	U.K. £
Unknown	Black	140.00	180.00	80.00

Photograph not available at press time

Note: Commissioned by Compton & Woodhouse.

RW4582
LADY JANE

Modeller:	Richard Moore
Height:	5", 12.7 cm
Colour:	Purple dress with white frills
Issued:	1995 in a limited edition of 9,500
Series:	The Fashionable Victorians (Victoria and Albert Museum)

Colourways	Backstamp	U.S. $	Price Can. $	U.K. £
Purple/white	Black	140.00	180.00	80.00

Note: Commissioned by Compton & Woodhouse.

RW4583
BAKER'S WIFE

Modeller:	Maureen Halson
Height:	8 ½", 21.6 cm
Colour:	Peach skirt; blue bodice with white frills; white apron and petticoat; straw hat with blue ribbon; brown basket of bread
Issued:	1995 in a limited edition of 5,000
Series:	Pastoral Collection

Colourways	Backstamp	U.S. $	Price Can. $	U.K. £
Peach/white/blue	Black	175.00	225.00	100.00

Note: Commissioned by Compton & Woodhouse.

RW4584
SWEET HOLLY

Modeller:	David Lyttleton
Height:	6 ¾", 17.2 cm
Colour:	Green coat and hat trimmed with rose-pink; white skirt decorated with holly and flowers
Issued:	1995 in a limited edition of 9,500
Series:	Sweet Posy Collection

Colourways	Backstamp	U.S. $	Price Can. $	U.K. £
Green/white	Black	150.00	200.00	90.00

Note: Commissioned by Compton & Woodhouse.

RW4585
SWEET VIOLET

Modeller:	David Lyttleton
Height:	6 ¾", 17.2 cm
Colour:	Lilac bodice and hat; white skirt decorated with lilacs; straw basket of lilacs
Issued:	1995 in a limited edition of 9,500
Series:	Sweet Posy Collection

Colourways	Backstamp	U.S. $	Price Can. $	U.K. £
Lilac/white	Black	150.00	200.00	90.00

Note: Commissioned by Compton & Woodhouse.

RW4586
A ROYAL PRESENTATION

Designer:	Raymond Hughes
Modeller:	John Bromley
Height:	8 ½", 21.6 cm
Colour:	Lilac gown with deeper lilac frills and ribbons; red roses and gold highlights
Issued:	1995 in a limited edition of 12,500
Series:	Splendour at Court

		Price		
Colourways	Backstamp	U.S. $	Can. $	U.K. £
Lilac	Black	275.00	375.00	165.00

Note: Commissioned by Compton & Woodhouse.

RW4587
JULIETTE / RACHEL (Style Two) / THANK YOU

Designer:	Elizabeth Greenshields
Modeller:	Jack Glynn
Height:	6 ½", 16.5 cm
Colour:	1. **Juliette:** Peach dress; darker peach highlights and shaw
	2. **Rachel:** Pink dress; white petticoats; lilac trim and shawl
	3. **Thank You:** White with gold highlights
Issued:	1. **Juliette:** 1996 to the present
	2. **Rachel:** 1996 to the present
	3. **Thank You:** 1998 to the present
Series:	1. **Juliette:** Les Petites
	2. **Rachel:** Les Petites
	3. **Thank You:** Golden Moments

			Price	
Description	Backstamp	U.S. $	Can. $	U.K. £
1. Juliette	Black	—	325.00	76.00
2. Rachel (Style Two)	Black	—	325.00	76.00
3. Thank You	Black	—	295.00	69.00

RW4588A
LADY HANNAH
Style One

Modeller:	David Lyttleton
Height:	5", 12.7 cm
Colour:	White dress with blue flowers, frills and neckline; gold highlights
Issued:	1995 in a limited edition of 9,500
Series:	The Fashionable Victorians (Victoria and Albert Museum)

		Price		
Colourways	Backstamp	U.S. $	Can. $	U.K. £
White/blue	Black	140.00	180.00	80.00

Note: Commissioned by Compton & Woodhouse.

RW4588B
LADY SARAH
Style One

Modeller:	Richard Moore
Height:	5", 12.7 cm
Colour:	White skirt with pink roses; green overdress; white hat with green ribbons
Issued:	1995 in a limited edition of 9,500
Series:	The Fashionable Victorians (Victoria and Albert Museum)

			Price	
Colourways	Backstamp	U.S. $	Can. $	U.K. £
White/pink/green	Black	140.00	180.00	80.00

Note: Commissioned by Compton & Woodhouse.

RW4589
FIRST KISS

Modeller:	Maureen Halson
Height:	8 ½", 21.6 cm
Colour:	Cream (Wallbody)
Issued:	1995 in a limited edition of 7,500
Varieties:	RW4777 Mother and Child
Series:	Tender Moments

			Price	
Colourways	Backstamp	U.S. $	Can. $	U.K. £
Cream	Black	150.00	200.00	90.00

Note: Commissioned by Compton & Woodhouse.

RW4591
FIRST DANCE
Style Two

Modeller:	Brian Diment
Height:	8 ½", 21.6 cm
Colour:	Pink dress with red trim; white gloves with black ribbons; gold fan
Issued:	1995 in a limited edition of 7,500
Series:	Tissot Collection

			Price	
Colourways	Backstamp	U.S. $	Can. $	U.K. £
Pink/red	Black	275.00	350.00	160.00

RW4594
WEDDING DAY (The)
Style Two

Designer:	Elizabeth Greenshields
Modeller:	Richard Moore
Height:	9 ½", 24.0 cm
Colour:	1. White dress; brown hair
	2. Ivory dress; blonde hair
Issued:	1996-1998
Series:	Golden Moments

		Price		
Colourways	Backstamp	U.S. $	Can. $	U.K. £
Coloured (as above)	Black	175.00	250.00	100.00

RW4595A
CHARLOTTE

Designer:	Elizabeth Greenshields
Modeller:	Jack Glynn
Height:	9 ½", 24.0 cm
Colour:	Pale yellow dress; pale blue overskirt decorated with white flowers; darker blue shawl; pale blue parasol
Issued:	1996 to the present
Series:	Summer Romance

		Price		
Colourways	Backstamp	U.S. $	Can. $	U.K. £
Yellow/blue	Black	—	475.00	145.00

Note: The same mould used to make Charlotte was also used to make Glyndebourne. Charlotte holds an open parasol in her right hand, Glyndebourne a rose.

RW4595B
GLYNDEBOURNE

Designer:	Elizabeth Greenshields
Modeller:	Jack Glynn
Height:	9", 22.9 cm
Colour:	Pale pink dress decorated with salmon-pink roses and edging; salmon-pink shawl; red rose
Issued:	1996 to the present
Series:	High Society

		Price		
Colourways	Backstamp	U.S. $	Can. $	U.K. £
Pale pink/salmon pink	Black	—	395.00	135.00

RW4597
A CELEBRATION AT WINDSOR

Modeller: Nigel Stevens
Height: 8 ½", 21.6 cm
Colour: Pink gown decorated with red roses, deeper pink underskirt and bow; gold highlights
Issued: 1995 in a limited edition of 12,500
Series: Splendour at Court

Colourways	Backstamp	U.S. $	Price Can. $	U.K. £
Pink	Black	275.00	375.00	165.00

Note: Commissioned by Compton & Woodhouse.

RW4599
SWEET FORGET-ME-NOT

Modeller: David Lyttleton
Height: 6 ¾", 17.2 cm
Colour: Blue bodice with white frill and bow; white skirt decorated with forget-me-not flowers
Issued: 1995 in a limited edition of 9,500
Series: Sweet Posy Collection

Colourways	Backstamp	U.S. $	Price Can. $	U.K. £
Blue/white	Black	150.00	200.00	90.00

Note: Commissioned by Compton & Woodhouse.

RW4600
EMBROIDERY

Modeller: Maureen Halson
Height: 8 ¼", 21.0 cm
Colour: Lilac and pink dress and hat decorated with roses
Issued: 1997 in a limited edition of 2,500
Series: The Graceful Arts

Colourways	Backstamp	U.S. $	Price Can. $	U.K. £
Lilac/pink	Black	425.00	550.00	245.00

Note: Commissioned by Compton & Woodhouse.

RW4601
FRIENDSHIP / LAURA

Designer:	Elizabeth Greenshields
Modeller:	Jack Glynn
Height:	8 ¼", 21.0 cm
Colour:	1. **Friendship:** White dress and hat, gold highlights
	2. **Laura:** Pale blue dress; gold highlights; straw hat
Issued:	1. **Friendship:** 1996 to the present
	2. **Laura:** 1996-1999
Series:	1. **Friendship:** Golden Moments
	2. **Laura:** Summer Romance

Description	Backstamp	U.S. $	Price Can. $	U.K. £
1. Friendship	Black	—	325.00	92.00
2. Laura	Black	175.00	250.00	100.00

RW4602A
SWEET PRIMROSE

Modeller:	David Lyttleton
Height:	6 ¾", 17.2 cm
Colour:	Pale green dress; white underskirt with green shading and primrose flowers
Issued:	1995 in a limited edition of 9,500
Series:	Sweet Posy Collection

Colourways	Backstamp	U.S. $	Price Can. $	U.K. £
Pale green/white/yellow	Black	150.00	200.00	90.00

Note: Commissioned by Compton & Woodhouse.

RW4602B
SWEET DAISY

Modeller:	David Lyttleton
Height:	6 ¾", 17.2 cm
Colour:	Blue bodice and overskirt; white underskirt with blue shading and daisies; yellow hat and shawl
Issued:	1995 in a limited edition of 9,500
Series:	Sweet Posy Collection

Colourways	Backstamp	U.S. $	Price Can. $	U.K. £
Blue/white/yellow	Black	150.00	200.00	90.00

RW4603
ANNIVERSARY / GOLDEN ANNIVERSARY / ROYAL PREMIERE / RUBY ANNIVERSARY / SILVER ANNIVERSARY

Designer: Elizabeth Greenshields
Modeller: Jack Glynn
Height: 6 ¾", 17.2 cm
Colour: 1. **Anniversary:** White with gold highlights
2. **Golden Anniversary:** Gold dress; pale yellow shawl
3. **Royal Premiere:** Peach dress; white shawl
4. **Ruby Anniversary:** Ruby dress; white shawl
5. **Silver Anniversary:** Silver grey dress with silver highlights
Issued: 1. **Anniversary:** 1996 to the present
2. **Golden Anniversary:** 1999 to the present
3. **Royal Premiere:** 1996 to the present
4. **Ruby Anniversary:** 1999 to the present
5. **Silver Anniversary:** 1999 to the present
Series: 1. **Anniversary:** Anniversary Collection
2. **Golden Anniversary:** Anniversary Collection
3. **Royal Premiere:** Glittering Occasions
4. **Ruby Anniversary:** Anniversary Collection
5. **Silver Anniversary:** Anniversary Collection

Description	Backstamp	U.S. $	Price Can. $	U.K. £
1. Anniversary	Black	—	350.00	92.00
2. Golden Anniversary	Black	—	395.00	99.50
3. Royal Premiere	Black	—	375.00	99.50
4. Ruby Anniversary	Black	—	395.00	99.50
5. Silver Anniversary	Black	—	395.00	99.50

RW4604
JANE / SARAH / WISTFUL

Designer: Elizabeth Greenshields
Modeller: Richard Moore
Height: 8 ¾", 22.2
Colour: 1. **Jane:** Pale green skirt and scarf, darker green bodice
2. **Sarah:** Lavender skirt and scarf, deeper lavender bodice; gold highlights
3. **Wistful:** Yellow skirt and scarf, deeper yellow bodice
Issued: 1. **Jane:** 1998 to the present
2. **Sarah:** 2000 in a limited edition of 950
3. **Wistful:** 1996-1999
Series: 1. **Jane:** Summer Romance
2. **Wistful:** Day Dreams

Description	Backstamp	U.S. $	Price Can. $	U.K. £
1. Jane	Black	—	395.00	99.50
2. Sarah	Black	—	—	190.00
3. Wistful	Black	175.00	225.00	100.00

Note: 'Sarah' was commissioned by Compton & Woodhouse.

254

RW4605
HOLLY

Designer: Elizabeth Greenshields
Modeller: Maureen Halson
Height: 8", 20.3 cm
Colour: Blue dress with pink bow; white apron; brown dog
Issued: 1995 in a limited edition of 7,500

Photograph not available at press time

Colourways	Backstamp	U.S. $	Can. $	U.K. £
			Price	
Blue	Black	175.00	250.00	100.00

Note: Commissioned by The Juvenile Diabetes Foundation.

RW4606
SWEET ANEMONE

Modeller: David Lyttleton
Height: 6 ¾", 17.2 cm
Colour: Mauve dress; white underskirt decorated with anemone flowers; yellow hat with pink and mauve flowers
Issued: 1995 in a limited edition of 9,500
Series: Sweet Posy Collection

Colourways	Backstamp	U.S. $	Can. $	U.K. £
			Price	
Mauve/white	Black	150.00	200.00	90.00

Note: Commissioned by Compton & Woodhouse.

RW4607
LUCY

Designer: Elizabeth Greenshields
Modeller: Jack Glynn
Height: 4", 10.1 cm
Colour: White dress and hat; tan dog
Issued: 1999
Series: Collectors Club Figure

Colourways	Backstamp	U.S. $	Can. $	U.K. £
			Price	
White	Black	—	—	75.00

RW4608
CAROLINE (Style Two) / FIONA

Designer: Elizabeth Greenshields
Modeller: Jack Glynn
Height: 6 ½", 16.5 cm
Colour: 1. **Caroline:** Pale brown skirt and hat; brown bows, ribbons and
bag; dark brown jacket
2. **Fiona:** Blue dress, hat and bag; pink bows and ribbons
Issued: 1. **Caroline:** 1996 to the present
2. **Fiona:** 1996 to the present
Series: Les Petites

Description	Backstamp	U.S. $	Price Can. $	U.K. £
1. Caroline (Style Two)	Black	—	350.00	76.00
2. Fiona	Black	—	350.00	76.00

RW4609
ANNE
Style One

Modeller: Maureen Halson
Height: 9 ¼", 23.5 cm
Colour: Peach
Issued: 1997-1997
Series: Special Events

Colourways	Backstamp	U.S. $	Price Can. $	U.K. £
Peach	Black	225.00	325.00	125.00

RW4611
CATHERINE / CONGRATULATIONS

Designer: Elizabeth Greenshields
Modeller: Jack Glynn
Height: 6 ¾", 17.3 cm
Colour: 1. **Catherine:** Pale blue dress and hat
2. **Congratulations:** White with gold highlights
Issued: 1. **Catherine:** 1996 to the present
2. **Congratulations:** 1998 to the present
Series: 1. **Catherine:** Les Petites
2. **Congratulations:** Golden Moments

Description	Backstamp	U.S. $	Price Can. $	U.K. £
1. Catherine	Black	—	350.00	76.00
2. Congratulations	Black	—	325.00	69.00

RW4612
SPECIAL OCCASION

Designer:	Elizabeth Greenshields
Modeller:	Richard Moore
Height:	8 ¾", 22.2 cm
Colour:	White with gold highlights
Issued:	1996 to the present
Varieties:	RW4676 May Ball
Series:	Golden Moments

| | | | Price | |
Description	Backstamp	U.S. $	Can. $	U.K. £
Special Occasion	Black	—	350.00	92.00

RW4613
SWEET PEONY

Modeller:	David Lyttleton
Height:	6 ¾", 17.2 cm
Colour:	Rose-pink dress and hat; white overskirt decorated with peony flowers
Issued:	1995 in a limited edition of 9,500
Series:	Sweet Posy Collection

| | | | Price | |
Colourways	Backstamp	U.S. $	Can. $	U.K. £
Rose-pink/white	Black	150.00	200.00	90.00

Note: Commissioned by Compton & Woodhouse.

RW4614
FLIRTATION (The)
Style Two

Modeller:	Maureen Halson
Height:	9 ½", 24.0 cm
Colour:	Female: Pink skirt; rose-pink bodice decorated with flowers
	Male: Blue suit; white waistcoat with blue and red design; white frills and cravat; brown shoes
Issued:	1996 in a limited edition of 2,450

| | | | Price | |
Colourways	Backstamp	U.S. $	Can. $	U.K. £
Pink/blue	Black	525.00	675.00	300.00

Note: Commissioned by Compton & Woodhouse.

RW4615
JESSICA

Designer: Elizabeth Greenshields
Modeller: Jack Glynn
Height: 9", 22.9 cm
Colour: Mauve and lilac dress; pink roses; gold highlights
Issued: 1996 to the present
Series: Summer Romance

Colourways	Backstamp	U.S. $	Price Can. $	U.K. £
Mauve/lilac	Black	—	425.00	99.50

RW4616
LADY CHARLOTTE

Modeller: Martin Evans
Height: 5", 12.7 cm
Colour: Turquoise dress with white bows
Issued: 1995 in a limited edition of 9,500
Series: The Fashionable Victorians (Victoria and Albert Museum)

Colourways	Backstamp	U.S. $	Price Can. $	U.K. £
Turquoise/white	Black	140.00	180.00	80.00

Note: Commissioned by Compton & Woodhouse.

RW4617
GOLDEN JUBILEE BALL (The)

Designer: Raymond Hughes
Modeller: John Bromley
Height: 8 ½", 21.6 cm
Colour: Blue dress trimmed with gold and red roses;
            white underskirt; pink gloves
Issued: 1996 in a limited edition of 12,500
Series: Splendour at Court

Colourways	Backstamp	U.S. $	Price Can. $	U.K. £
Blue	Black	275.00	375.00	165.00

Note: Commissioned by Compton & Woodhouse.

RW4619
LAST DANCE (The)

Modeller: David Lyttleton
Height: 9", 22.9 cm
Colour: Cream dress with gold design on the bodice
Issued: 1997
Series: Classical Sentiments

Colourways	Backstamp	Price U.S. $	Price Can. $	Price U.K. £
Cream/gold	Black	225.00	300.00	135.00

Note: Commissioned by Compton & Woodhouse.

RW4620
EMILY (Style Three) / KATE

Designer: Elizabeth Greenshields
Modeller: Jack Glynn
Height: 5 ¾", 14.6 cm
Colour: 1. **Emily:** Pale blue dress, hat and parasol, gold parasol stem
2. **Kate:** Pale green dress, hat and parasol; gold parasol stem
Issued: 1. **Emily:** 1996-1999
2. **Kate:** 1996 to the present
Series: Les Petites

Description	Backstamp	Price U.S. $	Price Can. $	Price U.K. £
1. Emily (Style Three)	Black	130.00	200.00	76.00
2. Kate	Black	—	350.00	76.00

RW4621
REBECCA (Style Three)/ SARAH (Style Two)

Designer: Elizabeth Greenshields
Modeller: Richard Moore
Height: 6 ¼", 15.9 cm
Colour: 1. **Rebecca:** Red dress and hat; white petticoat
2. **Sarah:** Pink dress with rose-pink bows; white petticoat
Issued: 1. **Rebecca:** 1996 to the present
2. **Sarah:** 1996 to the present
Series: Les Petites

Description	Backstamp	Price U.S. $	Price Can. $	Price U.K. £
1. Rebecca (Style Three)	Black	—	350.00	76.00
2. Sarah (Style Two)	Black	—	350.00	76.00

RW4622
FIRST SMILE

Modeller:	Maureen Halson
Height:	8 ¼", 21.0 cm
Colour:	Cream (Wallbody)
Issued:	1996 in a limited edition of 7,500
Series:	Tender Moments

			Price	
Colourways	*Backstamp*	*U.S. $*	*Can. $*	*U.K. £*
Cream	Black	150.00	200.00	90.00

Note: Commissioned by Compton & Woodhouse.

RW4623
SWEET ASTOR

Modeller:	David Lyttleton
Height:	6 ¾", 17.2 cm
Colour:	Dark peach jacket; peach skirt with astor flowers and a darker peach and orange border; white muff
Issued:	1995 in a limited edition of 9,500
Series:	Sweet Posy Collection

			Price	
Colourways	*Backstamp*	*U.S. $*	*Can. $*	*U.K. £*
Peach/peach/white	Black	150.00	200.00	90.00

Note: Commissioned by Compton & Woodhouse.

RW4624
LADY ALICE

Modeller:	Martin Evans
Height:	5", 12.7 cm
Colour:	Yellow dress; black hat and gloves
Issued:	1995 in a limited edition of 9,500
Series:	The Fashionable Victorians

			Price	
Colourways	*Backstamp*	*U.S. $*	*Can. $*	*U.K. £*
Yellow/black	Black	140.00	180.00	80.00

Note: Commissioned by Compton & Woodhouse.

RW4625
LADY VICTORIA

Modeller:	Martin Evans
Height:	5", 12.7 cm
Colour:	White dress trimmed with purple bands and pink, blue and gold flowers
Issued:	1995 in a limited edition of 9,500
Series:	The Fashionable Victorians

		Price		
Colourways	Backstamp	U.S. $	Can. $	U.K. £
White/purple	Black	140.00	180.00	80.00

Note: Commissioned by Compton & Woodhouse.

RW4627
SOPHIE / VIENNESE WALTZ

Designer:	Elizabeth Greenshields
Modeller:	Richard Moore
Height:	8 ¼", 21.0 cm
Colour:	1. **Sophie:** Pink dress with deeper pink shading; gold purse
	2. **Viennese Waltz:** Pale yellow dress; darker yellow shawl; gold purse
Issued:	1. **Sophie:** 1996 to the present
	2. **Viennese Waltz:** 1996 to the present
Series:	1. **Sophie:** Summer Romance
	2. **Viennese Waltz:** Glittering Occasions

		Price		
Description	Backstamp	U.S. $	Can. $	U.K. £
1. Sophie	Black	—	—	135.00
2. Viennese Waltz	Black	—	475.00	135.00

RW4628
WITH LOVE

Designer:	Elizabeth Greenshields
Modeller:	Jack Glynn
Height:	9", 22.9 cm
Colour:	Female: Pink dress; white underskirt; rose-pink hat
	Male: Dark grey suit; white shirt; grey stockings; black shoes
Issued:	1996 in a limited edition of 500
Series:	Age of Romance (Style Three)

		Price		
Colourways	Backstamp	U.S. $	Can. $	U.K. £
Pink/white/grey	Black	—	975.00	310.00

261

RW4629
BRIDESMAID (Style Two) / NICOLA

Designer: Elizabeth Greenshields
Modeller: Maureen Halson
Height: 6", 15.0 cm
Colour: 1. **Bridesmaid:** Pink and white dress; gold highlights; three
red roses
2. **Nicola:** Grey-blue and white dress; gold highlights; one red rose
Issued: 1. **Bridesmaid:** 1996-1998
2. **Nicola:** 1996-1998
Series: 1. **Bridesmaid:** Golden Moments
2. **Nicola:** Les Petites

Description	Backstamp	U.S. $	Price Can. $	U.K. £
1. Bridesmaid (Style Two)	Black	130.00	165.00	75.00
2. Nicola	Black	130.00	165.00	75.00

RW4630
LADY SOPHIE
Style One

Designer: Elizabeth Greenshields
Modeller: Maureen Halson
Height: 5", 12.7 cm
Colour: White overdress with pink edging; pink underskirt with white
shading; beige hat with pink ribbon; gold highlights
Issued: 1996 in a limited edition of 9,500
Series: The Fashionable Victorians

Colourways	Backstamp	U.S. $	Price Can. $	U.K. £
White/pink	Black	140.00	180.00	80.00

Note: Commissioned by Compton & Woodhouse.

RW4631
LADY BEATRICE

Modeller: Richard Moore
Height: 5", 12.7 cm
Colour: Dark blue jacket and skirt with pale blue shading; gold highlights
Issued: 1996 in a limited edition of 9,500
Series: The Fashionable Victorians

Colourways	Backstamp	U.S. $	Price Can. $	U.K. £
Blue	Black	140.00	180.00	80.00

Note: Commissioned by Compton & Woodhouse.

RW4632
BRIDE AND GROOM (Cake Decoration)

Designer:	Elizabeth Greenshileds
Modeller:	Maureen Halson
Height:	4 ¾", 12.1 cm
Colour:	White with gold highlights
Issued:	1996 to the present
Series:	Golden Moments

| | | | Price | |
Colourways	Backstamp	U.S. $	Can. $	U.K. £
White/gold	Black	—	225.00	54.00

RW4633
MIDNIGHT RENDEZVOUS

Designer:	Elizabeth Greenshields
Modeller:	Maureen Halson
Height:	9", 22.9 cm
Colour:	Red dress; white underskirt; white and grey marbled staircase; pink roses
Issued:	1996 in a limited edition of 1000
Series:	Precious Moments

| | | | Price | |
Colourways	Backstamp	U.S. $	Can. $	U.K. £
Red/white/grey	Black	—	695.00	195.00

RW4634
MOTHER AND CHILD
Style One

Designer:	Elizabeth Greenshields
Modeller:	Jack Glynn
Height:	9", 22.9 cm
Colour:	Peach and white
Issued:	1996 to the present
Series:	Golden Moments

| | | | Price | |
Colourways	Backstamp	U.S. $	Can. $	U.K. £
Peach/white	Black	—	395.00	135.00

RW4635
SWEET SNOWDROP

Modeller:	David Lyttleton
Height:	6 ¾", 17.2 cm
Colour:	Green dress and hat; white skirt with green shading and snowdrop flowers
Issued:	1996 in a limited edition of 9,500
Series:	Sweet Posy Collection

Colourways	Backstamp	U.S. $	Price Can. $	U.K. £
Green/white	Black	150.00	200.00	90.00

RW4637
AMY
Style One

Designer:	Elizabeth Greenshields
Modeller:	Jack Glynn
Height:	8 ¾", 22.2 cm
Colour:	Yellow dress; gold trim; black hair
Issued:	1996-1998
Series:	Summer Romance

Colourways	Backstamp	U.S. $	Price Can. $	U.K. £
Yellow	Black	175.00	225.00	100.00

RW4638
FROM ALL OF US / NIGHT AT THE OPERA

Designer:	Elizabeth Greenshields
Modeller:	Maureen Halson
Height:	9", 22.9 cm
Colour:	1. **From All of Us:** White with gold highlights
	2. **Night at the Opera:** Blue dress; cream fan; gold highlights
Issued:	1. **From All of Us:** 1999 to the present
	2. **Night at the Opera:** 1996 to the present
Series:	1. **From All of Us:** Golden Moments
	2. **Night at the Opera:** Glittering Occasions

Description	Backstamp	U.S. $	Price Can. $	U.K. £
1. From All of Us	Black	—	349.00	92.00
2. Night at the Opera	Black	—	475.00	145.00

RW4639
OLIVIA
Style Two

Designer:	Elizabeth Greenshields
Modeller:	Jack Glynn
Height:	8 ¼", 21.0 cm
Colour:	Pale aquamarine dress; gold trim
Issued:	1996-1999
Series:	Summer Romance

		Price		
Colourways	*Backstamp*	*U.S. $*	*Can. $*	*U.K. £*
Aquamarine	Black	250.00	350.00	135.00

RW4641
ROYAL ENCLOSURE

Designer:	Elizabeth Greenshields
Modeller:	Richard Moore
Height:	9", 22.9 cm
Colour:	Pale yellow skirt; white underskirt; dark green riding jacket and hat; yellow band and bow on hat; gold riding crop
Issued:	1996 to the present
Series:	High Society

		Price		
Colourways	*Backstamp*	*U.S. $*	*Can. $*	*U.K. £*
Yellow/white/green	Black	—	450.00	135.00

RW4642
SWEET PANSY

Modeller:	David Lyttleton
Height:	6 ¾", 17.2 cm
Colour:	Lilac jacket and hat; white skirt decorated with pansies; tan basket of flowers
Issued:	1996 in a limited edition of 9,500
Series:	Sweet Posy Collection

		Price		
Colourways	*Backstamp*	*U.S. $*	*Can. $*	*U.K. £*
Lilac/white	Black	150.00	200.00	90.00

Note: Commissioned by Compton & Woodhouse.

RW4643
SWEET DAFFODIL

Modeller: David Lyttleton
Height: 6 ¾", 17.2 cm
Colour: Blue bodice and hat; white skirt decorated with daffodils; yellow overskirt
Issued: 1996 in a limited edition of 9,500
Series: Sweet Posy Collection

Colourways	Backstamp	U.S. $	Price Can. $	U.K. £
Blue/white/yellow	Black	150.00	200.00	90.00

Note: Commissioned by Compton & Woodhouse.

RW4644
STROLLING IN SATIN

Modeller: John Bromley
Height: 8 ½", 21.6 cm
Colour: White
Issued: 1996 in a limited edition of 12,500
Series: House of Elliot

Colourways	Backstamp	U.S. $	Price Can. $	U.K. £
White	Black	165.00	215.00	95.00

Note: Commissioned by Compton & Woodhouse.

RW4645
SISTER, GUYS HOSPITAL, 1960

Designer: Elizabeth Greenshields
Modeller: Kenneth Potts
Height: 9", 22.9 cm
Colour: White uniform and cap; black and red cape
Issued: 1996
Series: Nursing Sisters

Colourways	Backstamp	U.S. $	Price Can. $	U.K. £
White/black/red	Black	500.00	675.00	300.00

RW4646
ANNABEL / JUST FOR YOU

Designer:	Elizabeth Greenshields
Modeller:	Maureen Halson
Height:	6 ¼", 15.9 cm
Colour:	1. **Annabel:** Pale yellow skirt; blue jacket; blue hat with yellow ribbon
	2. **Just For You:** Red jacket; pale yellow skirt; black hat
Issued:	1. **Annabel:** 1997 to the present
	2. **Just For You:** 2000 to the present
Series:	**Annabel:** Les Petites

			Price	
Colourways	*Backstamp*	*U.S. $*	*Can. $*	*U.K. £*
1. Annabel	Black	—	355.00	76.00
2. Just For You	Black	—	—	76.00

Note: Just For You is available only at the Royal Worcester Factory Shop. The name of your choice can be inscribed on the base of the figurine.

RW4647
ALICE (Style Three) / CELEBRATION / GARDEN PARTY

Designer:	Elizabeth Greenshields
Modeller:	Richard Moore
Height:	9", 22.9 cm
Colour:	1. **Alice:** Brown and peach dress; brown hat with peach ribbon
	2. **Celebration:** White dress and hat; gold highlights
	3. **Garden Party:** Pale yellow skirt; darker yellow bodice and overskirt
Issued:	1. **Alice:** 1996 to the present
	2. **Celebration:** 1996 to the present
	3. **Garden Party:** 1996-1999
Series:	1. **Alice:** Summer Romance
	2. **Celebration:** Golden Moments
	3. **Garden Party:** High Society

			Price	
Description	*Backstamp*	*U.S. $*	*Can. $*	*U.K. £*
1. Alice (Style Three)	Black	—	450.00	99.50
2. Celebration	Black	—	375.00	92.00
3. Garden Party	Black	250.00	325.00	135.00

RW4648
GRADUATION NIGHT

Designer: Elizabeth Greenshields
Modeller: Jack Glynn
Height: 8 ¾", 22.2 cm
Colour: Peach dress; gold highlights
Issued: 1996-1998
Series: Glittering Occasions

Colourways	Backstamp	U.S. $	Price Can. $	U.K. £
Peach	Black	175.00	225.00	100.00

RW4649
LADY ALEXANDRA

Modeller: Martin Evans
Height: 5", 12.7 cm
Colour: Lilac overdress; white skirt with lilac and pink flowers; gold trim
Issued: 1996 in a limited edition of 9,500
Series: The Fashionable Victorians

Colourways	Backstamp	U.S. $	Price Can. $	U.K. £
Lilac/white	Black	140.00	180.00	80.00

Note: Commissioned by Compton & Woodhouse.

RW4650
LADY LOUISE

Modeller: Martin Evans
Height: 5", 12.7 cm
Colour: Pale green crinoline; white sleeves and hat; gold highlights
Issued: 1996 in a limited edition of 9,500
Series: The Fashionable Victorians

Colourways	Backstamp	U.S. $	Price Can. $	U.K. £
Pale green/white	Black	140.00	180.00	80.00

Note: Commissioned by Compton & Woodhouse.

RW4651
QUEEN ELIZABETH I
Style Four

Modeller:	Michael Talbot
Height:	9", 22.9 cm
Colour:	Ivory sleeves and skirt with gold design; dark green overdress and cape with gold bows; white ruff with gold design; white ostrich feather fan
Issued:	1997 in a limited edition of 4,500

		Price		
Colourways	Backstamp	U.S. $	Can. $	U.K. £
Ivory/dark green/gold	Black	450.00	550.00	250.00

Note: Commissioned by Compton & Woodhouse.

RW4652
DANCE OF TIME

Modeller:	Maureen Halson
Height:	11", 27.9 cm
Colour:	Cream (Wallbody) with pearl lustre
Issued:	1997 in a limited edition of 5,000
Series:	Spirit of the Dance

		Price		
Colourways	Backstamp	U.S. $	Can. $	U.K. £
Cream/lustre	Black	350.00	450.00	200.00

Note: Commissioned by Compton & Woodhouse. This figure also appears on a lamp base.

RW4653
CLAIRE

Designer:	Elizabeth Greenshields
Modeller:	Richard Moore
Height:	8", 20.3 cm
Colour:	Peach dress; gold highlights; brown hair and shoes
Issued:	1996-1998
Series:	Summer Romance

		Price		
Colourways	Backstamp	U.S. $	Can. $	U.K. £
Peach	Black	250.00	350.00	135.00

RW4654
REFLECTION (Style One) / SPECIAL MUM

Designer:	Elizabeth Greenshields
Modeller:	Jack Glynn
Height:	8 ½", 21.6 cm
Colour:	1. **Reflection:** Pale blue skirt with yellow bodice and trim; gold hand mirror
	2. **Special Mum:** White with gold highlights
Issued:	1. **Reflection:** 1996-1999
	2. **Special Mum:** 1999 to the present
Series:	1. **Reflection:** Day Dreams
	2. **Special Mum:** Golden Moments

		Price		
Description	Backstamp	U.S. $	Can. $	U.K. £
1. Reflection	Black	175.00	275.00	100.00
2. Special Mum	Black	—	349.00	92.00

RW4656
MEMORIES

Designer:	Elizabeth Greenshields
Modeller:	Jack Glynn
Height:	4 ¾" x 7 ½", 12.1 x 19.1 cm
Colour:	Peach and yellow dress; brown and green chaise-lounge
Issued:	1996-1998
Series:	Day Dreams

		Price		
Colourways	Backstamp	U.S. $	Can. $	U.K. £
Peach/yellow	Black	175.00	225.00	100.00

RW4657
LADY MARGARET

Modeller:	Jack Glynn
Height:	6", 15.0 cm
Colour:	Rose-pink and pale pink
Issued:	1994 in a limited edition of 15,000
Series:	My Fair Ladies

		Price		
Colourways	Backstamp	U.S. $	Can. $	U.K. £
Rose-pink/pale pink	Black	125.00	150.00	70.00

Note: Commissioned by Compton & Woodhouse.

RW4659
MASKED BALL

Designer:	Elizabeth Greenshields
Modeller:	Maureen Halson
Height:	8 ¾", 22.2 cm
Colour:	Purple and lilac gown; gold mask
Issued:	1996 to the present
Series:	Glittering Occasions

Colourways	Backstamp	U.S. $	Price Can. $	U.K. £
Purple/lilac	Black	—	450.00	145.00

RW4660
NEW ARRIVAL
Style Two

Designer:	Elizabeth Greenshields
Modeller:	Jack Glynn
Height:	3 ½" x 4 ½", 8.9 x 11.9 cm
Colour:	1. Blue
	2. Pink
Issued:	1996 to the present
Series:	Golden Moments

Colourways	Backstamp	U.S. $	Price Can. $	U.K. £
Coloured (as above)	Black	—	199.00	43.00

RW4661
BIRTHDAY WISH / SUMMER REGATTA

Designer:	Elizabeth Greenshields
Modeller:	Richard Moore
Height:	8 ¾", 22.2 cm
Colour:	1. **Birthday Wish:** White with gold highlights
	2. **Summer Regatta:** Green dress; black gloves and hat
Issued:	1. **Birthday Wish:** 1997 to the present
	2. **Summer Regatta:** 1996-1999
Series:	1. **Birthday Wish:** Golden Moments
	2. **Summer Regatta:** High Society

Description	Backstamp	U.S. $	Price Can. $	U.K. £
1. Birthday Wish	Black	—	395.00	92.00
2. Summer Regatta	Black	175.00	250.00	100.00

RW4662
ASCOT LADY

Designer: Elizabeth Greenshields
Modeller: Richard Moore
Height: 9", 22.9 cm
Colour: Pale blue dress, darker blue cloak and hat; brown fur trim;
            yellow and blue parasol
Issued: 1996 to the present
Series: High Society

Colourways	Backstamp	U.S. $	Price Can. $	U.K. £
Blue	Black	—	450.00	145.00

RW4664
LADY LOUISA

Modeller: Martin Evans
Height: 4 ½", 11.9 cm
Colour: Pink and rose-pink crinoline decorated with rose-pink roses
            and gold highlights
Issued: 1996 in a limited edition of 15,000
Series: Debutantes

Colourways	Backstamp	U.S. $	Price Can. $	U.K. £
Pink/rose-pink	Black	125.00	150.00	70.00

Note: Commissioned by Compton & Woodhouse.

RW4665
LADY EMMA
Style Two

Modeller: Martin Evans
Height: 4 ½", 11.9 cm
Colour: Pale blue crinoline with deeper blue bodice and trim;
            gold highlights
Issued: 1996 in a limited edition of 15,000
Series: Debutantes

Colourways	Backstamp	U.S. $	Price Can. $	U.K. £
Blue	Black	125.00	150.00	70.00

Note: Commissioned by Compton & Woodhouse.

RW4666
LOVING YOU / THOUGHTFUL

Designer:	Elizabeth Greenshields
Modeller:	Richard Moore
Height:	8 ¼", 21.0 cm
Colour:	1. **Loving You:** White with gold highlights
	2. **Thoughtful:** Pale blue dress and jacket trimmed with lilac
Issued:	1. **Loving You:** 1997 to the present
	2. **Thoughtful:** 1996-1998
Series:	1. **Loving You:** Golden Moments
	2. **Thoughtful:** Day Dreams

Description	Backstamp	U.S. $	Price Can. $	U.K. £
1. Loving You	Black	—	350.00	92.00
2. Thoughtful	Black	175.00	225.00	100.00

RW4667
ESPECIALLY FOR YOU / LADIES DAY

Designer:	Elizabeth Greenshields
Modeller:	Maureen Halson
Height:	8 ¾", 22.2 cm
Colour:	1. **Especially For You:** Blue dress
	2. **Ladies Day:** Pale tan dress and hat; white petticoats; blue coat trimmed with fur; brown boot
Issued:	1. **Especially For You:** 2000 to the present
	2. **Ladies Day:** 1996-1998
Series:	**Ladies Day:** High Society

Colourways	Backstamp	U.S. $	Price Can. $	U.K. £
1. Especially For You	Black	—	—	99.00
2. Ladies Day	Black	175.00	250.00	100.00

Note: Especially For You is available only at the Royal Worcester Factory Shop. The name of your choice can be inscribed on the base of the figurine.

RW4668
LADY EMILY

Designer:	Unknown
Modeller:	Jack Glynn
Height:	6", 15.0 cm
Colour:	Green and white dress with black edging
Issued:	1996 in a limited edition of 15,000
Series:	My Fair Ladies

Colourways	Backstamp	U.S. $	Price Can. $	U.K. £
Unknown	Black	125.00	150.00	70.00

Note: Commissioned by Compton & Woodhouse.

RW4669
LADY HANNAH
Style Two

Modeller:	Martin Evans
Height:	4 ½", 11.9 cm
Colour:	Pale green and yellow crinoline; gold highlights
Issued:	1996 in a limited edition of 15,000
Series:	Debutantes

Colourways	Backstamp	U.S. $	Price Can. $	U.K. £
Green/yellow	Black	125.00	150.00	70.00

Note: Commissioned by Compton & Woodhouse.

RW4670
LADY CICELY

Designer:	Unknown
Modeller:	Richard Moore
Height:	4 ½", 11.9 cm
Colour:	Mauve and white crinoline with deeper mauve trim and rose-pink roses; deep mauve glove and shoe; gold highlights
Issued:	1996 in a limited edition of 15,000
Series:	Debutantes

Colourways	Backstamp	U.S. $	Price Can. $	U.K. £
Mauve/white	Black	125.00	150.00	70.00

Note: Commissioned by Compton & Woodhouse.

RW4671
LADY SOPHIE
Style Two

Designer:	Unknown
Modeller:	Richard Moore
Height:	4 ½", 11.9 cm
Colour:	Pink crinoline with white shading; rose-pink roses; gold highlights
Issued:	1996 in a limited edition of 15,000
Series:	Debutantes

Colourways	Backstamp	U.S. $	Price Can. $	U.K. £
Pink/white	Black	125.00	150.00	70.00

Note: Commissioned by Compton & Woodhouse.

RW4672
LADY CAMILLE

Designer:	Unknown
Modeller:	Jack Glynn
Height:	6", 15.9 cm
Colour:	Pink and burgundy
Issued:	1996 in a limited edition of 15,000
Series:	My Fair Ladies

		Price		
Colourways	Backstamp	U.S. $	Can. $	U.K. £
Pink/burgundy	Black	125.00	150.00	70.00

Note: Commissioned by Compton & Woodhouse.

RW4674
ROYAL ANNIVERSARY

Modeller:	John Bromley
Height:	8 ½", 21.6 cm
Colour:	Pale aqua and white gown decorated with red roses; gold highlights
Issued:	1996 in a limited edition of 12,500
Series:	Splendour at Court

		Price		
Colourways	Backstamp	U.S. $	Can. $	U.K. £
Pale aqua/white	Black	275.00	375.00	165.00

Note: Commissioned by Compton & Woodhouse.

RW4676
MAY BALL

Designer:	Elizabeth Greenshields
Modeller:	Richard Moore
Height:	8 ¾", 22.2 cm
Colour:	Pink dress; white fan; gold highlights
Issued:	1996 to the present
Varieties:	RW4612 Special Occasion
Series:	Glittering Occasions

		Price		
Description	Backstamp	U.S. $	Can. $	U.K. £
May Ball	Black	—	450.00	135.00

RW4677
KATIE
Style Two

Designer:	Elizabeth Greenshields
Modeller:	Maureen Halson
Height:	5 ¾", 14.0 cm
Colour:	White dress and hat; yellow hair
Issued:	2000-2000
Series:	Collectors Club Figure

Colourways	Backstamp	Price U.S. $	Can. $	U.K. £
White	Black	—	—	—

RW4678
LADY DOROTHY

Modeller:	Jack Glynn
Height:	6", 15.0 cm
Colour:	Turquoise dress trimmed with cream and black; turquoise hat with black and grey feathers
Issued:	1994 in a limited edition of 15,000
Series:	My Fair Ladies

Colourways	Backstamp	Price U.S. $	Can. $	U.K. £
Turquoise/cream	Black	125.00	150.00	70.00

Note: Commissioned by Compton & Woodhouse.

RW4679
LADY HELENA

Modeller:	Jack Glynn
Height:	6", 15.0 cm
Colour:	White dress with blue bands; blue hat with black and white bow, dark grey feather
Issued:	1997 in a limited edition of 15,000
Series:	My Fair Ladies

Colourways	Backstamp	Price U.S. $	Can. $	U.K. £
White/blue	Black	140.00	180.00	80.00

Note: Commissioned by Compton & Woodhouse.

RW4680
MUSIC
Style Two

Modeller: Maureen Halson
Height: 8 ¼", 21.0 cm
Colour: Turquoise dress; white underskirt with pink roses; gold harp
Issued: 1997 in a limited edition of 2,500
Series: The Graceful Arts

Colourways	Backstamp	Price U.S. $	Can. $	U.K. £
Turquoise/white/gold	Black	425.00	550.00	245.00

Note: Commissioned by Compton & Woodhouse.

RW4681
SERENA

Modeller: John Bromley
Height: 9", 22.9 cm
Colour: Pale green
Issued: 1997-1997
Series: Figurine of the Year

Colourways	Backstamp	Price U.S. $	Can. $	U.K. £
Pale green	Black	175.00	225.00	100.00

RW4682
FIRST TEDDY

Modeller: Maureen Halson
Height: 8 ¼", 21.0 cm
Colour: Cream (Wallbody)
Issued: 1997 in a limited edition of 7,500
Series: Tender Moments

Colourways	Backstamp	Price U.S. $	Can. $	U.K. £
Cream	Black	150.00	200.00	90.00

Note: Commissioned by Compton & Woodhouse.

RW4683
JEWEL IN THE CROWN

Modeller: John Bromley
Height: 8 ½", 21.6 cm
Colour: Pink gown with gold design
Issued: 1997 in a limited edition of 12,500
Series: Splendour at Court

Colourways	Backstamp	U.S. $	Price Can. $	U.K. £
Pink	Black	275.00	375.00	165.00

Note: Commissioned by Compton & Woodhouse.

RW4685
NATASHA
Style Two

Designer: Elizabeth Greenshields
Modeller: Richard Moore
Height: 9 ½", 24.0 cm
Colour: Tan skirt; coffee coloured coat trimmed with dark brown fur; dark brown fur muff and hat
Issued: 1998-1998
Series: Premiere Figurine of the Year

Colourways	Backstamp	U.S. $	Price Can. $	U.K. £
Tan/coffee/dark brown	Black	225.00	395.00	125.00

RW4686
SUMMER'S LEASE

Modeller: Maureen Halson
Height: 9 ½", 24.0 cm
Colour: Pink and white gown decorated with red roses; cream hat decorated with pink feather and red roses
Issued: 1998 in a limited edition of 2,950

Colourways	Backstamp	U.S. $	Price Can. $	U.K. £
Pink/white	Black	425.00	550.00	245.00

Note: Commissioned by Compton & Woodhouse.

RW4687
TRYST (The)

Modeller:	Maureen Halson
Height:	9 ½", 24.0 cm
Colour:	Female: Pale blue dress; white frills; gold edging; pink underskirt decorated with pink roses; pink shoes
	Male: Blue jacket with gold edging; flowered beige waistcoat; tan breeches; brown shoe
Issued:	1998 in a limited edition of 2,450
Series:	Dancing Lovers

		Price		
Colourways	Backstamp	U.S. $	Can. $	U.K. £
Blue/pink/tan/gold	Black	500.00	650.00	295.00

Note: Commissioned by Compton & Woodhouse.

RW4688
ISABELLE

Modeller:	John Bromley
Height:	8 ¼", 21.0 cm
Colour:	Pale blue dress with darker blue and gold top; pale blue and gold bow in hair
Issued:	1998-1998
Series:	Figurine of the Year

		Price		
Colourways	Backstamp	U.S. $	Can. $	U.K. £
Blue	Black	225.00	300.00	135.00

Note: Commissioned by Compton & Woodhouse.

RW4689
FLAME DANCE (Fire)

Modeller:	Richard Moore
Height:	11 ½", 29.2 cm
Colour:	Red and yellow
Issued:	1997-1999
Series:	Forces of Creation

		Price		
Colourways	Backstamp	U.S. $	Can. $	U.K. £
Red/yellow	Black	250.00	350.00	145.00

RW4690
A GIFT OF LOVE

Modeller: Richard Moore
Height: 9", 22.9 cm
Colour: Female: Peach dress and shoes; white petticoats
            Male: Jacket with brown lapels and cuffs; yellow
            waistcoat; white cravat and gloves
Issued: 1998 in a limited edition of 500
Series: Age of Romance, Series Three

Colourways	Backstamp	U.S. $	Price Can. $	U.K. £
Peach/brown	Black	—	995.00	310.00

RW4691
EMBASSY BALL (The)

Modeller: John Bromley
Height: 10", 25.4 cm
Colour: White dress with pale yellow overskirt embellished with gold
            embroidery and orange roses; yellow and gold fan
Issued: 1997 in a limited edition of 12,500
Series: Splendour at Court

Colourways	Backstamp	U.S. $	Price Can. $	U.K. £
White/yellow/orange/gold	Black	275.00	375.00	165.00

Note: Commissioned by Compton & Woodhouse.

RW4692
FIRST LOVE

Modeller: Maureen Halson
Height: 8 ¼", 21.0 cm
Colour: Cream (Wallbody)
Issued: 1998 in a limited edition of 7,500
Series: Tender Moments

Colourways	Backstamp	U.S. $	Price Can. $	U.K. £
Cream	Black	165.00	225.00	95.00

Note: Commissioned by Compton & Woodhouse.

RW4694
AQUAMARINE (Water)

Designer: Elizabeth Greenshields
Modeller: Richard Moore
Height: 9 ¼", 23.5 cm
Colour: Aquamarine and white
Issued: 1997-1999
Series: Forces of Creation

Colourways	Backstamp	U.S. $	Price Can. $	U.K. £
Aquamarine/white	Black	250.00	350.00	145.00

RW4695
MARY

Designer: Elizabeth Greenshields
Modeller: Carol Gladman
Height: 6 ¼", 15.9 cm
Colour: Peach skirt; brown jacket with fur trim; brown hat with peach ribbon and bow
Issued: 1998-1999
Series: Les Petites

Colourways	Backstamp	U.S. $	Price Can. $	U.K. £
Peach/brown	Black	150.00	195.00	80.00

RW4696
JENNIFER

Designer: Elizabeth Greenshields
Modeller: Maureen Halson
Height: 6 ¾", 17.2 cm
Colour: Rose-pink dress and hat with deep pink bow and ribbon
Issued: 1997 to the present
Series: Les Petites

Colourways	Backstamp	U.S. $	Price Can. $	U.K. £
Rose-pink	Black	—	375.00	76.00

RW4697
MISTRAL (Air)

Designer: Elizabeth Greenshields
Modeller: Richard Moore
Height: 11", 27.9 cm
Colour: Purple and pink
Issued: 1997-1999
Series: Forces of Creation

Colourways	Backstamp	U.S. $	Price Can. $	U.K. £
Purple/pink	Black	250.00	325.00	145.00

RW4698
I WISH

Modeller: Sheila Mitchell
Height: 8 ¼", 21.0 cm
Colour: Blue dress with darker blue design; pink ribbons; brown teddy bear
Issued: 1998 in a limited edition of 5,000
Series: Children of the Future (NSPCC)

Colourways	Backstamp	U.S. $	Price Can. $	U.K. £
Blue	Black	250.00	325.00	135.00

Note: Commissioned by Compton & Woodhouse.

RW4699
EARTH SONG

Designer: Elizabeth Greenshields
Modeller: Richard Moore
Height: 11", 27.9 cm
Colour: Peach and yellow
Issued: 1997-1999
Series: Forces of Creation

Colourways	Backstamp	U.S. $	Price Can. $	U.K. £
Peach/yellow	Black	250.00	350.00	145.00

RW4700
KNIGHTSBRIDGE

Designer:	Elizabeth Greenshields
Modeller:	Maureen Halson
Height:	9 ½" 24.0 cm
Colour:	Pale peach skirt; white bodice with gold decoration; black shawl and hat
Issued:	1997 to the present
Series:	High Society

			Price	
Colourways	Backstamp	U.S. $	Can. $	U.K. £
Yellow/white/dark green	Black	—	475.00	135.00

RW4701
MARY, QUEEN OF SCOTS
Style Two

Modeller:	Michael Talbot
Height:	9", 22.9 cm
Colour:	Burgundy and gold
Issued:	1998 in a limited edition of 4,500
Series:	Queens of Britain

			Price	
Colourways	Backstamp	U.S. $	Can. $	U.K. £
Burgundy/gold	Black	425.00	550.00	245.00

Note: Commissioned by Compton & Woodhouse.

RW4702
PAINTED FAN (The) (Lucinda)

Modeller:	John Bromley
Height:	9 ½", 24.0 cm
Colour:	Rose-pink and pale pink gown and fan; gold decoration
Issued:	1998 in a limited edition of 12,500
Series:	Age of Elegance, Series Two

			Price	
Colourways	Backstamp	U.S. $	Can. $	U.K. £
Pink/gold	Black	300.00	395.00	175.00

Note: Commissioned by Compton & Woodhouse.

RW4703
SECRET GARDEN

Designer: Elizabeth Greenshields
Modeller: Maureen Halson
Height: 9 ¼", 23.5 cm
Colour: Lilac gown decorated with red roses and bows
Issued: 1998 in a limited edition of 1,000
Series: Precious Moments

Colourways	Backstamp	U.S. $	Price Can. $	U.K. £
Lilac	Black	—	865.00	195.00

RW4705
EMMA (Woodhouse)

Modeller: Richard Moore
Height: 8 ½", 21.6 cm
Colour: Pink and white patterned dress; pink coat with ermine trim; pink hat with white feathers; white garden seat
Issued: 1998 in a limited edition of 4,500
Series: Jane Austen Heroines (Museum of Costume, Bath)

Colourways	Backstamp	U.S. $	Price Can. $	U.K. £
Pink/white	Black	425.00	550.00	245.00

Note: Commissioned by Compton & Woodhouse.

RW4706
MOONLIGHT CASCADE

Modeller: Richard Evans
Height: 8 ¾", 22.2 cm
Colour: Blue lustre gown with platinum highlights; blue ostrich feather fan
Issued: 1998 in a limited edition of 9,500
Series: The House of Eliott

Colourways	Backstamp	U.S. $	Price Can. $	U.K. £
Blue lustre/platinum	Black	275.00	375.00	165.00

Note: Commissioned by Compton & Woodhouse.

RW4707
GRAND ENTRANCE

Designer: Elizabeth Greenshields
Modeller: Richard Moore
Height: 9 ¼", 23.5 cm
Colour: Rose-pink dress, white underskirt with gold design
Issued: 1997 to the present
Series: Glittering Occasions

Colourways	Backstamp	U.S. $	Price Can. $	U.K. £
Rose-pink/white/gold	Black	—	595.00	135.00

RW4708
POETRY

Modeller: Maureen Halson
Height: 8 ¼", 21.0 cm
Colour: Pale green dress; white underskirt decorated with red roses
Issued: 1998 in a limited edition of 2,500
Series: Graceful Arts

Colourways	Backstamp	U.S. $	Price Can. $	U.K. £
Pale green/white	Black	425.00	550.00	245.00

Note: Commissioned by Compton & Woodhouse.

RW4709
A DAY TO REMEMBER

Modeller: Maureen Halson
Height: 9 ¼", 23.5 cm
Colour: Pearl lustre gown
Issued: 1998-1998
Series: Anniversary Figurine of the Year

Colourways	Backstamp	U.S. $	Price Can. $	U.K. £
Pearl lustre	Black	250.00	325.00	150.00

Note: Commissioned by Compton & Woodhouse.

RW4710
DINNER AT EIGHT

Modeller: John Bromley
Height: 8 ¾", 22.2 cm
Colour: Pearl lustre gown with platinum highlights
Issued: 1998 in a limited edition of 9,500
Series: Brief Encounters

Colourways	Backstamp	U.S. $	Price Can. $	U.K. £
Pearl lustre	Black	250.00	325.00	140.00

Note: Commissioned by Compton & Woodhouse.

RW4711
TANYA / TEA AT THE RITZ

Designer: Elizabeth Greenshields
Modeller: Richard Moore
Height: 8 ¾", 22.2 cm
Colour: 1. **Tanya:** Cream dress and hat; gold sash and bow on hat
        2. **Tea at the Ritz:** Blue dress and hat; gold sash and bow on hat
Issued: 1. **Tanya:** 1997-1998
        2. **Tea at the Ritz:** 1997 to the present
Series: 1. **Tanya:** Special Events
        2. **Tea at the Ritz:** High Society

Description	Backstamp	U.S. $	Price Can. $	U.K. £
1. Tanya	Black	225.00	300.00	130.00
2. Tea at the Ritz	Black	—	475.00	135.00

RW4712
EVENING ROMANCE

Designer: Elizabeth Greenshields
Modeller: Maureen Halson
Height: 9", 22.9 cm
Colour: Salmon-pink dress with gold decorated border
Issued: 1997 to the present
Series: Glittering Occasions

Colourways	Backstamp	U.S. $	Price Can. $	U.K. £
Salmon-pink/gold	Black	—	575.00	135.00

RW4713
MOTHER'S LOVE

Modeller:	Maureen Halson
Height:	7 ¾", 19.7 cm
Colour:	Cream (Wallbody)
Issued:	1998-1998
Series:	Mother of the Year Figurine

Colourways	Backstamp	U.S. $	Price Can. $	U.K. £
Cream	Black	175.00	250.00	100.00

Note: Commissioned by Compton & Woodhouse.

RW4715
CHRISTINA

Designer:	Elizabeth Greenshields
Modeller:	Richard Moore
Height:	6 ¾", 17.2 cm
Colour:	Red dress; black hat with pink flowers; gold highlights
Issued:	1997 to the present
Series:	Les Petites

Colourways	Backstamp	U.S. $	Price Can. $	U.K. £
Red	Black	—	375.00	76.00

RW4716
ELIZABETH
Style Two

Designer:	Elizabeth Greenshields
Modeller:	Richard Moore
Height:	9", 22.0 cm
Colour:	Dark blue jacket trimmed with paler blue fur; lemon overskirt; pale blue underskirt; blue hat with yellow band and feather; yellow gloves; blue umbrella
Issued:	1998-1998
Series:	Special Events

Colourways	Backstamp	U.S. $	Price Can. $	U.K. £
Blue/lemon	Black	200.00	250.00	110.00

Note: Commissioned by Compton & Woodhouse.

RW4717
JOANNE

Designer: Elizabeth Greenshields
Modeller: Ruth Hook
Height: 6 ½", 16.5 cm
Colour: Cream skirt with pink shading; black bodice and hat; gold highlights
Issued: 1997 to the present
Series: Les Petites

Colourways	Backstamp	Price U.S. $	Can. $	U.K. £
Cream/pink/black	Black	—	375.00	76.00

RW4718
A DAZZLING CELEBRATION (Lady Cecilia)

Modeller: John Bromley
Height: 9 ½", 24.0 cm
Colour: Ivory-white and pale pink gown with a pearl lustre sheen and gold embroidery
Issued: 1998 in a limited edition of 12,500
Series: Age of Elegance, Series Two

Colourways	Backstamp	Price U.S. $	Can. $	U.K. £
Ivory/pink/gold	Black	275.00	360.00	160.00

Note: Commissioned by Compton & Woodhouse.

RW4720
SONG OF SPRING

Modeller: Maureen Halson
Height: 9 ½", 24.0 cm
Colour: Pink dress with deeper pink, blue and green design; white frills; rose-pink ribbon and bows
Issued: 1998 in a limited edition of 2,950

Colourways	Backstamp	Price U.S. $	Can. $	U.K. £
Pink	Black	425.00	550.00	245.00

Note: Commissioned by Compton & Woodhouse.

RW4721
MILLENNIA

Modeller:	Richard Moore
Height:	9 ½", 24.0 cm
Colour:	White dress, shawl and dove; gold necklace and dials
Issued:	1999 in a limited edition of 1,000
Series:	Millennium Collection

Colourways	Backstamp	U.S. $	Price Can. $	U.K. £
White/gold	Black	350.00	450.00	195.00

RW4722
TRUE LOVE

Designer:	Elizabeth Greenshields
Modeller:	Richard Moore
Height:	9 ½", 24.0 cm
Colour:	Female: Red dress; cream shawl
	Male: Dark green jacket; pale green lapels and breeches; black boots
Issued:	1998 in a limited edition of 500
Series:	Age of Romance (Style Three)

Colourways	Backstamp	U.S. $	Price Can. $	U.K. £
Red/dark green	Black	—	975.00	310.00

Note: This model was issued with a wooden plinth.

RW4723
PROPOSAL (The)

Modeller:	Maureen Halson
Height:	9 ½", 24.0 cm
Colour:	Female: Pale lilac dress decorated with flowers
	Male: Purple coat with gold decoration; brown hair and breeches; black boots
Issued:	1999 in a limited edition of 2,450

Colourways	Backstamp	U.S. $	Price Can. $	U.K. £
Lilac/purple/brown/black	Black	500.00	650.00	295.00

Note: Commissioned by Compton & Woodhouse.

RW4724
LADY SARAH
Style Two

Modeller: Richard Moore
Height: 4 ½", 11.9 cm
Colour: Blue crinoline with gold highlights
Issued: 1999 in a limited edition of 15,000
Series: Debutantes

Colourways	Backstamp	U.S. $	Price Can. $	U.K. £
Blue	Black	125.00	150.00	70.00

Note: Commissioned by Compton & Woodhouse.

RW4725
GRACE
Style Three

Designer: Elizabeth Greenshields
Modeller: Richard Moore
Height: 9 ½", 24.0 cm
Colour: Cream skirt; tan and dark brown patterned top; gold highlights
Issued: 1999-1999
Series: Premiere Figurine of the Year 1999

Colourways	Backstamp	U.S. $	Price Can. $	U.K. £
Cream/tan/brown	Black	250.00	425.00	150.00

RW4726
ETERNITY

Designer: Elizabeth Greenshields
Modeller: Richard Moore
Height: 6 ½", 16.5 cm
Colour: White dress and shawl; gold trim, leaves and clock face
Issued: 1999-2000
Series: Millennium Collection

Colourways	Backstamp	U.S. $	Price Can. $	U.K. £
White/gold	Black	—	—	89.00

RW4727
I DREAM

Modeller: Sheila Mitchell
Height: 8 ¼", 21.0 cm
Colour: Pink dress
Issued: 1999 in a limited edition of 5,000
Series: Children of the Future (NSPCC)

Colourways	Backstamp	Price U.S. $	Price Can. $	Price U.K. £
Pink	Black	250.00	300.00	135.00

Note: Commissioned by Compton & Woodhouse.

RW4728
LADY HENRIETTA

Modeller: Richard Moore
Height: 4 ½", 11.9 cm
Colour: Pale blue crinoline
Issued: 1999 in a limited edition of 15,000
Series: Debutantes

Colourways	Backstamp	Price U.S. $	Price Can. $	Price U.K. £
Pale blue	Black	125.00	150.00	70.00

Note: Commissioned by Compton & Woodhouse.

RW4730
THE COURT OF TUTANKHAMUN TABLEAU (Three pieces)
The Fan Bearer

Modeller:	John Bromley
Height:	8", 20.3 cm
Colour:	White robes; turquoise, lapis lazuli and terra cotta
	embellishments; gold fan
Issued:	1999 in a limited edition of 500
Series:	The Court of Tutankhamun

Tutankhamun

Modeller:	John Bromley
Height:	6 ¼", 15.9 cm
Colour:	White robes; gold headdress, amulets and sandals;
	turquoise lapus lazuli and terra cotta decoration;
	brown and blue chair
Issued:	1999 in a limited edition of 500
Series:	The Court of Tutankhamun

The Wine Pourer

Modeller:	John Bromley
Height:	8", 20.3 cm
Colour:	White robes; turquoise, lapis lazuli and terra cotta
	embellishments
Issued:	1999 in a limited edition of 500
Series:	The Court of Tutankhamun

			Price	
Tableau	Backstamp	U.S. $	Can. $	U.K. £
1. The Fan Bearer	Black			
2. Tutankhamun	Black		Complete set £495.00	
3. The Wine Pourer	Black			

Note: Commissioned by Compton & Woodhouse.

RW4731
VICTORIA

Designer:	Elizabeth Greenshields
Modeller:	Richard Moore
Height:	9", 22.9 cm
Colour:	Cream skirt; red jacket with gold buttons; red hat with white feather; black gloves and shoes; green striped packages tied with red ribbon
Issued:	1999-1999
Series:	Special Events

			Price	
Colourways	Backstamp	U.S. $	Can. $	U.K. £
Cream/red	Black	200.00	275.00	110.00

RW4733
QUEEN VICTORIA
Style Two

Modeller:	Richard Moore
Height:	8", 20.3 cm
Colour:	Red cloak with gold border and cream lining; cream and gold skirt
Issued:	1999 in a limited edition of 4,500
Series:	Queens of Britain

			Price	
Colourways	Backstamp	U.S. $	Can. $	U.K. £
Red/cream/gold	Black	425.00	550.00	245.00

Note: Commissioned by Compton & Woodhouse.

RW4734
HANNAH
Style One

Designer:	Elizabeth Greenshields
Modeller:	Richard Moore
Height:	6 ¼", 15.9 cm
Colour:	Pale green dress; peach rose and bows; pale yellow shawl; dark green hat
Issued:	1999 to the present
Series:	Les Petites

			Price	
Colourways	Backstamp	U.S. $	Can. $	U.K. £
Pale green/yellow	Black	—	338.00	76.00

RW4735
SPIRIT OF PEACE

Modeller:	Maureen Halson
Height:	12", 30.5 cm
Colour:	1. Pearl lustre
	2. White with pale blue highlights
Issued:	1. Pearl lustre: 1999 in a limited edition of 2,000
	2. White/blue: 1999 in a limited edition of 2,000

			Price	
Colourways	Backstamp	U.S. $	Can. $	U.K. £
1. Pearl lustre	Black	—	—	295.00
2. White/blue	Black	—	—	295.00

Note: Commissioned by Compton & Woodhouse.

RW4736
AMY
Style Two

Modeller:	David Lyttleton
Height:	9", 22.9 cm
Colour:	Pink dress, hat and shoe
Issued:	1999-1999
Series:	Figurine of the Year

				Price
Colourways	Backstamp	U.S. $	Can. $	U.K. £
Pink	Black	275.00	375.00	150.00

RW4737
FRANCESCA

Designer:	Elizabeth Greenshields
Modeller:	Richard Moore
Height:	9", 22.9 cm
Colour:	Yellow dress; brown fur-trimmed jacket; tan Afghan dog
Issued:	1999-1999
Series:	Collectors Society Exclusive

			Price	
Colourways	Backstamp	U.S. $	Can. $	U.K. £
Yellow/brown/tan	Black	250.00	300.00	135.00

RW4739
MOTHER AND CHILD
Style Two

Modeller: John Bromley
Height: 8 ¼", 21.0 cm
Colour: White
Issued: 1999

Colourways	Backstamp	U.S. $	Price Can. $	U.K. £
White	Black	175.00	250.00	110.00

Note: Commissioned by Compton & Woodhouse.

RW4741
MAISIE

Modeller: John Bromley
Height: 8 ½", 21.6 cm
Colour: Cream (Wallbody)
Issued: 1999 in a limited edition of 2,000
Series: Fashion Figurine of the Year (1920s)

Colourways	Backstamp	U.S. $	Price Can. $	U.K. £
Cream	Black	175.00	225.00	100.00

Note: Commissioned by Compton & Woodhouse.

RW4742
MARGERY

Designer: Elizabeth Greenshields
Modeller: Richard Moore
Height: Unknown
Colour: Blue dress with trim; marble base
Issued: 1999

Colourways	Backstamp	U.S. $	Price Can. $	U.K. £
Blue	Black	175.00	250.00	100.00

Note: Commissioned by the Townswomen's Guild.

RW4745
WORCESTERSHIRE COUNTY CRICKET CLUB

Designer: Elizabeth Greenshields
Modeller: Tim Perks
Height: Unknown
Colour: White
Issued: 1999

Colourways	Backstamp	U.S. $	Price Can. $	U.K. £
Unknown	Black	225.00	325.00	125.00

Photograph not available at press time

Note: Commissioned by Worcestershire County Cricket Club.

RW4749
I PRAY

Modeller: Sheila Mitchell
Height: 8 ¼", 21.0 cm
Colour: Blue pyjamas; brown teddy bear
Issued: 2000 in a limited edition of 2,000
Series: Children of the Future (NSPCC)

Colourways	Backstamp	U.S. $	Price Can. $	U.K. £
Unknown	Black	235.00	295.00	135.00

Note: Commissioned by Compton & Woodhouse.

RW4756
BETROTHAL (The)

Modeller: Maureen Halson
Height: 9 ½", 24.0 cm
Colour: Female: Pink dress with deeper pink flowers
           Male: Turquoise jacket and pants with gold buttons
Issued: 1999 in a limited edition of 2,450
Series: Dancing Lovers

Colourways	Backstamp	U.S. $	Price Can. $	U.K. £
Pink/turquoise/gold	Black	525.00	675.00	300.00

Photograph not available at press time

Note: Commissioned by Compton & Woodhouse.

RW4758
CELESTIA / DESTINY

Designer:	Elizabeth Greenshields
Modeller:	Richard Moore
Height:	9 ½", 24.0 cm
Colour:	1. Celestia: White dress; white ribbon with gold stars; gold star and crescent moon; gold numerals around base
	2. Destiny: Blue dress; white ribbon with gold stars; gold star and crescent moon; gold numerals around base
Issued:	1999 in a limited edition of 1,000
Series:	Millennium Collection

			Price	
Description	Backstamp	U.S. $	Can. $	U.K. £
1. Celestia	Black	—	—	200.00
2. Destiny	Black	—	—	200.00

RW4761
REFLECTION
Style Two

Modeller:	John Bromley
Height:	5", 12.7 cm
Colour:	White dress; pink ballet slippers
Issued:	1999 in a limited edition of 4,500
Series:	Waiting in the Wings

			Price	
Colourways	Backstamp	U.S. $	Can. $	U.K. £
White/pink	Black	—	—	145.00

Note: Commissioned by Compton & Woodhouse.

RW4765
BEST BUDDIES

Modeller:	Valerie Slusar
Height:	7 ¼", 18.4 cm
Colour:	Maroon sweater; lilac shorts and cap; brown hair and boots; white dog
Issued:	1999 in a limited edition of 1,000
Series:	Children of the World (UNICEF)

			Price	
Colourways	Backstamp	U.S. $	Can. $	U.K. £
Maroon/lilac/brown	Black	175.00	250.00	95.00

RW4768
LITTLE PRINCESS

Modeller: Valerie Slusar
Height: 6", 15.0 cm
Colour: Pale blue dress and hat; darker blue hat ribbon and shoes; doll wears pale pink dress
Issued: 1999 in a limited edition of 1,000
Series: Children of the World (UNICEF)

Colourways	Backstamp	U.S. $	Price Can. $	U.K. £
Pale blue	Black	175.00	250.00	95.00

RW4769
QUEEN ELIZABETH THE QUEEN MOTHER

Modeller: John Bromley
Height: 9", 22.9 cm
Colour: Red
Issued: 2000 in a limited edition of 9,500

Colourways	Backstamp	U.S. $	Price Can. $	U.K. £
Red	Black	—	—	198.00

Note: Commissioned by Compton & Woodhouse.

RW4770
PURR-FECT FRIENDS

Modeller: Valerie Slusar
Height: 6", 15.0 cm
Colour: Yellow dress edged in white; yellow hair ribbon; grey kitten
Issued: 1999 in a limited edition of 1,000
Series: Children of the World (UNICEF)

Colourways	Backstamp	U.S. $	Price Can. $	U.K. £
Yellow/white/grey	Black	175.00	250.00	89.00

RW4771
TWO'S COMPANY

Modeller: Valerie Slusar
Height: 6", 15.0 cm
Colour: Purple top; tan shorts and boots; white and black rabbit
Issued: 1999 in a limited edition of 1,000
Series: Children of the World (UNICEF)

Colourways	Backstamp	U.S. $	Price Can. $	U.K. £
Purple/tan	Black	175.00	225.00	89.00

RW4772
I HOPE

Modeller: Sheila Mitchell
Height: 8 ¼" 21.0 cm
Colour: White dress and dove; auburn hair
Issued: 2000 in a limited edition of 5,000
Series: Children of the Future (RSPCC)

Colourways	Backstamp	U.S. $	Price Can. $	U.K. £
Unknown	Black	—	—	135.00

Note: Commissioned by Compton & Woodhouse.

RW4773
PRETTY IN PINK

Modeller: Valerie Slusar
Height: 7 ¼", 18.4 cm
Colour: Pink dress with white frills; pink hair ribbon; brown basket and shoes
Issued: 1999 in a limited edition of 1,000
Series: Children of the World (UNICEF)

Colourways	Backstamp	U.S. $	Price Can. $	U.K. £
Pink/white/brown	Black	175.00	225.00	95.00

RW4774
QUEEN ELIZABETH II
Style Two

Modeller: Richard Moore
Height: 10", 25.4 cm
Colour: Cream gown; purple cloak trimmed with ermine and
decorated in gold
Issued: 1999 in a limited edition of 4,500

Colourways	Backstamp	U.S. $	Price Can. $	U.K. £
Cream/purple/gold	Black	—	—	245.00

Note: Commissioned by Compton & Woodhouse.

RW4776
PIGGYBACK RIDE

Modeller: Valerie Slusor
Height: 7", 17.8 cm
Colour: White T-shirt; blue dungarees; purple shoe;
golden brown teddy bear
Issued: 1999 in a limited edition of 1,000
Series: Children of the World (UNICEF)

Colourways	Backstamp	U.S. $	Price Can. $	U.K. £
White/blue/purple	Black	175.00	225.00	95.00

RW4777
MOTHER AND CHILD 2000

Modeller: Maureen Halson
Height: 8 ¾", 22.2 cm
Colour: Pale blue
Issued: 1999 in a limited edition of 5,000
Varieties: RW4589 First Kiss
Series: Tender Moments

Colourways	Backstamp	U.S. $	Price Can. $	U.K. £
Pale blue	Black	—	—	124.00

Note: Commissioned by Compton & Woodhouse.

RW4778
ANNIVERSARY 2000

Modeller:	John Bromley
Height:	8 ½", 21.6 cm
Colour:	White dress; brown hair; bouquet of red roses
Issued:	2000-2000
Series:	Anniversary Figurine of the Year

			Price	
Colourways	Backstamp	U.S. $	Can. $	U.K. £
White	Black	—	—	150.00

Note: Commissioned by Compton & Woodhouse.

RW4779
HANNAH
Style Two

Modeller:	John Bromley
Height:	8 ½", 21.6 cm
Colour:	Tinted lustre dress; blonde hair; silver-plated purse
Issued:	2000-2000
Series:	Figurine of the Year

			Price	
Colourways	Backstamp	U.S. $	Can. $	U.K. £
Tinted lustre	Black	—	—	160.00

Note: Commissioned by Compton & Woodhouse.

RW4791
THE JEWELS OF CLEOPATRA TABLEAU (Four pieces)
Cheetah

Modeller:	John Bromley
Height:	4", 10.1 cm
Colour:	Naturalistically coloured; bronze collar with gold cross
Issued:	2000 in a limited edition of 500
Series:	The Jewels of Cleopatra

Cleopatra

Modeller:	John Bromley
Height:	9", 22.9 cm
Colour:	White tunic; red, blue and gold jewelled collar; gold headdress, sandals and bracelets; terracotta throne
Issued:	2000 in a limited edition of 500
Series:	The Jewels of Cleopatra

Jewel Box

Modeller:	John Bromley
Height:	2", 5.0 cm
Colour:	Terracotta; gold treasures
Issued:	2000 in a limited edition of 500
Series:	The Jewels of Cleopatra

Slave

Modeller:	John Bromley
Height:	5 ½", 14.0 cm
Colour:	Blue and gold headdress
Issued:	2000 in a limited edition of 500
Series:	The Jewels of Cleopatra

Tableau	Backstamp	U.S. $	Price Can. $	U.K. £
1. Cheetah	Black			
2. Cleopatra	Black			
3. Jewel Box	Black		Complete set £550.00	
4. Slave	Black			

Note: Commissioned by Compton & Woodhouse.

RW4795
MARGARET

Designer: Elizabeth Greenshields
Modeller: Richard Moore
Height: 9 ¼", 23.5 cm
Colour: Dark green jacket; yellow skirt and hat; gold walking cane
Issued: 2000-2000
Series: Premiere Figurine of the Year

| | | | Price | |
Colourways	Backstamp	U.S. $	Can. $	U.K. £
Dark green/yellow	Black	—	532.00	125.00

RW4796
CHARIS (Day - bust)

Modeller: Arnold Machin
Height: 10", 25.4 cm
Colour: Porcelain, glazed
Issued: 1999 in a limited edition of 500
Varieties: P18 Day (bust)

| | | | Price | |
Description	Backstamp	U.S. $	Can. $	U.K. £
Porcelain, glazed	Black	225.00	300.00	130.00

Note: Commissioned by Compton & Woodhouse.

RW4797
MILLIE
Style Two

Designer: Elizabeth Greenshields
Modeller: Richard Moore
Height: 9 ¼", 23.5 cm
Colour: Red jacket with fur trim; tan skirt; tan hat with red ribbon and bow; black and white dog
Issued: 2000-2000
Series: Collectors Club Exclusive

| | | | Price | |
Colourways	Backstamp	U.S. $	Can. $	U.K. £
Red/tan	Black	—	—	135.00

RW4805
ANNE
Style Two

Designer: Elizabeth Greenshields
Modeller: Richard Moore
Height: 6 ¼", 15.9 cm
Colour: Lavender and mauve
Issued: 1999 to the present
Series: Les Petites

Colourways	Backstamp	U.S. $	Price Can. $	U.K. £
Lavender/mauve	Black	—	306.00	76.00

RW4806
NEW DAWN

Modeller: Carolyn Froud
Height: 9", 22.9 cm
Colour: White dress; dark brown hair; circlet of flowers in her hair
Issued: 2000 in a limited edition of 4,950

Colourways	Backstamp	U.S. $	Price Can. $	U.K. £
White	Black	—	—	175.00

Note: Commissioned by Compton & Woodhouse.

Copy of the *Watteau Figure (Female, standing)*
sketch by Agnes Pinder-Davis (RW3403)

P SERIES

Copy of the *Salvage* sketch
by Eileen Soper (RW3370)

Collectors Society

...exclusively for collectors of Royal Worcester

With a heritage which spans almost 250 years, Royal Worcester has established an unrivalled reputation for excellence which has earned royal patronage continuously since 1789. It is in this great tradition that Royal Worcester continues to manufacture products to the highest standards today, ensuring that there is no better time to enhance or start a Royal Worcester collection.

SOCIETY MEMBERSHIP BENEFITS INCLUDE:

• Exclusive complimentary gift, Royal Worcester's Fine Bone China figurine, Katie, when you join in the year 2000.

• Opportunity to purchase products created exclusively for Society members, including the second annual Collectors Society figurine, Millie. Millie is limited to manufacture during the year 2000 only and is available to purchase only upon presentation of your Royal Worcester Collectors Society membership card.

• Personalised membership card, valid for 12 months from the date of joining the Society.

• VIP invitation to visit Royal Worcester's Visitor Centre, Factory and Museum. Free entry for up to four people (includes member) upon presentation of your valid membership card. (It is advisable to book in advance).

• Royal Worcester's exclusive magazine for members, 'Society' with a variety of features, product news, competitions, letters, and exclusive offers.

• Invitation to Royal Worcester Special Events.

Join today to receive your complimentary gift

Please send your completed application form and payment to:
Royal Worcester Collectors Society, Royal Worcester, Severn Street, Worcester WR1 2NE.

All applications in Canada should be sent to:
Royal Worcester Collectors Society (Canadian Division)
c/o Northdale Trading Ltd., 55-D East Beaver Creek Road, Richmond Hill, Ontario L4B IE8.

Please complete all details on reverse in ink and <u>BLOCK CAPITALS.</u>

MEMBERSHIP DETAILS

The Royal Worcester Collectors Society is open to applicants aged 18 and over.
I am pleased to join The Royal Worcester Collectors Society for one year at a cost of:
UK Residents £28.00. Canada Residents C$60.00 (plus applicable taxes).

I am joining for Myself ☐   As a Gift ☐

Please complete details of new member below:

Title (Mr/Mrs/Ms etc.): ....   Sex: Male ☐ Female ☐

1st name: ....   2nd Initial: ....

Last name: ....   Date of Birth: ☐☐ / ☐☐ / ☐☐

Address: ....

Town/City: ....   Postcode: ....

Country: ....   Tel No: ....

Preferred stockist: Where you purchase/would like to purchase Royal Worcester products.

Stockist's name: ....   Town: ....

Please tick box if you do not wish to receive information from associated companies.   ☐

IN THE UK, TO JOIN PLEASE COMPLETE THIS APPLICATION FORM AND EITHER:

A) take it to a Royal Worcester Collectors Society participating retailer with your payment of £28.00 (by cheque or credit card payable to the retailer) who will present you with your complimentary gift Katie and Temporary Membership Card. Royal Worcester will send your Welcome Pack directly to your home.* OR:

B) send it FREEPOST to Royal Worcester with your payment. Your Complimentary Gift Katie and Welcome Pack, including your 12 month membership card, will be sent directly to your home.*

*Allow 28 days for delivery

IN CANADA, APPLICATIONS MAY ONLY BE MADE BY POST TO NORTHDALE TRADING LIMITED.

For postal applications only, please tick one of the following:

☐ I enclose a cheque/postal order for £28.00 for membership made payable to Royal Worcester (UK)/or C$60.00 plus applicable taxes made payable to Northdale Trading Limited (Canada). Please ensure that your address is clearly written on the reverse of all cheques.

☐ Please charge my Visa/Mastercard/Switch/Delta/Diners/Amex with the sum of £28.00 (UK)/or charge my Visa/Mastercard with the sum of C$60.00 plus applicable taxes (Canada).

Card No: ☐☐☐☐☐☐☐☐☐☐☐☐☐☐☐☐☐☐☐

Expiry Date: ☐☐ / ☐☐   Valid From: ☐☐ / ☐☐

Name on Card: ....   Switch Issue No: ☐☐

Signature: ....   Date: ....

Name and billing address of cardholder (*if different from the name and address given above*).

Title (Mr/Mrs/Ms etc.): ....   Last name: ....

Address: ....

Town/City: ....   Postcode: ....

Country: ....   Tel No: ....

P2
ALPHEUS / CORYDON

Modeller: Neal French
Height: 5 ½", 14.0 cm
Colour: 1. **Alpheus:** Turquoise jacket; striped breeches; pink hat
2. **Corydon:** Purple breeches; white top with purple pattern; green hat
3. Porcelain, glazed
Issued: 1970-1971
Series: Fontainebleau Series

Description	Backstamp	U.S. $	Price Can. $	U.K. £
1. Alpheus	Black	210.00	275.00	120.00
2. Corydon	Black	210.00	275.00	120.00
3. Porcelain, glazed	Black	175.00	225.00	100.00

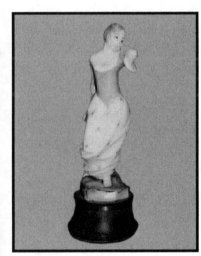

P3
DELIA / HELENA

Modeller: Neal French
Height: 5 ½", 14.0 cm
Colour: 1. **Delia:** White skirt with pink dots; pink top
2. **Helena:** Red skirt; red, black and white striped top
3. Porcelain, glazed
Issued: 1970-1971
Series: Fontainebleau Series

Description	Backstamp	U.S.$	Price Can. $	U.K. £
1. Delia	Black	210.00	275.00	120.00
2. Helena	Black	210.00	275.00	120.00
2. Porcelain, glazed	Black	175.00	225.00	100.00

P4
DAPHNIS / SYLVANUS

Modeller: Neal French
Height: 5 ½", 14.0 cm
Colour: 1. **Daphnis:** Turquoise breeches; striped jacket; white stockings; black shoes
2. **Sylvanus:** Green jacket; white breeches; green and white striped stockings; red shoe
3. Porcelain, glazed
Issued: 1970-1971
Series: Fontainebleau Series

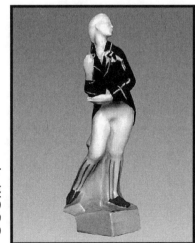

Description	Backstamp	U.S. $	Price Can. $	U.K. £
1. Daphnis	Black	210.00	275.00	120.00
2. Sylvanus	Black	210.00	275.00	120.00
3. Porcelain, glazed	Black	175.00	225.00	100.00

P5
CHLOE / SCYLLA

Modeller:	Neal French
Height:	5 ½", 14.0 cm
Colour:	1. **Chloe:** White skirt with green pattern; yellow bodice
	2. **Scylla:** Yellow skirt; turquoise and white bodice
	3. Porcelain, glazed
Issued:	1970-1971
Series:	Fontainebleau Series

		Price		
Description	Backstamp	U.S. $	Can. $	U.K. £
1. Chloe	Black	210.00	275.00	120.00
2. Scylla	Black	210.00	275.00	120.00
3. Porcelain, glazed	Black	175.00	225.00	100.00

P6
PARIS /STREPHON

Modeller:	Neal French
Height:	5 ½", 13.3 cm
Colour:	1. **Paris:** Brown shirt; blue and white striped breeches; purple shoes and hat; yellow sack
	2. **Strephon:** White shirt with red dots; yellow breeches; green hat; black shoes; white sack
	3. Porcelain, glazed
Issued:	1970-1971
Series:	Fontainebleau Series

		Price		
Description	Backstamp	U.S. $	Can. $	U.K. £
1. Paris	Black	210.00	275.00	120.00
2. Strephon	Black	210.00	275.00	120.00
3. Porcelain, glazed	Black	175.00	225.00	100.00

P7
FLORINDA / PHYLLIS

Modeller:	Neal French
Height:	5 ½", 14.0 cm
Colour:	1. **Florinda:** Pink skirt; blue bodice; yellow bow
	2. **Phyllis:** White skirt with blue pattern; yellow overskirt; pink and white striped bodice; turquoise bow
	3. Porcelain, glazed
Issued:	1. **Florinda:** 1970-1971
	2. **Phyllis:** 1970-1971
	3. Porcelain, glazed: 1971
Series:	Fontainebleau Series

		Price		
Desscription	Backstamp	U.S. $	Can. $	U.K. £
1. Florinda	Black	210.00	275.00	120.00
2. Phyllis	Black	210.00	275.00	120.00
2. Porcelain, glazed	Black	175.00	225.00	100.00

P10
SPRING
Style Three

Modeller: Arnold Machin
Height: 17 ¾", 45.1 cm
Colour: Porcelain and ormalou
Issued: 1968 in a limited edition of 150
Series: The Four Seasons, Series Two

Colourways	Backstamp	U.S. $	Price Can. $	U.K. £
Porcelain, glazed	Black	600.00	775.00	350.00

Note: Commissioned by Thomas Goode & Co.

P11
SUMMER
Style Two

Modeller: Arnold Machin
Height: 18", 45.7 cm
Colour: Porcelain and ormalou
Issued: 1968 in a limited edition of 50
Series: The Four Seasons, Series Two

Colourways	Backstamp	U.S. $	Price Can. $	U.K. £
Porcelain, glazed	Black	600.00	775.00	350.00

Note: Commissioned by Thomas Goode & Co.

P12
AUTUMN
Style Two

Modeller: Arnold Machin
Height: 17 ¾", 45.1 cm
Colour: Porcelain and ormalou
Issued: 1968 in a limited edition of 150
Series: The Four Seasons, Series Two

Colourways	Backstamp	U.S. $	Price Can. $	U.K. £
Porcelain, glazed	Black	600.00	775.00	350.00

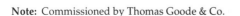

Note: Commissioned by Thomas Goode & Co.

P13
WINTER
Style Two

Modeller: Arnold Machin
Height: 17 ¾", 45.1 cm
Colour: Porcelain and ormalou
Issued: 1968 in a limited edition of 150
Series: The Four Seasons, Series Two

Colourways	Backstamp	U.S. $	Price Can. $	U.K. £
Porcelain, glazed	Black	600.00	775.00	350.00

Note: Commissioned by Thomas Goode & Co.

P17
NIGHT (BUST)

Modeller: Arnold Machin
Height: 10 ½", 26.7 cm
Colour: Porcelain, glazed
Issued: 1970 in a limited edition of 250
Varieties: RW4780 Charis (Night)

Colourways	Backstamp	U.S. $	Price Can. $	U.K. £
Porcelain, glazed	Black	600.00	775.00	350.00

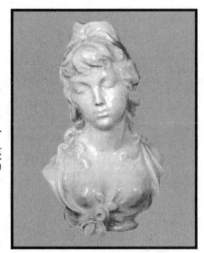

Note: Also available on wooden plinth.

P18
DAY (bust)
Style One

Modeller: Arnold Machin
Height: 10 ½", 26.7 cm
Colour: Porcelain, glazed
Issued: 1970 in a limited edition of 250

Colourways	Backstamp	U.S. $	Price Can. $	U.K. £
Porcelain, glazed	Black	600.00	775.00	350.00

Note: Also available on wooden plinth.

INDICES

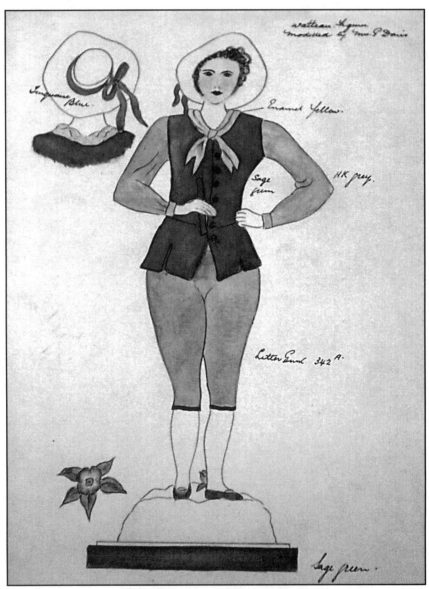

Copy of the *Watteau Figure (Male, standing)*
sketch by Agnes Pinder-Davis (RW3402)

COLLECTING BY SERIES

À LA MODE

Chic (1933)	RW4150
En Repose (1926)	RW4139
Promenade (1922)	RW4153
Soirée (1926)	RW4140

AGE OF ELEGANCE
Series One

The Dandy	RW3986
Delettante	RW3984
Grace, Style One	RW4011
Innocence	RW3985
The Paramour	RW3987
Philanderer	RW4012

Series Two

A Dazzling Celebration (Lady Cecilia)	RW4718
The Painted Fan (Lucinda)	RW4702

AGE OF ROMANCE
Series One

Rachel, Style One	RW3546
Sarah, Style One	RW3547
Spring Morn	RW3546
Summer's Day	RW3547

Series Two

Autumn Song	RW4087
Belle of the Ball, Style One	RW4079
The Bride	RW4119
Charity	RW4044
Coming of Age	RW4064
Crinoline Lady	RW4032
Debutante	RW4090
Diana, Style One	RW4090
Emily, Style Two	RW4079
Equestrienne	RW4066
Flirtation, Style One	RW4065
Fragrance	RW4039
Invitation, Style Two	RW4038
Masquerade, Style Two	RW4149
Morning Walk	RW4023
Rebecca, Style Two	RW4083
Sincerity	RW4062
Spring Fair	RW4024
Summertime	RW4058
Sunday Morning	RW4041
Wedding Day (Boy)	RW4026
Wedding Day (Girl)	RW4025
Winter Waltz	RW4033
Winter's Morn	RW4083

Series Three

A Gift of Live	RW4690
True Love	RW4722
With Love	RW4628

AGE OF ROMANCE MINIATURES

Affection	RW4113
Coquette, Style Two	RW4091
Evening Engagement	RW4114
March Winds	RW4115
Mary, Mary	RW4098
Modesty	RW4086
Party Dress	RW4097
Rendezvous	RW4112

ALICE IN WONDERLAND

Alice, Style One	RW3608
Cheshire Cat	RW3609
The Dodo	RW3613
The Duchess	RW3612
Mock Turtle	RW3610
Old Father William	RW3614
White Rabbit	RW3611

ANNIVERSARY COLLECTION

Anniversary	RW4603
Golden Anniversary	RW4603
Ruby Anniversary	RW4603
Silver Anniversary	RW4603

ANNIVERSARY FIGURINE OF THE YEAR

A Day to Remember	RW4709
Anniversary 2000	RW4778

ART DECO

Blithe Spirit	RW3175
The Fan	RW3398
Grace, Style Two	RW3177
The Greeting	RW3397
Joy, Style One	RW3172
Pirouette	RW3176
Soubrette	RW3171

BALLET DANCERS

Alicia	RW3175
Anita	RW3171
Anna	RW3174
Irina	RW3177
Natasha, Style One	RW3176
Tamara	RW3172
Tatiana	RW3173

BISQUE FIGURES

La Fleur	RW3586
Le Miroir	RW3588
Le Panier	RW3585
L'Oiseau	RW3587

BOER WAR SOLDIERS

Colonial Trooper	RW2108
Guardsman	RW2111
Handy Man	RW2110
Imperial Yeoman	RW2107
Soldier of the Black Watch, First Version	RW2109A
Soldier of the Black Watch, Second Version	RW2109B
Soldier of the Imperial Forces	RW2106

BOYS AND GIRLS COME OUT TO PLAY

Ballet	RW4508
Dressing Up	RW4509
First Flight	RW4517
First Prize	RW4522
See-Saw	RW4515

BRIEF ENCOUNTERS

Dinner at Eight	RW4710

CHILDREN OF THE FUTURE (NSPCC)

I Dream	RW4727
I Hope	RW4772
I Pray	RW4749
I Wish	RW4698

CHILDREN OF THE NATIONS

Burmah	RW3068
China	RW3073
Egypt	RW3066
England	RW3075
Greece	RW3069
Holland	RW3074
India	RW3071
Ireland	RW3178
Italy	RW3067
Japan	RW3072
Scotland	RW3104
Spain	RW3070
Wales	RW3103

CHILDREN OF THE WORLD (UNICEF)

Best Buddies	RW4765
Little Princess	RW4768
Piggyback Ride	RW4776
Pretty in Pink	RW4773
Purr-fect Friends	RW4770
Two's Company	RW4771

CHINESE DANCERS

Chinese Dancer (Female)	RW3195
Chinese Dancer (Male)	RW3194

CHINOISERIE CHILDREN

Chinoiserie Boy	RW3354
Chinoiserie Girl (Head down)	RW3348
Chinoiserie Girl (Head up)	RW3362

CHINOISERIE FIGURES

Chinoiserie Figure Holding Bird (Female)	RW3446
Chinoiserie Figure Holding Bird (Male)	RW3447
Chinoiserie Figure (Female, kneeling)	RW3398
Chinoiserie Figure (Female, standing)	RW3400
Chinoiserie Figure (Male, kneeling)	RW3397
Chinoiserie Figure (Male, standing)	RW3399

CHINOISERIE SAYINGS

Apple of Your Eye	RW3497
Don't Let the Cat Out of the Bag	RW3494
Early Bird	RW3498
Funny Fish	RW3493
Hen Party	RW3501
Joy Ride	RW3496
Lucky Spider	RW3492
Mad as a Hatter	RW3502
Sea Scout	RW3491
Slow Coach	RW3495
Two's Company, Three's None	RW3499
Wise as an Owl	RW3500

CLASSICAL SENTIMENTS

The Last Dance	RW4619

COLLECTORS CLUB FIGURES

Katie, Style Two	RW4677
Lucy	RW4607

COLLECTORS SOCIETY EXCLUSIVES

Francesca	RW4737
Millie, Style Two	RW4797

THE COURT OF TUTANKHAMUN (TABLEAU)

The Fan Bearer	RW4730
Tutankhamun	RW4730
The Wine Pourer	RW4730

THE CRIES OF LONDON

"A Mery New Song"	RW3252
Daisy, Style One	RW3560
"Delicate Cowcumbers to Pickle"	RW3227
"Fair Cherryes"	RW3300
"Fine Writeing Inkes"	RW3299
Heather	RW3543
"London Gazette Here"	RW3271
"Ripe 'Speragus"	RW3250
Rose, Style Two	RW3541
Violet	RW3542

DANCING LOVERS

The Betrothal	RW4657
The Tryst	RW4687

DAY DREAMS

Memories	RW4656
Reflection, Style One	RW4654
Thoughtful	RW4666
Wistful	RW4604

DAYS OF THE WEEK

Monday's Child (Boy)	RW3519
Monday's Child (Girl)	RW3257
Tuesday's Child (Boy)	RW3534
Tuesday's Child (Girl)	RW3258
Wednesday's Child (Boy)	RW3521
Wednesday's Child (Girl)	RW3259
Thursday's Child (Boy)	RW3260
Thursday's Child (Girl)	RW3522
Friday's Child (Boy)	RW3261
Friday's Child (Girl)	RW3523
Saturday's Child (Boy)	RW3524
Saturday's Child (Girl)	RW3562
Sunday's Child (Boy)	RW3256
Sunday's Child (Girl)	RW3518

DEBUTANTES

Lady Cicely	RW4670
Lady Emma, Style Two	RW4665
Lady Hannah, Style Two	RW4669
Lady Henrietta	RW4728
Lady Louisa	RW4664
Lady Sarah, Style Two	RW4724
Lady Sophie, Style Two	RW4671

ENCHANTED EVENINGS

Belle of the Ball, Style Two	RW4562
The Fairest Rose	RW4547
The First Quadrille (Henrietta)	RW4538
The Last Waltz	RW4524
The Masquerade Begins	RW4507
Queen of Hearts	RW4532
Royal Debut	RW4569
Sweetest Valentine	RW4552

ENGLISH GIRLS

City Girl	RW4423
Country Girl	RW4412
Mayfair Girl	RW4411
Richmond Girl	RW4288
Weekend Girl	RW4414
West End Girl	RW4413

EQUESTRIAN SERIES

At the Meet	RW3114
Cantering to the Post	RW3117
Huntsman and Hounds	RW3115
Over the Sticks	RW3116

FASHIONABLE VICTORIANS

Lady Alexandra	RW4649
Lady Alice	RW4624
Lady Beatrice	RW4631
Lady Charlotte	RW4616
Lady Elizabeth	RW4581
Lady Emma, Style One	RW4580
Lady Hannah, Style One	RW4588A
Lady Jane	RW4582
Lady Louise	RW4650
Lady Sarah, Style One	RW4588B
Lady Sophie, Style One	RW4630
Lady Victoria	RW4625

FASHION FIGURINE OF THE YEAR

Lady Violet (1909)	RW4577
Maisie (1920s)	RW4741

FEMALE DANCING FIGURES

Female Dancing Figure, Style One	RW2654
Female Dancing Figure, Style Two	RW2655
Lady with Mask - Falsehood	RW2650
Lady with Mirror - Truth	RW2649

FESTIVE COUNTRY DAYS

Noelle	RW4539
The Queen of the May	RW4529
The Village Bride	RW4548

FIGURINE OF THE YEAR

Amy, Style Two (1999)	RW4736
Hannah, Style Two (2000)	RW4779
Isabelle (1998)	RW4688
Serena (1997)	RW4681

FIRST WORLD WAR SOLDIERS

French Soldier	RW2582
Soldier of the First World War (Seated)	RW2646
Soldier of the First World War (Standing)	RW2645
Soldier of the Worcestershire Regiment	RW2591
Territorial Soldier	RW2588

FONTAINEBLEAU

Alpheus	P2
Chloe	P5
Corydon	P2
Daphnis	P4
Delia	P3
Helena	P3
Florinda	P7
Paris	P6
Phyllis	P7
Scylla	P5
Strephon	P6
Sylvanus	P4

FORCES OF CREATION

Aquamarine (Water)	RW4694
Earth Song	RW4699
Flame Dance (Fire)	RW4689
Mistral (Air)	RW4697

FOUR SEASONS
Series One

Autumn, Style One	RW3341
Spring, Style Two	RW3342
Summer, Style One	RW3339
Winter, Style One	RW3340

Series Two

Autumn, Style Two	P12
Spring, Style Three	P10
Summer, Style Two	P11
Winter, Style Two	P13

Series Three

Autumn, Style Three	RW4262
Spring, Style Four	RW4168B
Summer, Style Three	RW4261
Winter, Style Three	RW4207

Series Four

Autumn, Style Four	RW4518
Spring, Style Five	RW4504
Summer, Style Four	RW4510
Winter, Style Four	RW4523

GLITTERING OCCASIONS

Evening Romance	RW4712
Graduation Night	RW4648
Grand Entrance	RW4707
Masked Ball	RW4659
May Ball	RW4676
Night at the Opera	RW4638
Royal Premiere	RW4603
Viennese Waltz	RW4627

GOLDEN MOMENTS

Anniversary	RW4603
Birthday Wish	RW4661
Bride and Groom (Cake Decoration)	RW4632
Bridesmaid, Style Two	RW4629
Celebration	RW4647
Congratulations	RW4611
Friendship	RW4601
From All of Us	RW4638
Loving You	RW4666
Mother and Child, Style One	RW4634
New Arrival, Style Two	RW4660
Special Mum	RW4654
Special Occasion	RW4612
Thank You	RW4587
The Wedding Day, Style Two	RW4594

THE GRACEFUL ARTS

Embroidery	RW4600
Music, Style Two	RW4680
Painting	RW4579
Poetry	RW4708

HIGH SOCIETY

Ascot Lady	RW4662
Garden Party	RW4647
Glyndebourne	RW4595B
Knightsbridge	RW4700
Ladies Day	RW4667
Royal Enclosure	RW4641
Summer Regatta	RW4661
Tea at the Ritz	RW4711

HISTORICAL FIGURES

Anne Boleyn	RW2652
Charles I	RW2651
Charles II	RW2672
Elizabeth I, Style One	RW2648
Edward VI	RW2643
Henry VIII, Style One	RW2637
Mary, Queen of Scots, Style One	RW2634
Sir Walter Raleigh	RW2668

HISTORICAL MILITARY FIGURES

The Admiral 1780	RW2661
Officer of the Coldstream Guards 1815	
First Version	RW2635
Second Version	RW2676
Third Version	RW3675
Officer of the French Marines	RW2629
Officer of the Royal Artillery 1815	RW2658
Officer of the Seaforth Highlanders 1812	RW2657
Officer of the Scots Guards	RW3677
Officer of the 17th Dragoon Guards 1814	RW2677
Officer of the 3rd Dragoon Guards 1806	RW2675
Officer of the 29th Foot (Worcestershire Regiment) 1812	RW3535

HOLLYWOOD GLAMOUR

Olivia, Style One	RW4571
Liz	RW4573
Bette	RW4575

HOUSE OF ELLIOT

Moonlight Cascade	RW4706
Strolling in Satin	RW4644

JANE AUSTEN COLLECTION

Anne Elliot	RW4349
Catherine Morland	RW4362
Elizabeth Bennet	RW4348
Emma Woodhouse	RW4347
Fanny Price	RW4361
Lady Susan	RW4363

JANE AUSTEN HEROINES
(Museum of Costume, Bath)

Emma (Woodhouse)	RW4705

THE JEWELS OF CLEOPATRA (TABLEAU)

Cheetah	RW4791
Cleopatra	RW4791
Jewel Box	RW4791
Slave	RW4791

KATIE'S DAY

Bath Time	RW4466
Bed Time	RW4473
Play Time	RW4484
School Time	RW4472
Story Time	RW4483
Tea Time, Style Two	RW4474

MICHAEL, TOMMY, MISCHIEF AND JOAN

Joan	RW2915
Michael	RW2912
Mischief	RW2914
Tommy	RW2913

MILITARY COMMANDERS

Alexander (The Great)	RW3956
The Duke of Marlborough	RW3914
The Duke of Wellington	RW3870
Eugene de Beauharnais	RW4055
(George) Washington	RW3897
Napoleon Bonaparte	RW3860
Richard Coeur de Lion	RW4034
Simon Bolivar	RW4076
William The Conqueror	RW4067

MILLENNIUM COLLECTION

Celestia	RW4758
Destiny	RW4758
Eternity	RW4726
Millennia	RW4721

MONTHS OF THE YEAR

January	RW3452
February	RW3453
March	RW3454
April	RW3416
May	RW3455
June, Style Two	RW3456
July	RW3440
August	RW3441
September	RW3457
October	RW3417
November	RW3418
December	RW3458

MOTHER'S LOVE

First Steps	RW4459
New Arrival, Style One	RW4488
Once Upon a Time	RW4468
Sweet Dreams	RW4408

MOTHER OF THE YEAR FIGURINES

Mother's Love	RW4713

MY FAIR LADIES

Lady Camille	RW4672
Lady Dorothy	RW4678
Lady Emily	RW4668
Lady Helena	RW4679
Lady Margaret	RW4657

NATIONAL SOCIETY FOR THE PREVENTION OF CRUELTY TO CHILDREN (NSPCC)

Love	RW4323
Lullaby	RW4442
A Posy For Mother	RW4499

THE 1920S VOGUE COLLECTION

Annie (1927)	RW4543
Bea (1922)	RW4550
Clara (1925)	RW4514
Constance (1924)	RW4561
Daisy, Style Two (1922)	RW4519
Diana, Style Two (1921)	RW4512
Dolly	RW4576
Eleanor (1928)	RW4555
Ellen	RW4540
Evie (1923)	RW4554
Irene (1920)	RW4567
Kitty (1928)	RW4537
Millie, Style One (1926)	RW4520
Minnie (1929)	RW4544
Molly	RW4527
Poppy (1924)	RW4521

NURSERY RHYMES

Goosey Goosey Gander	RW3304
Little Boy Blue	RW3306
Little Jack Horner	RW3305
Little Miss Muffet	RW3301
Polly Put the Kettle On	RW3303

NURSING SISTERS

Sister, Guys Hospital, 1960	RW4645
Sister, Nightingale Training School St. Thomas' Hospital (London)	RW3663
Sister, The London Hospital	RW3662
Sister, The University College Hospital, London	RW3771

OLD COUNTRY WAYS

A Farmer's Wife	RW4373
The Milkmaid	RW4458
Rosie Picking Apples	RW4322
The Shepherdess, Style Two	RW4441

OUR CHERISHED MOMENTS

A Present for Santa	RW4565
The Christening	RW4545
Mothering Sunday	RW4560
The Wedding Day, Style One	RW4551

PAPAL GUARD

An Officer of the Palatine Guard	RW3595
Colonel of the Noble Guard in Gala Uniform	RW3594
Papal Gendarme	RW3596
The Privy Chamberlain of the Sword and Cape to the Pope in the Spanish Costume	RW3589
Trooper of the Swiss Guard of His Holiness the Pope	RW3580

PASTORAL COLLECTION

Baker's Wife	RW4583
Goose Girl	RW4566
Market Day	RW4549
Sunday Best	RW4557

LES PETITES

Annabel	RW4646
Anne, Style Two	RW4805
Bridesmaid	RW4629
Caroline, Style Two	RW4608
Catherine	RW4611
Christina	RW4715
Emily, Style Three	RW4620
Fiona	RW4608
Hannah, Style One	RW4734
Jennifer	RW4696
Joanne	RW4717
Juliette	RW4587
Kate	RW4620
Mary	RW4695
Nicola	RW4629
Rachel, Style Two	RW4587
Rebecca, Style Three	RW4621
Sarah, Style Two	RW4621

PLAYTIME

First Aid	RW3756
Master Mariner	RW3755
Poupée	RW3754
Sheriff	RW3757
Treasure Trove	RW3748
Young England	RW3747

PRECIOUS MOMENTS

Midnight Rendezvous	RW4633
Secret Garden	RW4703

PREMIERE FIGURINE OF THE YEAR

Grace, Style Three (1999)	RW4725
Margaret (2000)	RW4795
Natasha, Style Two (1998)	RW4685

QUEENS OF BRITAIN

Mary, Queen of Scots, Style Two	RW4701
Queen Victoria, Style Two	RW4733

QUEENS REGNANT

Queen Anne	RW3938
Queen Elizabeth I, Style Two	RW3937
Queen Elizabeth II, Style One	RW3941
Queen Mary I	RW3936
Queen Mary II	RW3939
Queen Victoria, Style One	RW3940

RACING STUDIES

At the Start, Style One, No. 4	RW3959A
At the Start, Style Two No. 6	RW3959B
By a Short Head	RW3948
Cheltenham	RW3952
Grundy with Pat Eddery Up	RW3982
Mistral and Lester Piggot	RW4015

RED INDIAN SERIES

Indian Brave	RW2908
Indian Chief	RW2907
Indian Squaw with Child on Back	RW2909
Indian Squaw with Child on Shoulder	RW2910

THE ROARING TWENTIES

Annie (1927)	RW4543
Bea (1922)	RW4550
Clara (1925)	RW4514
Constance (1924)	RW4561
Daisy, Style Two (1922)	RW4519
Diana, Style Two (1921)	RW4512
Dolly	RW4576
Eleanor (1928)	RW4555
Ellen	RW4540
Evie (1923)	RW4554
Irene (1920)	RW4567
Kitty (1928)	RW4537
Millie, Style One (1926)	RW4520
Minnie (1929)	RW4544
Molly	RW4527
Poppy (1924)	RW4521

SPECIAL EVENTS

Anne, Style One (1997)	RW4609
Elizabeth, Style Two (1998)	RW4716
Tanya (1998)	RW4711
Victoria (1999)	RW4731

SPIRIT OF THE DANCE

Dance of Time	RW4652
Scarf Dancer	RW4503

SPLENDOUR AT COURT

A Celebration at Windsor	RW4597
A Royal Presentation	RW4586
The Embassy Ball	RW4691
The Golden Jubilee Ball	RW4617
Jewel in the Crown	RW4683
Royal Anniversary	RW4674

SUMMER ROMANCE

Alice, Style Three	RW4647
Amy, Style One	RW4637
Charlotte	RW4595A
Claire	RW4653
Jane	RW4604
Jessica	RW4615
Laura	RW4601
Olivia, Style Two	RW4639
Sophie	RW4627

SUR LA PLAGE

Baigneuse (La Plongée Attendue)	RW3947
Jeux de Plage	RW3950
L'Impetueux	RW3953
Leçon à la Mer	RW3954
Plonguer	RW3946
Preference	RW3945

SWEET POSY COLLECTION

Sweet Anemone	RW4606
Sweet Astor	RW4623
Sweet Daffodil	RW4643
Sweet Daisy	RW4602B
Sweet Forget-Me-Not	RW4599
Sweet Holly	RW4584
Sweet Pansy	RW4642
Sweet Peony	RW4613
Sweet Primrose	RW4602A
Sweet Rose	RW4574
Sweet Snowdrop	RW4635
Sweet Violet	RW4585

SYLVAN NYMPHS

Nymph with Convoulvulus	RW4226
Nymph with Daisy	RW4222
Nymph with Hairbell	RW4228
Nymph with Snowdrop	RW4227
Nymph with Viola	RW4229
Nymph with Winter Jasmine	RW4223

TENDER MOMENTS

First Kiss	RW4589
First Love	RW4692
First Smile	RW4622
First Teddy	RW4682
First Touch	RW4572
Mother and Child 2000	RW4777

TISSOT COLLECTION

First Dance, Style Two	RW4591

UPSTAIRS, DOWNSTAIRS

Chamber Maid	RW4368
Cook	RW4385
Daughter of the House	RW4440
Gentleman of the House	RW4428
Governess and Child	RW4446
Lady of the House	RW4415
Laundry Maid	RW4357
Parlour Maid	RW4369
Scullery Maid	RW4371

VICTORIAN LADIES

Alice, Style Two	RW3887
Beatrice	RW3681
Bridget	RW3842
Caroline, Style One	RW3682
Cecilia	RW3892
Charlotte and Jane	RW3804
Elaine	RW3877
Elizabeth, Style One	RW3774
Emily, Style One	RW3841
Felicity	RW3878
Lisette	RW3642
Louisa	RW3688
Madelaine	RW3775
Marion	RW3803
Melanie	RW3749
Penelope	RW3643
The Picnic	RW3881
Rebecca, Style One	RW3687
Rosalind	RW3750
The Tea Party	RW3700

VICTORIAN MUSICIANS

The Flute Player	RW2901
The Harpist	RW2898
The Lute Player	RW2899
The Song	RW2902

WAITING IN THE WINGS

Reflection, Style Two	RW4761

WALKING-OUT DRESS OF THE 19TH CENTURY
(Victoria and Albert Museum)

The Bustle	RW4454
The Crinoline	RW4422
The Regency	RW4372
The Romantic, Style One	RW4409

WARTIME

Evacuees	RW3347
The Letter	RW3382
The Rescue	RW3346
Salvage	RW3370
Spitfire	RW3352
Stowaway	RW3369
Take Cover	RW3351

WATTEAU FIGURES

Watteau Figure (Female, seated)	RW3405
Watteau Figure (Female, standing)	RW3403
Watteau Figure (Male, seated)	RW3404
Watteau Figure (Male, standing)	RW3402

THE WORCESTER CHILDREN

At the Seaside	RW4190
Ballerina	RW4188
Birthday Girl	RW4194
Christopher	RW4156
Country Boy	RW4201
Daisy Chain	RW4203
Fisherman	RW4165
Gardener	RW4192
Hometime	RW4159
Katie, Style One	RW4154
Let's Run	RW4161
Little Grandmother's Dress	RW4155
Little Mermaid	RW4191
Little Parakeet Boy	RW4163
Lost Slipper	RW4200

Mother's Helper / Polly Kettle	RW4205
Musical Moments	RW4204
Old Friends	RW4193
Peace	RW4167
Poor Teddy	RW4195
Skating	RW4199
Slide (The)	RW4189
Snowball	RW4166
Solitaire	RW4206
Springtime	RW4168A
Sunshine Days	RW4164
Teatime, Style One	RW4160
Three's Company	RW4158
Windy	RW4202
Woodland Walk	RW4157

THE WORLD OF THE IMPRESSIONISTS

Alphonsine	RW4085
Ballet Master	RW4124
Camille	RW4084
Cha-u-Kau (Female clown)	RW4216
Germaine	RW4072
Jeanne	RW4073
La Midinette	RW4100
Le Cerceau	RW4231
La Leçon	RW4126
L'Étude	RW4127
Marguerite and Don Pedro	RW4088
Mary Cassat	RW4230
Nina La Loge	RW4215
Norbert	RW4089

ALPHABETICAL INDEX